Th

CLASSIC *f*M

Hall *of* Fame
Collection

The

CLASSIC fM

Hall *of* Fame
Collection

Keith Shadwick

Virgin

First published in Great Britain in 2000 by

Virgin Publishing Ltd
Thames Wharf Studios
Rainville Road
London W6 9HA

Book design: Roger Kohn Designs
Printed and bound by Butler & Tanner,
Frome and London

ISBN 0 7535 0476 6

A catalogue record for this book is available
from the British Library.

Contents

Acknowledgements page 6

Introduction page 7

About the Hall of Fame page 11

The Top 100 page 19

101-200 page 119

201-300 page 169

301-400 page 220

Statistics page 231

401-500 page 232

1999 Top 50 and new entries page 236

1998 Top 50 and new entries page 238

1997 Top 50 and new entries page 240

1996 Top 50 page 242

Selected Charts page 243

Index page 261

Acknowledgements

In a project of this size and scope, the end result is always the work of many hands. To get things in perspective, the first people who must be acknowledged are the composers themselves. It is their music that is central to the book and which is a blessing to so many lives. May their sounds always fill the air. Down here on the ground, Anna Gregory at Classic FM was always a catalyst and a dependable organising force for the overview as well as the details, ably assisted by Jo Wilson. Kate Sampson got the deal together, along with David Gould and Rob Shreeve at Virgin, who gave the brief so that the whole thing could take shape. Aiding the process greatly was Ian Paten, project editor and man of discretion.

The third parties who helped are many and various. At the record companies, the following earned my gratitude through their outstanding levels of patience and resourcefulness as the project deadlines grew tighter and the goalposts shifted from time to time: Chris White at EMI, Matt Phillips and Talia Hull (even in the middle of an office move) at Warner Classics, Celia Ballantyne at Harmonia Mundi, Jo Carpenter, Jonathan Fry and Alexandra Spicer at Naxos. Likewise Tom Norden, unflappably representing a host of smaller companies, Jo Nicholson at ASV, Alf Goodrich at Nimbus and Jenny Wegg at Hyperion all helped quickly and efficiently. Paul Westcott at Chandos and Kathy Tyler at BMG and their colleagues were prompt and very helpful on numerous occasions, while Johanna Knowles at Sony dealt with a plethora of enquiries during a major campaign for a key Sony artist. Similarly, Pippa Sharpe at Universal was helpful under difficult circumstances. If there is anyone I've omitted, it is by accident, not design, and I apologise in advance: your efforts were appreciated at the time.

Keith Shadwick

Introduction

This book is a testament and a celebration. It is a testament to the taste and perspicacity of Classic FM's audience in selecting the fine music which makes up the greater part of this all-time Hall of Fame. It is a celebration of the beauty, joy and humanity to be found in just about every avenue classical music has explored in the past 500 years.

The resulting list has more than enough quality to make it a very useful set of recommendations for anyone looking for a start in the classical music field. After all, one of the hardest things with this music is to find an entry point. It's like going to a great party but not knowing a soul in the room – how do you get in on the action? Here the weight of opinion across the United Kingdom can be your guide as to what music is worth listening to. And believe me, this is the only party in town – no one else has gone to the trouble of asking such a large cross-section of British music-lovers to express their opinion in this way.

It has been my responsibility, after the votes had been counted, to undertake all the necessary comparisons so that I could guide interested parties to the best currently available versions on CD of every work in the chart. This last point should be stressed, if only because it entailed so much extra work on my part!

Each and every recording recommended in this book has been carefully checked to ensure that, as we go to press, it is currently available and can be purchased through any well-stocked record store or ordered from the supplier of your choice.

Some CDs are going to be a lot easier to find than others. For example, there are just a handful of currently available complete recordings of Borodin's String Quartet No. 2, and many versions listed in other well-known general guides have been deleted. Some compositions are covered by so many orchestras (the Beethoven symphonies can all boast scores of currently available recordings) that the proliferation is bamboozling for all but the most canny shopper. With this guide, you can be confident that all the CDs recommended are high quality and can be supplied (occasionally with a little effort on their part) by any decent CD retailer.

To help you find your way around the many recommendations, we've used a couple of special symbols:

★ indicates an outstanding recording which merits a special recommendation.

✔ means 'good value' and denotes a very respectable mid- or budget-price recording.

A brief look at the list will confirm that the 'core music' continues to be that of the golden age that, by general consensus, started with Mozart and Haydn in the 1770s and ended with the death of Mahler early in the 20th century. This 'core repertoire' represents, at a rough estimate, three quarters of all the music listed here. Honourable exceptions include Vivaldi and Bach prior to Mozart, with Sibelius and Gershwin being the major favourites after Mahler. In the world of opera, only Gluck, Puccini and Richard Strauss really make any impact outside these parameters, and none of these could be called musical revolutionaries. Strauss may have lived to see the other side of World War II, but his musical language remained that of Wagner, Brahms and Mahler.

Another lesson from the Hall of Fame is that people are most comfortable with shorter works or what Wagner called 'bleeding chunks' – excerpts from longer works. The most obvious examples are also to be found in opera – the overtures of Wagner and Rossini, for example. At number 130 in the all-time Hall of Fame, Rossini's *La gazza ladra* ('Thieving Magpie') is one of the most popular overtures in all classical music, but it comes from an opera so obscure that there has been only one commercial recording in the past 30 or more years. Equally, the famous arias from Puccini, Verdi and Mozart are certainly visited much more often by the average listener than the complete operas from which they stem.

The great aria 'Nessun dorma' may forever be associated with tears on a football field or three men in black suits, but who could recount the story of *Turandot*, the opera from which the aria came (and number 97 in our chart), without considerable prompting?

Such 'sampling' has also regularly taken place in orchestral music, often inspired by the music's presence in a film; this has certainly helped Rachmaninov's Piano Concertos Nos 2 and 3 to reach numbers 2 and 36 respectively. The eternal popularity of Mahler's *adagietto* from his Fifth Symphony, at number 9 in the chart, stems partly from its use as the soundtrack to Visconti's 1971 masterpiece, *Death In Venice*. Similarly, Shostakovich's *The Gadfly* (number 53) would be virtually unknown in the West if it had not been used as a source of theme music for more than one television series.

All of which makes it the more extraordinary that Górecki's Symphony No. 3 continues to hold a respectable position in the hearts of contemporary Britain, and to be represented at number 113 in the Hall of Fame Collection. As I was directly responsible for this music's first airing on Classic FM (on the show Rob Cowan and I co-hosted, Classic Verdict) during the very first week the station was on air in September 1992, this is particularly heartening. I can still remember the excitement after that first broadcast when the phones began ringing, enquiring about this strangely moving piece of music. During the writing of this book I revisited the brilliant Upshaw/Zinman recording of this work – the one Górecki himself prefers – and reaffirmed its timeless and devastating impact. Regardless of its recent vintage, it communicates simply and directly, electrifying its audience in a unique way. With a very different musical style, John Tavener, in his *Song for Athene* (number 168), manages to establish a similar mesmerising effect on his listeners as the depth of his inspiration (courtesy of the Orthodox Church and its tenets) communicates itself to us anew with every listening.

The other great theme in this poll is the prevalence of British music. We need not make any apologies for this, for any nation would be proud to number among its native sons Purcell, Elgar, Delius, Vaughan Williams, Holst, Warlock, Walton and Britten. I only wish that the delights of such composers as Howells, Finzi and Gurney were more widely known. Come to think of it, a wider look at half the names on the above list would unearth some extremely palatable music in no time at all. But that, of course, is true of many of the composers in this book, as Darren Henley points out in the following introduction to the Hall of Fame. Even Max Bruch, who has consistently topped the chart since its inception, has only recently begun to register some of his other equally fine orchestral works in the list. What about the neglected beauties of Grieg, Debussy, Vivaldi, Haydn, Mendelssohn ...? The list could go on indefinitely.

Some people would regard this as a discouraging, indeed daunting, aspect of the classical music world: there is just so much music to hear and digest. This is akin to the 'glass half full' or 'glass half empty' argument. My feeling is that it is one of the great joys of classical music: all you need is a bit of courage. In my case it was foolhardiness when, as a naïve teenager, I went into a record shop with hard-earned pocket money burning a hole in my wallet and a determination to buy an opera. At the time I knew little of Richard Strauss or his work, but I talked myself into buying the latest version of his opera *Salome* without the benefit of hearing a note prior to purchase. It could have been a disaster, but when I got home and listened to it I became fascinated by what I discovered. It is that same thrill of adventure I still get when I hear new music, of any genre.

This list may be the first step into the exciting unknown for many people: I surely hope so, for that unknown really is one of the most thrilling places to be on this planet. Come on in – the music's fine!

Keith Shadwick

About the Classic FM Hall of Fame

When we launched the Classic FM Hall of Fame back in the winter of 1996, we had no idea that we were giving birth to a phenomenon. It has become so much more than just an annual chart – spawning a daily radio programme and no fewer than six bestselling CDs.

Since we started our quest to identify the United Kingdom's favourite pieces of classical music, we have produced four annual charts. Each one offers a snapshot of our listeners' favourites at a given point in time. We are often asked how we go about compiling the chart. What happens is that at the beginning of each year we ask our listeners to send us their top three all-time classical favourites. Every single one of these votes is registered on a computer, which creates a running tally of the relative positions of each of the pieces. The final chart is produced just before Easter. Classic FM's team of music producers then set about the unenviable task of fitting all 300 works into one 45-hour countdown, which is broadcast from dawn to dusk on Easter Saturday, Sunday and Monday.

During the first four years of the chart, one composer has reigned supreme: Max Bruch. In 1996 he surprised all of us by beating the likes of Mozart and Beethoven to take the No. 1 spot with his Violin Concerto No. 1 in G minor. At No. 300 that same year was another work by Bruch, *Kol Nidrei*. So a lesser-known composer, born in Cologne in 1838, not only topped but also tailed our debut chart. He has retained pole position every year since, confounding the pundits who claimed that his early success was merely a fluke. Indeed, in 1998 Bruch built on his achievements in the previous two years: his Second Violin Concerto was the fourth-highest new entry at No. 120 and his Third Violin Concerto made its first-ever appearance at 206. There were also jumps of 71 places for *Kol Nidrei* and 13 places for the *Scottish Fantasy*. This evidence of a major Bruch revival seems all the more remarkable when you consider that, by the time he died in 1920, his music had drifted out of fashion to such an extent that his reputation had dwindled to almost nothing. It also proves that looks count for very little with Classic FM listeners – a German contemporary of Bruch once said of him: 'In personal appearance, he is by no means as majestic as one would suppose from his works.'

Rachmaninov's Second Piano Concerto has been a constant bridesmaid to Bruch's bride, taking the No. 2 position each year.

But in 1997 the film *Shine* did the same job for his Third Piano Concerto as *Brief Encounter* had done for his Second. The biopic of Australian pianist David Helfgott's battle with the 'Rach Three' and with psychiatric illness, which won Geoffrey Rush a Best Actor Oscar, struck a chord with Classic FM's listeners. Rachmaninov's Third Piano Concerto leapt up 61 places to No. 24, while his First Piano Concerto made its debut in the chart at No. 262. Twelve months on, though, *Shine*'s star had faded, as had the Rach Three – to the tune of 36 places. But, proving that the Classic FM Hall of Fame evolves continuously, in the 1999 chart it had jumped back up to No. 31.

Cinema successes and failures always have a part to play in our annual charts, and in 1998 there was one movie that hit the headlines more than any other. There are very few superlatives that haven't already been used to describe the film *Titanic*. Among the eleven Oscars it won was that for Best Dramatic Score. Classic FM listeners gave this award their seal of approval by voting James Horner's majestic score into the No. 75 slot, the second-highest new entry to the chart that year. It was a particularly outstanding achievement given that the film soundtrack only went on sale at the beginning of the voting period. A year later, Horner had consolidated his position in the chart. Far from sinking, *Titanic* had risen a further three places.

In 1999, Elgar's Cello Concerto shone on the silver screen, moving up five places to equal its 1997 position at No. 4 after being the central theme in the film *Hilary and Jackie*, the 'true' story of the rollercoaster life of cellist Jacqueline du Pré. The final major cinema hit of the 20th century was the latest Star Wars film: *The Phantom Menace*. It just nudged into the 1999 Classic FM Hall of Fame, but votes were counted when only the soundtrack, rather than the film itself, had been released in the UK.

In 1997, the highest new entry in the chart was *Adiemus*, which shot in at No. 134. The haunting voice of Miriam Stockley performing Karl Jenkins's best-known work was one of the biggest-selling classical records of the last decade. By 1998 *Adiemus* had jumped 78 places to 56. It was joined by two further new entries from Jenkins: *Adiemus II: Cantata Mundi* was new at 213 and *Palladio* just squeezed into the chart at 296. However, a year on and Karl Jenkins's fortunes had changed, with the original *Adiemus* his only composition in the chart – and that down 71 places.

Operatic works have performed strongly every year and Bizet's 'Au fond du temple saint' from *The Pearl Fishers* has consistently been the highest-placed representative of the genre. But special praise should be saved for three sopranos, the much-loved Lesley Garrett, the lesser-known Inessa Galante and the Classic FM Magazine Artist of the Year 1999, Emma Kirkby. Effervescent Lesley has become a big hit with both our listeners and our presenters over the past few years – not least because she sings the vocal jingles which you hear on Classic FM. Her CD

Soprano in Red was one of the bestselling albums of 1996. It featured the 'Nuns' Chorus' from Johann Strauss II's *Casanova*, which was a new entry in 1997, arriving at 254. Latvian Inessa Galante made her first appearance in 1997 at No. 179, performing Caccini's 'Ave Maria', which shot from obscurity to popularity in just a few months. A year later, this baroque hit had moved up another 20 places, after being recorded by Lesley Garrett. In 1998 it was Emma Kirkby's turn. She played a big part in bringing Vivaldi's haunting *Nulla in Mundo Pax Sincera* to a wider audience. A new entry at No. 193 in the 1997 Hall of Fame, it became the chart's highest climber twelve months later – up a massive 138 places to No. 55.

It is interesting to note how some of the more reflective works have risen up the chart over the years. Tárrega's beautiful work for guitar, *Recuerdos de la Alhambra*, evocative of a fountain playing in the courtyard of a Spanish palace, was the highest climber of all in the 1997 chart – up 118 places to No. 180. The highest new entry in the 1998 chart came from John Tavener. His *Song for Athene* was performed at the funeral of Diana, Princess of Wales, and it is easy to understand why so many Classic FM listeners took this haunting choral work to their hearts. In the same year, the *adagietto* from Mahler's Fifth Symphony entered the Top Ten for the first time at No. 6, Allegri's *Miserere* moved from No. 33 to No. 14, and both the Verdi and Fauré Requiems made solid gains.

However, it is 1999 which will be remembered as the year of the requiem. John Rutter's *Requiem* – straight in at No. 80 – was the highest new entry in that year's chart, Zbigniew Preisner's *Requiem for My Friend* was fresh in at 236, and Andrew Lloyd Webber's *Requiem* a brand-new entry at 268 – all three composers appearing in the Hall of Fame for the first time. Rutter and Preisner had released critically acclaimed recordings of their works over the previous year, but Lloyd Webber had the teenage soprano Charlotte Church to thank for his success – she recorded his 'Pie Jesu' on her debut album *Voice of an Angel*, which became an instant bestseller.

Some pieces become popular with Classic FM listeners because of particular programmes on the station. Among these are the music of the 18th-century Italian Jesuit priest, Domenico Zipoli, and in particular his beautiful *Elevazione*. The 'Meditation' from Massenet's opera *Thaïs* and Vaughan Williams' beautiful soaring melody *The Lark Ascending* have also benefited from regular airplay. Arvo Pärt's deeply spiritual music grows in popularity year by year, and his *Spiegl im Spiegl* – a favourite of our late-night broadcasting – is likely to give him his first Hall of Fame Top 300 entry. I am also waiting for a breakthrough into the chart for Ludovico Einaudi's strikingly original piano composition Le *Onde*, first released in 1988.

It never ceases to surprise me how many 'one-hit wonders' appear in the chart each year – pieces from composers with one *magnum opus* which puts all their other work in the shade. It seems ironic that among them are some of the greatest pieces of classical music ever written: Pachelbel's *Canon in D*, Mascagni's *Cavalleria Rusticana*, Holst's *Planets* Suite and Allegri's *Miserere*. At the other end of the scale comes Mozart, who has had more entries in the chart each year than any other composer, beating Beethoven into second place every time. Edward Elgar has been a consistent performer, flying the flag as our most prolific home-grown composer in terms of number of entries in the chart.

T his book is the first to be centred around the Classic FM Hall of Fame. It follows on from six highly successful CD releases, all of which are on the Classic FM record label: *Classic FM Hall of Fame* (CFMCD7); *More Classic FM Hall of Fame* (CFMCD10); *Classic FM Opera Hall of Fame* (CFMCD20); *Classic FM Hall of Fame at the Movies* (CFMCD22); *Adverts Hall of Fame* (CFMCD26); and the brand-new *Classic FM Hall of Fame 2000* (CFMCD31).

The book is divided into two parts. The first section contains the Classic FM Hall of Fame All-Time Top 300. This is based on an aggregation of votes from the first four years of the Hall of Fame, between 1996 and 1999 – almost 400,000 listeners' votes in all, making it one of the most representative lists of British classical music taste ever published. Each entry is accompanied by Keith Shadwick's description of the piece and his recommendations of the finest available recordings. Keith has been involved with Classic FM since the week the station first went on air back in 1992, both as a presenter and as a producer. He is a respected writer and broadcaster who has brought his immense knowledge of both the music industry and music itself to play in the book. We have also included an extra 200 entries that have not quite made it into the Top 300. So towards the back of the book you'll find Nos. 301 to 400 (each with a single recommended recording) and 401 to 500. These are the works that are either climbing their way up into the main chart or which are losing favour with our listeners and are on the way out. You can discover an amazing array of riches among the recommended recordings. There are definitive historic performances, such as Jacqueline du Pré's version of the Elgar Cello Concerto conducted by Sir John Barbirolli, as well as original recordings of newly composed works, such as Paul McCartney's *Standing Stone* performed by the London Symphony Orchestra and Choir under the baton of Lawrence Foster.

The second section of the book comprises a series of statistics based on the All-Time Top 300. It is here that you will find details of the most successful composers, side by side with those who have had just one hit. We have listed all the new entries to the chart through the years and have also identified the Hall of Fame hits that enjoy a life beyond the concert hall: in the cinema and in television advertisements, for example.

We have also chosen some of the biggest hits to suit you if you are in a particular mood – with, among others, the Top 20 Stirring Classics and the Top 20 Relaxing Classics. If Opera is your bag, then we have identified the Top 20 operatic choices for you to sing along to.

It is our intention to update this book regularly. The Classic FM Hall of Fame is very much a living, breathing entity, reflecting fashions and events in the world around us. For this reason there can never be a single definitive chart – only a series of snapshots of tastes at any given moment in time. By the time this book is published, we will have broadcast the new Classic FM Hall of Fame 2000 and will already have started working on the 2001 chart. Who knows which composers will come to the fore, which film scores will capture our collective imagination, or which long-forgotten pieces will be revitalised by a new recording. Whatever they may be, you can rest assured that we will be here at Classic FM to share your delight in discovering them.

So sit back, read, listen... and relax.

Darren Henley
Managing Editor, Classic FM
March 2000

THE CLASSIC FM
HALL OF FAME
COLLECTION

Bruch

1) VIOLIN CONCERTO NO. 1

M ax Bruch's first violin concerto became a poisoned chalice for the composer. He lived and composed to the age of 82 but was never to repeat his 1864 triumph with his first concerto: this made him an embittered man. However, none of his admirers has cause to complain, for we have the concerto to enjoy for ever. It has lyric passion, intensity and deft control of the soloist's virtuosity, so that the flash and filigree serve only to illuminate rather than just dazzle the listener. It is also scored not just for maximum volume all the way: there is great naturalness in the way the piece develops, while the *adagio* is memorably tender.

An outstanding recording of this work has to have a soloist whose skills long ago moved past technique alone to embrace passionate communication with the audience. It also requires an alert and entirely sympathetic conductor and orchestra: this is not a warhorse that simply plays itself. The two full-price versions chosen here both make very strong cases for themselves: Kyung-Wha on EMI manages to convey full-on passion without pushing the notes too hard, forcing them beyond what they are meant to convey into histrionics. In this she is intelligently guided by Klaus Tennstedt's conducting. Maxim Vengerov has the Leipzig Gewandhaus Orchestra and Kurt Masur pacing him superbly, and while his typically forceful playing drives the piece along faster than usual, the *adagio* benefits, its melody flowing unstoppably and with conviction. This approach is shared by the famous old Ricci Decca recording from 1958 (now on Belart) which, although the orchestra is somewhat hazy at times, has perfectly acceptable sound quality, especially at budget price.

● If you like this, try Bruch's *Scottish Fantasia* (95)

★

EMI CDC7 54072-2
**Kyung-Wha Chung (violin)/
London Philharmonic Orchestra/
Klaus Tennstedt**

Teldec 4509-90875-2
**Maxim Vengerov (violin)/
Leipzig Gewandhaus Orchestra/
Kurt Masur**

Belart 461 142-2
**Ruggiero Ricci (violin)/
London Symphony Orchestra/
Sir Adrian Boult**

Rachmaninov
2) PIANO CONCERTO NO. 2

Rachmaninov may have made his name through his astounding keyboard technique and the concerts he gave worldwide after his exile from Russia in the wake of the Revolution, but he grew to hate playing to audiences, preferring to be alone rather than 'in company'. This paradox comes through in his music, especially in the most famous piano concerto written this century, his Second (completed in 1901). With one of the most famous openings of any concerto (those eight brooding piano chords followed by the rolling arpeggios, like waves of bad news engulfing the listener), it also has a serene and comfortably melancholy second movement where the piano is like a perfect voice against the strings. It is no doubt this quality which has attracted so many film-makers to the idea of using it as soundtrack music, most memorably in *Brief Encounter*.

Perhaps the best recent recording in a highly competitive field is that of Lilya Zilberstein and Claudio Abbado on DGG.

She has plenty of attack and fire, but she plays cleanly and does not drag the music out of shape. In the slow movement she has a beautiful tone and touch and wisely does not linger, allowing the music to flow. Abbado keeps the BPO under control and terse in its support. The famous 1972 Decca recording by Ashkenazy and Previn has been reissued countless times: the number quoted is its latest incarnation.

It is almost classically restrained: a performance to treasure. The Earl Wild / Jascha Horenstein performance comes from a two-CD set of all four concertos with the Paganini *Variations*. It was recorded in 1966 and suffers from a sound that is just a little too reverberant, but the playing sparkles, the music is treated with utmost respect and, for the price, it is highly recommendable.

● If you like this, try Rachmaninov's Piano Concerto No. 3 (36)

★

Deutsche Grammophon DG 439 930-2
Lilya Zilberstein (piano)/
Berlin Philharmonic Orchestra/
Claudio Abbado

✔

Decca 417 702-2
Vladimir Ashkenazy (piano)/
London Symphony Orchestra/
André Previn

✔

Chandos CHAN 6507
Earl Wild (piano)/
Royal Philharmonic Orchestra/
Jascha Horenstein

Mozart
③ CLARINET CONCERTO K622

It is tempting to describe the clarinet part in this extraordinarily beautiful concerto as 'liquid gold', such beauty of tone and line does Mozart extract from the instrument. It is one of the very last orchestral compositions he completed before his death in late 1791, and it glows with that special autumnal peace and grace which inhabit all of Mozart's late orchestral works.

There are a great many versions of the concerto on disc: many of them can be immediately discounted either because the poor soloist simply cannot remain in tune (it's that sort of instrument) or lacks expressivity. Then there are the few, three of which are recommended here, which give unbroken pleasure. If you are after the heavenly route, then Emma Johnson is the one for you. Her tone and attack are sweet, her phrasing unexaggerated. The recording quality (from 1985) is not wonderful – plenty of breathing noises and a rather dull edge on the strings – but it is acceptable. Johnson has a conventional

approach to the music's performance, but one that will satisfy many. For something truly out of the usual, we turn to Sabine Meyer on EMI, whose 1990 recording is so full of character, so will-of-the-wisp in its twists and turns of expression and the way it moves from one mood to another, that it is utterly fascinating. Another reason for its special quality is that Meyer chooses to use the long-discarded basset clarinet, the instrument Mozart originally wrote the concerto for, which is pitched rather lower than the conventional instrument used today. This gives additional warmth to the playing and changes the personality of the piece in pleasing and surprising ways. For those unwilling to pay full price for Johnson, the 1960s brilliance of the incomparable Jack Brymer is still available on disc (mid-price) on a Philips compilation, and the sound is reasonable.

● If you like this, try Weber's Clarinet Concerto No. 2 (304)

ASV CDDCA 532
**Emma Johnson (clarinet)/
English Chamber Orchestra/
Raymond Leppard**

★ ✔

EMI CDM 566897-2
**Sabine Meyer (clarinet)/
Staatskapelle Dresden/
Hans Vonk**

✔

Philips 416 483-2
**Jack Brymer (clarinet)/
Academy of St Martin-in-the-Fields/
Sir Neville Marriner**

Beethoven

(4) SYMPHONY NO. 6 (PASTORAL)

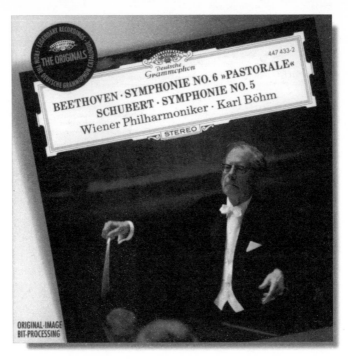

Beethoven is usually envisaged as a dour, Olympian figure. To those with such preconceptions his 'pastoral' symphony is a rude awakening. The first notes announce a happy state of mind and bright expectations: these are borne out by the music that follows and confirmed by the words Beethoven himself wrote at the symphony's beginning: 'Awakening of joyful feelings on arriving in the country'. The good mood is sustained for the whole of the first movement and flows into the second, subtitled by Beethoven 'scene at the brook'. This is translated into ebullience and gaiety in the *scherzo* of the third movement, where the rounds and dances are mixed into a carnival of musical colours. The colours darken for the dramatic storm of the fourth movement, but the mood does not sour: this is Beethoven observing, not condemning, the sometimes terrible forces of nature. Still, the happiness and gratitude of the final movement, the 'peace after the storm', reassert the sense of wellbeing with which our composer set off into the Viennese countryside.

The symphony needs interpreters who are prepared to allow Beethoven a more relaxed and smiling mien than usual: the three listed assuredly manage that, their understanding of the man and his music built over a long period of time. All three conductors allow the music to unfold naturally. Harnoncourt is more apt to point up little details of the scoring as we go along, while Böhm leaves us to find our own highlights and Zinman keeps us on our toes by the brilliance of his ensemble's playing and the generally quicker speeds he adopts. All three orchestras show tremendous discipline and loyalty to their director's vision, but it is the wondrous lyricism of Böhm's reading, as well as its mid-price tag, which gains him the nod here.

● If you like this, try Mendelssohn's Symphony No. 4 (109)

Teldec 9031 75709-2
**Chamber Orchestra of Europe/
Nikolaus Harnoncourt**

★

Deutsche Grammophon DG 447 433-2
**Vienna Philharmonic Orchestra/
Karl Böhm**

Arte Nova 74321 496952
**Zurich Tonhalle Orchestra/
David Zinman**

Elgar

5) CELLO CONCERTO

Separated from the Violin Concerto by close on a decade, one in which the world indulged in four calamitous years of war, this heartfelt work shows Elgar, in Coleridge's famous phrase, 'a sadder and a wiser man', one who was profoundly shocked by the brutality of the Great War. His musical language had become tauter, more inward. The first movement spells out the emotional landscape and introduces the themes that will dominate the work. The short second movement encompasses plucked strings, a yearning *lento* theme and a short but strident orchestral outburst finishing up in a fast *scherzo* featuring soloist and orchestra together. The *adagio* follows, displaying the emotional core of the piece and spotlighting the cellist for almost the entire time. This is the point at which an individual performance succeeds or fails: indifference to the music, or lack of concentration, makes for a miserable experience. The long last movement moves through a succession of moods and themes, often leaving the orchestra silent for considerable stretches before calling it back into the fray. Its end is not triumphal: there is a resolution of sorts, but it is weighed down with the melancholy of Elgar's new knowledge of the world.

One version has stood out above all others for decades: Jacqueline du Pré's EMI recording with Sir John Barbirolli. Barbirolli and the LSO give supple and completely sympathetic support to the soloist, and du Pré brings incredible expressiveness to the work. The whole piece vibrates with her spirit. With Yo-Yo Ma's excellent latter-day version on Sony currently unavailable, a cheaper modern alternative is Maria Kliegel's admirable performance with the RPO and Michael Halasz on Naxos. There is also an excellent budget-price performance by Ralph Kirshbaum from 1979 on Chandos. But du Pré is the top recommendation and is likely to remain so.

● If you like this, try Dvořák's Cello Concerto (94)

★

EMI CDC 556219 2
Jacqueline du Pré (cello)/
London Symphony Orchestra/
Sir John Barbirolli

✔

Naxos 8.550503
Maria Kliegel (cello)/
Royal Philharmonic Orchestra/
Michael Halasz

✔

Chandos CHAN 6607
Ralph Kirshbaum (cello)/Royal Scottish
National Orchestra/Sir Alexander Gibson

Elgar

ENIGMA VARIATIONS

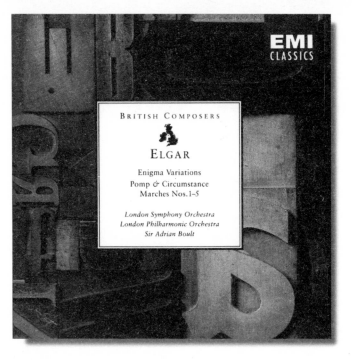

This was the breakthrough orchestral work for Elgar, with which he made his reputation. Written in the winter and spring of 1898/99, this set of miniatures, conceived as 'variations on an original theme', was composed not to a commission, but on a personal impulse as a musical tribute to family and friends. The original theme upon which the variations are based has never been revealed, although plenty have claimed to have cracked the 'enigma'. But there is no mistaking the warmth of feeling in the musical portraits, whether they be playful, forceful, ironic or passionate. With the tenth miniature, *Nimrod*, Elgar created one of the most famous pieces he ever wrote.

Three recordings made for one company – EMI – all have clear merits. The most recent is from Sir Simon Rattle and the CBSO and dates from 1993. Rattle brings gusto and insight to the pieces and is especially successful in the brighter, more vivacious selections. His *Nimrod* is curiously studied and ill-at-ease. The accompanying music is *Falstaff* and the incidental music to *Grania and Diarmid*. The oldest of the three performances is from Sir John Barbirolli with the Hallé Orchestra. This dates from 1962 and is a wonderfully vivacious, alert account. Barbirolli's *Nimrod*, quietly bursting with feeling, is close to a minute shorter than Rattle's but seems to have all the time in the world to unfold its splendour. Again the coupling is with *Falstaff*. The 1970 recording by Boult and the LSO is perhaps the pick of the three, for its conductor's insights into the score are matched by the recording quality, which is richer than that for Barbirolli, and generally better balanced than Rattle's. It is coupled with all five *Pomp & Circumstance* marches. All are mid-price releases.

● If you like this, try Elgar's *Serenade for Strings* (162)

EMI CDC 555001-2
**City of Birmingham
Symphony Orchestra/
Sir Simon Rattle**

✔

EMI CDM 566322-2
**Hallé Orchestra/
Sir John Barbirolli**

★

EMI CDM 764015-2
**London Symphony Orchestra/
Sir Adrian Boult**

Beethoven
7) PIANO CONCERTO NO. 5

Beethoven's Fifth Concerto (known as the 'Emperor' in Britain) was composed in 1809 and was the last of his piano concertos. He certainly went out with a bang: this is quite possibly the single most famous concerto ever written, although there may be more popular concertos written for both piano and violin, as the Classic FM chart readily suggests. The Fifth Concerto is conceived on a scale that, in its day, would have been described as vast. Its first movement alone lasts as long as a good many of Mozart's most popular concertos – for piano, flute or horn – while the soloist's role is more focused and spotlighted than in anything by Mozart. This reflects changing tastes as much as Beethoven's own drive to establish new parameters for the concerto form.

Given the ambitious nature of his quest, it is only natural that a great many performers of this work take a grand, Olympian approach. This is certainly the case with Alfred Brendel and Sir Simon Rattle, who between them

manage to bring rather too much 'significance' to every bar of the music. The orchestra is trying so hard at the opening exposition that it sounds ragged and diffuse. Meanwhile, the transition from the beautiful second movement *adagio* to the third movement *rondo allegro* is about as subtle as a London bus pulling out into peak-hour traffic. More poised and alert is Pollini who, along with Abbado and the BPO, brings clarity and spirit to the music rather than a rather cool gravitas. Meanwhile, if authentic instruments appeal to you, then probably the most enjoyable current version is that by Jos van Immerseel accompanied by Tafelmusik and Bruno Weil on Sony Vivarte (available on one disc or as part of a complete piano concerto cycle). The accompanying work is the Violin Concerto played by Vera Befies.

● If you like this, try Beethoven's *Triple Concerto* (159)

Philips 462 781-2
Alfred Brendel (piano)/
Vienna Philharmonic Orchestra/
Sir Simon Rattle

★

Deutsche Grammophon DG 4397702
Maurizio Pollini (piano)/
Berlin Philharmonic Orchestra/
Claudio Abbado

Sony SK 63365
Jos van Immerseel (piano)/
Tafelmusik/
Bruno Weil

---

8) SYMPHONY NO. 9 (CHORAL)

Many people regard the Choral Symphony as Beethoven's last word on what the symphonic form can do or be, and given its gigantic proportions and ambitions, this is not an unreasonable hypothesis. It is undermined, of course, by the fact that Beethoven went on to leave a 10th Symphony incomplete at his death, but it helps us appreciate the scale of his achievement here. This is heroic music; it is also wild and barbaric at times, forcing the orchestra to play distorted and ugly sounds in its long search for peace and reconciliation in the last-movement setting of Schiller's 'Ode to Joy'. Its searching melodies, its drama and agony, its switching between extremes, all proved to be a legacy for later symphonists, especially Mahler, who passionately loved Beethoven's music.

The three recordings recommended here each have very individual approaches, reflecting the conductor's personal relationship with the music built up over years of study. The first version is the famous Philharmonia

recording by Klemperer from 1957. It is spacious in sound and in Klemperer's ideas of what Beethoven had in mind. The second, by Fricsay and the BPO, was made in 1958 and was DGG's first stereo recording with the Berlin Philharmonic. It remains an alternately savage and dignified interpretation, alive to the keenness of Beethoven's creative vision. The sound is a little dry but quite serviceable. Both these releases are mid-price. Nicely straddling the interpretative traditions personified by these two is David Zinman's 1999 performance for Arte Nova with the Zurich Tonhalle Orchestra. Zinman manages the savagery and the drama of this almost programmatic symphony, but also blesses us with peace at the appropriate moments. Neither he nor the listener loses concentration for a second. To make this budget-price version even more of a bargain, an alternative reading of the last movement is also included.

● If you like this, try Beethoven's *Fantasia for Piano, Chorus and Orchestra* (257)

✔
EMI CDM 566797-2
Aase Nordmo-Løvberg (soprano)/Christa Ludwig (mezzo-soprano)/Waldemar Kmentt (tenor)/Hans Hotter (bass baritone)/ Philharmonia Choir & Orchestra/Otto Klemperer

Deutsche Grammophon DG 445 400-2
Irmgard Seefried (soprano)/Maureen Forrester (contralto)/Ernst Haefliger (tenor)/Dietrich Fischer-Diskau (baritone)/Berlin Philharmonic Orchestra/St Hedwig's Cathedral Choir, Berlin/Ferenc Fricsay

★ ✔
Arte Nova 74321 65411-2
Ruth Ziesak (soprano)/Birgit Remmert (contralto)/Steve Davislim (tenor)/Detlef Roth (baritone)/Zurich Tonhalle Orchestra/ Swiss Chamber Choir/David Zinman

Mahler

9) SYMPHONY NO. 5 ✓

This is a huge, uncompromising, noisy and strident work. Mahler makes no bones about bearing his agonised soul to the world: the work begins with a funeral march and the gloom lifts only after nearly half an hour of music, when the sunny *scherzo* is announced by the bright sound of the horns. After that comes the *adagietto* – since the film *Death in Venice* almost exclusively associated with death and dissolution, but in fact written by Mahler as a love song to his new young wife, Alma. Most conductors have tended to milk the *adagietto* for all it's worth: some performances last close to 15 minutes, while Mahler's original markings in the score suggest it should last somewhere around seven or eight: a proper *adagietto*, not a fully fledged *adagio*.

Of the three performances here, Boulez's *adagietto* lasts the longest, at 11 minutes: it starts correctly enough but has slowed appreciably before the first run-through of the melody. After that it becomes funereal. The rest of the work Boulez manages very

well indeed, getting a fine, full sound and committed playing from the VPO. Sir John Barbirolli's 1969 recording for EMI is justly famous: Barbirolli had an instinct for Mahler's special musical voice. His *adagietto* is a good minute shorter than Boulez's and gains immensely in poise and expressivity for the extra momentum. This is a mid-price release. The final recommendation is a surprise. It is a budget-price performance in RCA's 'Navigator' series, and features Erich Leinsdorf with the Boston Symphony in a well-judged 1962 recording. The trumpets occasionally blare a little too much but the *adagietto* is a revelation, at 8 minutes 30 seconds closer to Mahler's intentions than anything since Bruno Walter's landmark 1947 Columbia recording, and played with frightening intensity – truly a song of love, from composer and conductor alike.

● If you like this, try Mahler's Symphony No. 2 (74)

Deutsche Grammophon DG 453 416-2
**Vienna Philharmonic Orchestra/
Pierre Boulez**

★

EMI CDM 566910-2
**New Philharmonia Orchestra/
Sir John Barbirolli**

RCA 74321 29249-2
**Boston Symphony Orchestra/
Erich Leinsdorf**

Mozart

10) PIANO CONCERTO NO. 21 K467
(ELVIRA MADIGAN)

MOZART · PIANO CONCERTOS
NO. 21, K. 467 · NO. 27, K. 595
THE CHAMBER ORCHESTRA OF EUROPE

MURRAY PERAHIA

It's not only because this concerto was used in the film *Elvira Madigan* that it remains so popular. The music is in turns so sunny, so pensive, so graceful, that it is always irresistible. This is especially the case in the second movement. This picks up the touch of melancholy underlying the quick-witted and decorous first movement, which is mostly upbeat but which occasionally takes a backward glance. This, in the *andante*, becomes a fully fledged bout of introspection while the strings, often plucked, add their sympathetic entreaties. The two melodies that Mozart develops during this movement are almost painfully beautiful as well as being in perfect musical proportion. Yet Mozart does not leave us in this enervated condition: his *allegro vivace* final movement restores us to full vigour and appreciation of life in general and his melodic gifts in particular.

Grace under pressure and a sense of the religious sublime are two qualities which do not go amiss for pianists hoping to deliver something out of the ordinary when playing this famous concerto. Mitsuko Uchida and Jeffrey Tate, recording in 1985, certainly have the latter quality, especially in the *andante*, but they are inclined to promote it perhaps at the expense of the other, higher spirits that are as much part of Mozart as his pensive moments. Uchida gets a stunningly beautiful tone from her instrument, however, at all times. Murray Perahia and the Chamber Orchestra of Europe manage a happier balance of elements in their 1990 version for Sony. Friedrich Gulda and Claudio Abbado, recording in 1975, take the route aspired to by Uchida and Tate and do it with spine-tingling effect. Their version is available on a mid-price DGG two-CD set of four Mozart concertos, and while its sonic limitations exclude it from an unreserved recommendation, the playing is wonderful.

● If you like this, try Mozart's Flute and Harp Concerto (66)

Philips 416 381-2
Mitsuko Uchida (piano)/
English Chamber Orchestra/
Jeffrey Tate

★

Sony SK 34562
Murray Perahia (piano)/
Chamber Orchestra of Europe

✔

Deutsche Grammophon DG 453 079-2
Friedrich Gulda (piano)/
Vienna Philharmonic Orchestra/
Claudio Abbado

Vaughan Williams

 11) **THE LARK ASCENDING**

Edward Elgar
Violin Concerto

Ralph Vaughan
Williams
The Lark Ascending

Kennedy
Simon Rattle

City of Birmingham
Symphony Orchestra

This is one of those pieces of music – like Beethoven's Fifth or The Beatles' 'Help' – which grabs the listener's attention from the first bar. Built on the simple idea of a soaring solo violin melody arching against hushed strings, it combines Vaughan Williams's powers of musical description with his incredible melodic gift. The key to a great performance, then, lies in the balance between the landscape (depicted by the orchestra) and the bird (the violin). Too much grandstanding by the violinist and the piece loses all its mystery and magic; giving the orchestra the upper hand means that the poor old lark's song is lost to the elements.

Of the three versions recommended here, Kennedy takes the prize for the most sumptuous tone and birdlike phrasing. Rattle and the CBSO generally keep out of the way (and may be a little too discreet for some tastes), but come to life in the dreamlike waltz section. Bryden Thomson and the LSO are treated much more as equals to violin soloist Michael Davis by the Chandos engineers, but Davis hasn't the quicksilver imagination of Kennedy in his phrasing.

Both these versions were recorded in the 1990s: our last recommendation comes from the mid-1960s. This is the famous and popular Hugh Bean/Sir Adrian Boult version from 1967. Once again the balance favours the violin, leaving the string section in quiet passages sounding as if they're in the next field, but the woodwinds are given equal weighting to Bean in the middle section, making for a nice swell of nature sounds. Bean himself plays with spirit and poise, though his tone can't match Kennedy's. Interestingly, Kennedy and Rattle take over 17 minutes to ascend while Bean and Boult do it in just over 14. Davis and Thomson nestle nicely in between at 15 minutes. Kennedy is at full price; the other two are mid-price issues.

● If you like this, try Vaughan Williams's *Fantasia on a Theme of Thomas Tallis* (42)

★
EMI CDC 556413 2
Kennedy (violin)/
City of Birmingham Symphony Orchestra/
Sir Simon Rattle

CHAN 9775
Michael Davis (violin)/
London Symphony Orchestra/
Bryden Thomson

EMI CDM 764022-2
Hugh Bean (violin)/
New Philharmonia Orchestra/
Sir Adrian Boult

Bizet

12) LES PÊCHEURS DE PERLES
(THE PEARL FISHERS)

This opera, premièred in 1863, was Bizet's first, and a moderate success at the time. Its exotic setting (Ceylon) and its tale of love versus state, culture and religion hardly make for an original plot, but Bizet compensates for any clichés in the drama by his liberal use of soaring melody and his transparent orchestral scoring. The heroine, Leila, abandons her virginal vows in her quest for love from Nadir, while his friend Zurga, elected leader of the village and also in love with Leila, has to pronounce on their profane relationship after they are uncovered by the murderous priest, Nourabad.

As with most operas of the time, *Les Pêcheurs* suffered its fair share of cuts and rearrangements. It is not that often produced on-stage, so new recordings are infrequent. Happily, the latest version is also the best and the most consistently faithful to Bizet's original. This is on EMI and conducted by Michel Plasson, featuring a strong front-line cast of Barbara Hendricks, John Aler and Gino Quilico. It dates from 1989 and restores a number of cuts and revisions (especially the opera's actual conclusion). The singing is outstanding, the characterisation excellent, the recording sound and balance realistically like those achieved in an opera house. With such a good version currently available there is little point recommending other complete recordings. Better, if you're just after the famous duet, to turn to the legendary Bjoerling/Merrill recording of 1951, which is now on a mid-price RCA CD of Bjoerling which includes music from Puccini and Verdi as well. But this opera has much more to thrill the listener than just this one duet: try the complete set and make a great discovery.

● If you like this, try Bizet's *Carmen* (76)

★
EMI CDS 749837 2
John Aler (tenor)/
Gino Quilico (baritone)/
Toulouse Capitole Chorus & Orchestra/
Michel Plasson

✔
RCA GD 87799
Jussi Bjoerling (tenor)/
Robert Merrill (baritone)/
RCA Victor Symphony Orchestra/
Renato Cellini

Pachelbel
13) CANON IN D

None of Pachelbel's other works has the charm of his famous Canon & Gigue in D. This is perhaps because its simple musical elements are so skilfully knitted together (and so hypnotic in style) that it is impossible to resist its temptations once you have begun listening. The bass line is a strong and ever-present pattern (using a chord progression well known to rock songwriters), supporting the melody and counter-melody as they unfold above it, spreading out among the different instruments for added colour.

The secret to this short work is to play it in such a way that the music does not become disconnected: the whole piece should flow, one theme arising naturally from the other like voices overlapping. There is also a need to keep the instrumental forces small so that the sound does not become unfocused. This is something I Musici know how to do in their sleep, and which they unfailingly deliver on their sprightly 1982 reading of the piece for Philips. The harpsichord adds sufficient colour to keep the harmony moving nicely while the strings sustain a light, airy canon. These people sound as if they are enjoying what they are doing. Equally spirited, but not with quite the same clarity of recording, are Capella Istropolitana under Richard Edlinger for Naxos. These musicians deliver a wholly competent and enjoyable performance, but the zing is a little lacking. If you want authentic instruments (not to everyone's taste so not a general recommendation) there is a fine chamber version on Harmonia Mundi by London Baroque.

● If you like this, try Zipoli's *Elevazione* (208)

★
Philips 410 606-2
I Musici

✔
Naxos 8.550104
**Capella Istropolitana/
Richard Edlinger**

Harmonia Mundi HMC90 1539
**London Baroque/
Charles Medlam**

Barber

14) ADAGIO FOR STRINGS

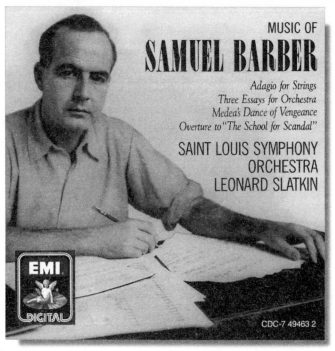

MUSIC OF
SAMUEL BARBER

Adagio for Strings
Three Essays for Orchestra
Medea's Dance of Vengeance
Overture to "The School for Scandal"

SAINT LOUIS SYMPHONY
ORCHESTRA
LEONARD SLATKIN

EMI
DIGITAL

CDC-7 49463 2

Barber's famous piece was first heard as the slow movement of his only string quartet, composed in 1938. It consciously imitates the style and method of Renaissance composers and achieves its intensity through the simplicity and economy of its construction. Barber, pleased to find the movement so enthusiastically welcomed, made an arrangement for string orchestra which then allowed it to be heard in concert halls. It soon became his most famous piece, and although it has been repeatedly associated with war films it seems not to have suffered in the minds of the listening public.

Of the thousands of recordings there are many which, in their haste to squeeze every last drop of pathos from the music, distort it to such an extent that it becomes a very ill-used and unhappy piece. The three recommended here achieve their impact by respecting the message the music is offering, rather than imposing one. The best-judged of the three is by American conductor Leonard Slatkin with the St Louis Symphony. This is part of an all-Barber CD programme. Slatkin takes things slowly, but he respects the music's integrity. There is sorrow and sober re-evaluation here, but not hysteria. Raymond Leppard and the Indianapolis Symphony include Barber in a tour of early 20th-century American composers, of whom, other than Barber, only Gershwin is widely known. The performance is superb, the climax and resolution well judged, but the recording quality rather thin (surprisingly, for it is a new recording). Another American conductor, Michael Tilson Thomas, brings heart-on-sleeve emotion to his rendition. The pace is a little too funereal, but the playing makes up for it well enough. This disc benefits from the *Adagio* being paired with Copland's *Emily Dickinson Songs* and the wonderful Barber orchestral song *Knoxville: Summer of 1915*. Barbara Hendricks sings superbly in both.

● If you like this, try Albinoni's *Adagio* (24)

★
EMI CDC 749463 2
**St Louis Symphony Orchestra/
Leonard Slatkin**

Decca 458 157-2
**Indianapolis Symphony Orchestra/
Raymond Leppard**

EMI CDC 555358 2
**London Symphony Orchestra/
Michael Tilson Thomas**

Saint-Saëns

15) SYMPHONY NO. 3 (ORGAN)

Some composers are so closely identified with a country that it would seem ill-mannered to recommend recordings of their music made by 'foreigners'. Saint-Saëns quite consciously set himself the task of writing music full of what he regarded as French virtues, as opposed to Germanic ones, at a time when the music of Schumann, Brahms, Strauss and Wagner was the *ne plus ultra* of fashion.

At the risk of seeming churlish, then, we'll recommend only one performance with a Frenchman as principal artist, although the EMI recording featuring Wayne Marshall on organ and conducted by Mariss Jansons at least has a francophile at the orchestra's helm. This recording is also the most recent and certainly benefits from of-the-minute technology when it comes to shaking the house's foundations in the last movement, when the organ comes into its own. Chandos's version, which handily combines Saint-Saëns's Third and Second Symphonies on one disc, has a real honest-to-goodness Frenchman conducting, and Yan Pascal Tortelier certainly

brings to the work his innate sense of flair and balance. The organist is Gillian Weir (no francophobe she), and the usual Chandos meticulousness about sound quality means that the last movement should never be played too early on a Sunday morning if you want to stay friendly with the neighbours.

Finally, a perfectly serviceable version with absolutely no French connection is available at budget price in the Sony Essential Classics range. This dates from 1962 and features that winning combination, the Philadelphia Orchestra conducted by Eugene Ormandy. Edward Power-Biggs is on organ. The playing is immensely neat, powerful and disciplined, though there could be a little more elegance from time to time. But at budget level this lets you know just why Saint-Saëns's Third is still worth getting excited about. The disc also comes with serviceable versions of *Carnival of the Animals* and *Danse Macabre*.

● If you like this, try Widor's Symphony No. 5 (75)

EMI CDC 555184 2
Wayne Marshall (organ)/
Oslo Philharmonic Orchestra/
Mariss Jansons

★

Chandos CHAN 8822
Gillian Weir (organ)/
Ulster Orchestra/Yan Pascal Tortelier

Sony SBK 47655
Edward Power-Biggs (organ)/
Philadelphia Orchestra/
Eugene Ormandy

Vivaldi
16) LE QUATTRO STAGIONE

The Four Seasons (Le Quattro Stagioni) are the first four concertos in Vivaldi's eight-concerto group published in 1725 under the title 'Il cimento dell'armonia e dell'inventione' ('challenges of harmony and invention'), Opus 8. They are early examples of 'programme music', being vivid musical illustrations of the earth's seasons, which Vivaldi took the pains to accompany with short, evocative poems. The music starts in Spring, with flowers in bud and birds singing, and runs all through Summer and Autumn to Winter, which is full of stormy blasts of icy winds contrasted with cosy times spent in front of a warm hearth.

Given the almost tangible presence of the everyday natural world in the music, it is a prime concern of any performance to bring these images to radiant life. Too many recordings are colourless and merely stately: this music should thrill and transfix. All three of our chosen performances attempt to do this, but in different ways. The most dazzling and exciting recording by

some distance is by Il Giardino Armonico: some of their ensemble playing takes the breath away, it is so dramatic, so perfectly played, so passionate. They also know how to shape every phrase to give it maximum impact. Nigel Kennedy's recording, with the English Chamber Orchestra, is very spirited, and Kennedy plays with his usual high levels of imagination, but the pictures conjured are not so vivid, the playing a little more traditional in its approach. The Freiburg Baroque Orchestra on Deutsche Harmonia Mundi use original instruments and supply a barer texture than Kennedy's forces. They also take a more studied approach, but the case they argue becomes progressively more convincing as the CD runs on. It is an impressive overall performance, even if the octane levels are down. This, by the way, is the only CD of the three to include Vivaldi's poems for each concerto, although Il Giardino include in theirs Vivaldi's score notes.

● If you like this, try Vivaldi's Mandolin Concerto RV425 (133)

★
Teldec 0630 14619-2
Enrico Onofri (violin)/
Giardino Armonico Ensemble/
Giovanni Antonini

EMI CDC5 56253 2
Kennedy (violin/director)/
English Chamber Orchestra

DHM 05472 77384-2
Gottfried von der Goltz (violin/director)/
Freiburg Baroque Orchestra

Mascagni
17) CAVALLERIA RUSTICANA

This one-act opera, premièred in Rome in 1890, launched both Pietro Mascagni's career and the curiously Italian operatic genre called *verismo*. This supposedly ushered 'realism' onto the operatic stage after decades of operatic hyperbole. However, the situations and plots were generally new twists on the same old melodrama. Mascagni's one massive success, *Cavalleria Rusticana*, doesn't stint on the drama while dealing with low-life characters from 'rustic' Italy to deliver 19th-century 'street credibility'.

Given this approach to music-making, a tenor with a brilliant, large and flexible voice combined with superb acting skills is essential. Equally important is a soprano who will give her all to her part. Certainly the RCA version of the opera conducted by James Levine and featuring a young Placido Domingo and Renata Scotto at her peak delivers all this and more. The 'more' comes in the form of wonderfully detailed orchestral playing, fine late-1970s recording sound and balance, plenty of pace at the right

moments, and singing that combines zest with gimlet-eyed perfectionism. At mid-price this is a bargain (a libretto is included), and you needn't look further. Unless, that is, you'd like to hear the whole thing in English translation. If that's the case, then you're in luck, because Chandos made a recording in English in 1997. A little more sedate than Levine's (this is England, after all), it has David Parry conducting the LPO, with Dennis O'Neill and Nelly Miricioiu in the lead roles. O'Neill in particular comes across as a fully rounded character with believable motivations.

Finally, if it's just the famous bits that generally attract you to classical music, then a goodly proportion of them are contained on a recital CD by Swedish legend Jussi Bjoerling. Recorded in 1952, but in fine sound, it finds his voice in spine-tingling good shape – his *'Brindisi'* has everyone breaking open the wine cases. A mid-price wonder.

● If you like this, try Humperdinck's *Hänsel und Gretel* (363)

★ ✔
RCA 74321 39500-2
Renata Scotto (soprano)/Placido Domingo (tenor)/Ambrosian Opera Chorus/National Philharmonic Orchestra/James Levine

Chandos CHAN 3004
Nelly Miricioiu (soprano)/Dennis O'Neill (tenor)/Geoffrey Mitchell Choir/London Philharmonic Orchestra/David Parry

RCA 09026 68429-2
Jussi Bjoerling (tenor)/RCA Victor Orchestra/Renato Cellini

Fauré

18) REQUIEM

FAURÉ · REQUIEM version 1893

LA CHAPELLE ROYALE · ENSEMBLE MUSIQUE OBLIQUE
PHILIPPE HERREWEGHE

harmonia
mundi
FRANCE
901292

Fauré's *Requiem* is something of a minefield for the record-buyer, for there are at least three different performing texts and whole movements are included or excluded, depending on which version the conductor decides to follow. The John Rutter version here was one of the very first to begin plumbing the mysteries of this musical puzzle, presenting the original 1888 score with its 1893 additions and accompaniment as edited by Rutter himself. This version is entirely different from the 1901 choir-with-orchestra version, standard for most of this century and not authorised by Fauré. The Rutter choir gives us the work in fine detail and good voice, making this a treasurable and enlightening experience.

Herreweghe's version includes all seven movements, first gath·red together in 1893, and uses a boys' choir alongside soprano Agnes Mellon and baritone Peter Kooy. The emphasis is on the gentle, pure sounds Fauré coaxed from his ensemble, with the whole rarely rising above a moderate volume. Fauré was adamantly against the hellfire-and-brimstone idea of a requiem, and there is no doubt that delicacy is a keyword in the performance of this sublime music.

The version presented by Jeremy Summerly and his forces on Naxos is not only a bargain, it's something of a coup for the music, too. Summerly combines the original 1888 performing manuscript along with the movements completed later, with additional orchestration that first appeared in 1897. Apart from that, this is a first-rate performance on its own terms. All of which makes it a tough call when choosing a single version. The only clear conclusion to be drawn is that no sensible Fauré fan would buy a CD performance based on the outmoded 1901 soloists, women's chorus and orchestra version. Bear that in mind when making your choice.

● If you like this, try Fauré's *Cantique de Jean Racine* (50)

Collegium COLCD 109
Caroline Ashton (soprano)/Stephen Varcoe (baritone)/Cambridge Singers/City of London Sinfonia/John Rutter

★

Harmonia Mundi HMC90 1292
Agnes Mellon (soprano)/Peter Kooy (bass)/Petits Chanteurs de Saint-Louis/Chorus of La Chapelle Royale/Ensemble Musique Oblique/Philippe Herreweghe

Naxos 8.550765
Lisa Beckley (soprano)/Nicholas Gedge (bass baritone)/Oxford Schola Cantorum/Oxford Camerata/Jeremy Summerly

---

Handel

19) MESSIAH

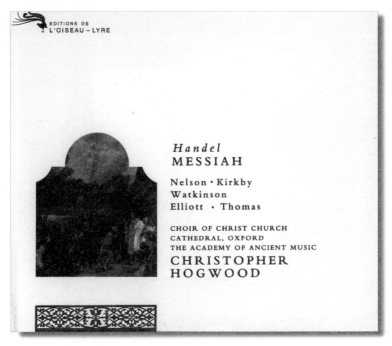

Handel
MESSIAH

Nelson · Kirkby
Watkinson
Elliott · Thomas

CHOIR OF CHRIST CHURCH
CATHEDRAL, OXFORD
THE ACADEMY OF ANCIENT MUSIC
CHRISTOPHER
HOGWOOD

Handel's great *Messiah* has been a cornerstone of British music-making for over two centuries. This is such a powerful work, with such a gripping story, its narrative structure so liberally punctuated by great climaxes and natural pauses, that its oratorio status could be seen as nominal, so close to opera does it sail. This means that the best way to enjoy this pulsating work is not in what Wagner called 'bleeding chunks', but by listening to the whole thing, so that the full meaning of such favourites as the Hallelujah chorus, 'Unto us a child is born' and 'I know that my Redeemer liveth' is revealed and savoured. After all, this is primarily a religious musical experience, and is best enjoyed in that context.

There have been scores of complete recordings of the *Messiah*, such has been its continuing popularity during this century. Of those on conventional modern instruments and using modern singing techniques, the Colin Davis Philips recording from 1966 featuring Helen Watts and Heather

---

✔

Philips 438 356-2
Heather Harper (soprano)/Helen Watts (contralto)/John Wakefield (tenor)/John Shirley-Quirk (baritone)/London Symphony Orchestra & Chorus/Sir Colin Davis

★

L'Oiseau-Lyre 430 488-2
Emma Kirkby (soprano)/Judith Nelson (soprano)/Carolyn Watkinson (contralto)/Paul Elliot (tenor)/David Thomas (bass)/Christ Church Cathedral Choir/Academy of Ancient Music/Christopher Hogwood

✔

Naxos 8.550667
Kym Amps (soprano)/Helen Parker (soprano)/Angus Davidson (alto)/Frances Jellard (mezzo-soprano)/Robin Doveton (tenor)/John Bowen (tenor)/David van Asch (bass/director)/Adrian Peacock (bass)/Scholars Baroque Ensemble

---

Harper represents a tradition that will be recognised by many as a familiar and comfortable one. They also have English accents, which may seem a pedantic point to make, but it does actually help in this most British of baroque oratorios. Both other versions here are also with British singers and musicians, but both use authentic singing and instrumental techniques. This helps unveil the dimensions of the work and restore its most engaging elegance. Christopher Hogwood's pioneering effort of 1980 featuring Emma Kirkby and Judith Nelson with the Christ Church Cathedral Choir still holds up well, striking a fine balance between majesty and delicacy. At the budget end of things, the Scholars Baroque Ensemble on Naxos make a splendid effort on their 1992 recording, although there is perhaps the occasional lack of weight in their 'big' numbers and the instrumental accompaniment.

● If you like this, try Vivaldi's *Gloria in D* (140)

Mendelssohn

20) VIOLIN CONCERTO IN E MINOR
OP. 64

The opening burst of melody from the violin, so urgent, so full of flaming romance, is a sound likely to accompany the listener for hours after a successful rendition of the concerto has finished. It has overtones of Jewish folk music, but its quick urgency also seems to have roots in Romantic literature, as if it were a portrait of a great Byronic figure shrouded in mystery and obscure melancholy. Yet this troubled entry recedes as the pace slackens after the first handful of minutes, and as the orchestra ushers in a change of tonality the violin moves into a more restful, consoling theme. The dialogue between urgent fretfulness and open-hearted serenity continues to the movement's close. Then the great *andante* arrives, with its lullaby melody from the violin and gentle rocking rhythm from the accompanying strings. Midway through the movement the orchestra takes up the serenading briefly, allowing the violinist to regather his forces. This is certainly not a concerto composed merely to impress violinist and audience alike with its technical challenges and ingenious technique. It is meant to convey real and substantial feelings and thoughts through its content. The merry, skipping melody of the last movement affirms that, its sense of happiness a tonic to any troubled brow. There is something childlike in this music, but nothing childish. Its innocence is an emotional rather than an intellectual one. And its charm is complete.

Many violinists have brought their interpretative genius to bear on this quite modestly proportioned work (it lasts just over 25 minutes – short by Romantic standards). At present, the most charismatic modern recording is undoubtedly that of Maxim Vengerov on Teldec, although the traditional approach taken by Josef Suk in 1963 on a mid-price Supraphon reissue is highly convincing and beautifully played.

● If you like this, try Beethoven's Violin Concerto (31)

★

Teldec 4509 90875-2
**Maxim Vengerov (violin)/
Leipzig Gewandhaus Orchestra/
Kurt Masur**

✔

Supraphon 11 1939-2
**Josef Suk (violin)/
Czech Philharmonic Orchestra/
Karel Ancerl**

Decca 421 145-2
**Joshua Bell (violin)/
Academy of St Martin-in-the-Fields/
Sir Neville Marriner**

Dvořák

21) SYMPHONY NO. 9
('FROM THE NEW WORLD')

The movement the whole world knows from this symphony is the *largo*. This contains Dvořák's most obvious – and most inspired – use of what used to be called Negro spirituals. But this is not the only attraction of this dramatic and colourful work. It is stocked full of melodies from both sides of the Atlantic as Dvořák marries the folk traditions of America with those of his native Bohemia in a heady potpourri. The first movement is full of anticipation and excitement, its sense of discovery giving an impression of a tourist's point of view on the world. The third movement has the energy and positive bustle of a modern 19th-century metropolis (which is what Dvořák found in New York), as well as the common touches the flute and woodwinds provide intermittently. The final movement sums up Dvořák's generally positive impression of his adopted country (he was there, fêted and honoured, for three years). There are moments of doubt and what sounds like nostalgia for his homeland – this,

after all, gives the work its necessary tension – but it is an overwhelmingly positive experience.

Karel Ancerl was long associated with the best in Czech conducting traditions and with Dvořák in particular, and his Supraphon recording, though from 1961, gives a good account of that tradition. A Hungarian, Istvan Kertesz, made a complete Dvořák symphony cycle for Decca in the 1960s, regarded as one of the greatest Dvořák sets to this day. It is now available only as a complete cycle in a special budget-priced boxed set. Lastly, Rafael Kubelik, a Czech with this music in his bones, made a number of recordings of the Ninth: the best currently available is that with the Berlin Philharmonic for DGG from 1973. The remastering has kept an old recording fresh enough for a mid-price recommendation.

● If you like this, try Dvořák's Symphony No. 8 (212)

Supraphon 11 1242-2
**Czech Philharmonic Orchestra/
Karel Ancerl**

✔

Decca 430 046-2
**London Symphony Orchestra/
Istvan Kertesz**

★ ✔

Deutsche Grammophon DG 447 412-2
**Berlin Philharmonic Orchestra/
Rafael Kubelik**

---

22) PIANO CONCERTO IN A MINOR

The piano's opening falling octave arpeggio is one of the most famous passages in all classical music and has been copied, parodied and imitated to the point of saturation. However, if one sticks with this concerto it rapidly becomes clear that it deserves its wide popularity. It is cast in the large and tempestuous mould of the great Romantic piano concertos from the likes of Schumann, Tchaikovsky and Brahms, giving the piano the spotlight and all the best melodies while the large orchestra keeps up its commentary on what the soloist is getting up to. Grieg confidently uses his themes in cyclic ways, re-examining them and making them anew by various shifts in emphasis and orchestral colour. By the time the lyrical second movement is upon us we are convinced that this is a concerto to settle in and listen to carefully, for it feels as comfortable as a conversation between old friends. The *adagio* is the concerto's emotional core, and is one of almost unadulterated, uncloying sweetness. The finale is relatively short for a concerto of this era,

but it has its own stunningly beautiful melody, which emerges from the piano some three or so minutes in and transforms the mood into one of dreamy happiness before the upbeat and rapid ending (using a Norwegian dance melody) brings the concerto to a climax begging for a standing ovation.

The type of performance deserving of such an ovation is available from a number of sources, but the most beautiful and poetic version currently on record comes, appropriately enough, from BIS, a label closely associated with quality versions of Scandinavian music. The pianist is Roland Pöntinen, the conductor Leif Segerstam, and the playing is consistently beautiful. Of the other listed versions, the Jandó is utterly traditional in approach but cheap and cheerful; the more interesting of the rest is probably that by the dynamic young Andsnes on Virgin.

● If you like this, try Clara Schumann's Piano Concerto (346)

★
BIS CD 375
Roland Pöntinen (piano)/Bamberg Symphony Orchestra/Leif Segerstam

Naxos 8.550118
Jeno Jandó (piano)/Budapest Symphony Orchestra/Andras Ligeti

Virgin VC 759613 2
Leif Ove Andsnes (piano)/ Bergen Philharmonic Orchestra/ Dmitri Kitaenko

---

Holst

THE PLANETS

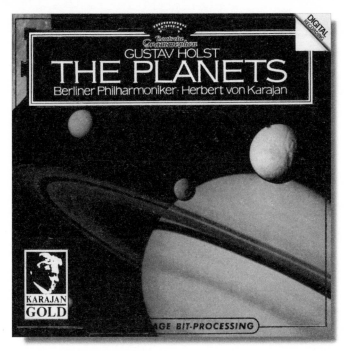

olst had his first big success in 1917 with this suite. Until then he had been one of the lesser-known members of the so-called 'New English Renaissance' in music. The uncompromising modernity of *The Planets* stimulated the imagination of its contemporary audience rather than driving them in terror to the exits. Everybody could – and still can – imagine the character of each planet as it is musically evoked, from the hateful Mars through the venerable Saturn to the mystic Neptune. All the orchestra and conductor have to do is match Holst's imagination. Needless to say, many don't, but our three choices have no problems responding to the challenge.

Sir Adrian Boult's is the oldest of the three recordings, dating from 1967. Boult was chosen by Holst himself to give the 1917 première, so there is little doubt that he knows what he is doing here. This, his fourth recording of the suite, finds him and the New Philharmonia in fine fettle, although the recording balance is not too impressive. Still, there is

no denying the magic of Boult's vision of the piece: he is one of a handful wanting to balance the blood-and-glory approach with a puckish spirit.

Such considerations are swept aside by the famous but brutal aural assault organised by Karajan and the BPO. In a DGG recording dating from 1980, Karajan sets the pulses racing and the nervous diving for cover. He is also in control of the score's intricacies, as are his engineers. This is a convincing juggernaut. Interestingly, Karajan makes Holst's music sound less English, more part of the European mainstream of his day: understandably, then, Puck doesn't make an appearance.

In the same year as Karajan, Sir Alexander Gibson made a highly creditable recording of the work for Chandos, and although he rushes Mars somewhat this is an organised approach. Certainly good enough to be recommended at mid-price.

● If you like this, try Saint-Saëns's *Carnival of the Animals* (101)

EMI CDM566934 2
**New Philharmonia Orchestra & Chorus/
Sir Adrian Boult**

★

Deutsche Grammophon DG 439 011-2
**Berlin RIAS Chamber Choir/
Berlin Philharmonic Orchestra/
Herbert von Karajan**

Chandos CHAN 7082
**Royal Scottish National Orchestra/
Sir Alexander Gibson**

Albinoni
24) ADAGIO

BAROQUE MASTERPIECES

NAXOS

DDD
8.553221

ALBINONI: Adagio
CORELLI: Christmas Concerto
HANDEL: Largo • Alexander's Feast
MARCELLO: Oboe Concerto
PACHELBEL: Canon & Gigue

Most people know by now that Albinoni didn't in fact compose the single most famous piece of music associated with his name, the so-called *Adagio*. This was cobbled together by 20th-century musicologist Remo Giazotto from various Albinoni excerpts, and scored by him for organ and strings. What Albinoni would have made of this we cannot possibly know, but he was a gifted amateur addicted to the spotlight, so there is good reason to believe he would have been happy to have his name in front of the public again, even by proxy. Since the initial success of this short but intense fragment, recordings of it have poured from the studios of the world in abundance, using virtually every instrumentation known to man. In the spirit of the original, which was an arrangement to start with, John Cameron arranged Giazotto's arrangement, this time for choir, organ and strings, setting it to the words of the Gospel of St Matthew. It makes as much of the music as any other reading, so it can be bought with safety in the version delivered by Edward Higginbottom's New College Choir. The accompanying selections are all pretty lugubrious, so be prepared for a wet Kleenex afternoon.

Both I Musici and Capella Istropolitana (directed by Richard Edlinger) stick to the Giazotto arrangement, and both are pretty slow, making the whole experience almost funereal. It is possible to buy versions where the pace is just a little more sprightly, the atmosphere not quite so desolate, but that may defeat the purpose. Choosing between two such well-played instrumental versions is not that easy – both are part of programmes of famous baroque music, with the Naxos collection being the fresher repertoire and also available at budget price. That, combined with its digital sound quality, must make it a best buy.

● If you like this, try Tallis's *Spem in Alium* (157)

Erato 3984 21659-2
**Choir of New College, Oxford/
Capricorn/
Edward Higginbottom**

Philips 410 606-2
I Musici

★

Naxos 8.553221
**Pavel Bogacz (violin)/
Capella Istropolitana/
Richard Edlinger**

Allegri
25) MISERERE

Allegri was of the generation of Italian composers that came to maturity following Palestrina's death. Few of his works are performed or recorded with any regularity, which is one of the reasons why this list of recommendations consists exclusively of choral music compilations. Allegri's famous motet is in a minor key and its text, Psalm 50, deals with a sinner's humble supplication to God to absolve him of his many wrongdoings. Its stately pace and sense of humility in the light of the Creator are immediately attractive when sung by any competent choir, while its repeated use of the solo high C for a boy soprano is heart-stopping when performed properly.

Edward Higginbottom and the Choir of New College take an ethereal approach on their *Agnus Dei* compilation for Erato. They sing the piece in F# minor, whereas the other two choirs sing it in G minor, so the sonorities are different. The soprano voice tends to get a little lost in the diffuse recorded sound favoured by the Erato engineers. Hyperion also use a 'cathedral' sound for their rendition (which, unlike Erato's, sticks with Renaissance choral music rather than wandering through the centuries), but the music sounds much better knitted together, and every line is quite clearly delineated. EMI's King's College recital directed by Stephen Cleobury features a well-structured programme, concentrating on music from the Renaissance. The sound is considerably more distinct than either of the others, which occasionally exposes some vocal imperfections and minor wobbles, but it has a persuasive point of view.

● If you like this, try Tavener's *Song for Athene* (168)

Erato 0630 14634-2
**Choir of New College, Oxford/
Edward Higginbottom**

★

Hyperion CDA 66850
**Westminster Cathedral Choir/
James O'Donnell**

EMI CDC 747065 2
**Choir of King's College, Cambridge/
Stephen Cleobury**

J. S. Bach

26) CONCERTO FOR TWO VIOLINS
BWV 1043

J. S. BACH
Solo & Double
Violin Concertos

Andrew Manze · Rachel Podger
The Academy of Ancient Music
Andrew Manze, *dir.*

S ome of Bach's most melodically seductive music was written, appropriately enough, under the influence of his great Italian contemporaries, Albinoni and Vivaldi. What makes the double concerto BWV so diverting is a wonderful combination of robust compositional intellect and utter sweetness of melodic and harmonic simplicity. Any classically trained violinist with an intact soul will give heartfelt performances of this work, so it is hardly surprising to find hearts conspicuously worn on sleeves in the chosen recordings here. Most interesting is the balance struck by the authentic instrument brigade, represented by Andrew Manze and the Academy of Ancient Music, for Harmonia Mundi. In the faster outer movements both the ensemble and the two soloists are full of bustle and trenchant tones. When it comes to the famous *largo*, the tones sweeten and the long dual lines of Bach's inspiration are spun to mesmerising effect. This is no milk-and-water study: the blood is coursing freely through the veins of this performance.

It is a similar end result for Yehudi Menuhin and the Bath Festival Orchestra (recorded in 1960), although the methods are a little different. Menuhin and his cohorts are using modern instruments and techniques, but the passion is equal to that displayed by Manze's group. This is great music-making, regardless of era, and the sound quality holds up well. A bargain at mid-price.

With the third of our selections, Jeanne Lamon and Tafelmusik take the authentic instruments approach. This yields a more fragile sound to the whole enterprise, though Lamon is a player who likes to establish her presence and takes a lyrical approach. Tafelmusik's precision and clarity bring a chamber-like elegance to the music which it wears well, but those in search of the more universal side of Bach's masterpiece may prefer the Academy's Harmonia Mundi outing.

● If you like this, try Vivaldi's Double Concerto for Mandolins (299)

★
Harmonia Mundi HMU90 7155
Rachel Podger (violin)/
Andrew Manze (violin/director)/
Academy of Ancient Music

✔
EMI CES 568517 2
Yehudi Menuhin (violin/director)/
Christian Ferras (violin)/
Bath Festival Orchestra

Sony SK 66265
Jeanne Lamon (violin)/
Linda Melstead (violin)/Tafelmusik

Verdi
27) NABUCCO

With its vast chorus, large orchestra and heroic arias depicting the deliverance of the Jews from Babylonian captivity, everything about *Nabucco*, premièred in 1842, is larger than life. For a start, although there are starring roles for the usual soprano, tenor and baritone, the chorus itself plays as much of a front-line role as anyone else. Even though the usual combination of doomed love across political and societal (and, in this opera, racial) divides dominates the plot, it is the context given by the chorus which makes it really matter, just as with Aida's tragedy within the top echelons of Pharaohonic Egyptian society.

Both recordings of *Nabucco* recommended here have strong front-line casts, with perhaps Gardelli's Tito Gobbi having the edge as Nabucco (Nebuchadnezzar) over his rival. The tragic role of Abigail is perhaps best served by Guadagno's Monica Pick-Hieronimi, a German singer who has made her mark in Italian opera roles. Which leaves us with the choruses and the conducting. Gardelli's chorus and orchestra are suitably overwhelming, sometimes blasting the unwary listener with walls of sound, but they are not the most disciplined of crews. Guadagno's version, although recorded live at Verona's huge Roman amphitheatre, manages a good balance between orchestra and choir and delivers the weight of sound while not neglecting the tidiness essential to a convincing delivery. Too much raggedness destroys the sense of monumentality and just makes things sound chaotic on a grand scale. So if it's the choruses and the general heroic nature of the work which grab you, then go for the Guadagno.

● If you like this, try Verdi's *Aida* (55)

★

Decca 417 407-2
Tito Gobbi (baritone)/
Elena Suliotis (soprano)/
Vienna State Opera Orchestra & Chorus/
Lamberto Gardelli

Koch 36427-2
Paolo Gavanelli (bass)/
Monica Pick-Hieronimi (soprano)/
Verona Arena Orchestra & Chorus/
Anton Guadagno

Rimsky-Korsakov
28) SCHEHERAZADE

Written in 1888, at the height of the late Romantic movement's obsession with exoticism of all types, this symphonic suite is for many people some of the most wonderfully descriptive 'programme music' ever composed. Rimsky-Korsakov loved the tales of the *1001 Nights* and decided that this symphonic suite would bear the name of the great story-teller Scheherazade herself. The keynotes here are excess, sensuality, hedonism and luxury, and woe betide the conductor who evokes a less than enthusiastic response from his orchestra. No fear of that occurring with the three conductors selected here.

Mariss Jansons demands a brooding, menacing atmosphere from the LPO in the first movement, *The Sea and Sinbad's Ship*, as Scheherazade desperately manoeuvres to outwit her vengeful husband and begins her tale: the restless rhythmic surge sweeps us all along as if we were on board deck in the most frightful storm. Elsewhere he unveils a delicate and romantic touch.

Barenboim and the Chicago Symphony generally take a more sophisticated approach to the music and its images, stressing not only the drama of the tales but also the skill and humour of the storyteller herself. Both orchestras sound almost opulent in timbre and tone, with Barenboim going more for painterly subtleties than the broad brush strokes favoured by Jansons. They are equally rewarding in their approach and both sets, recorded in the 1990s, have spectacular sound.

The version recorded by Fritz Reiner in the 1960s, also with the Chicago Symphony Orchestra, still scares the unwary listener witless with its forceful, precise and vivid accounts of the stories. Only in the string section sound, which lacks a fully rounded tone, is the date of the recording obvious. The Young Lovers also sound like they're approaching middle age. Yet at mid-price these are minute drawbacks. Add in Reiner's perfectionist discipline and you have a memorable evening of musical storytelling before you should you plump for this version.

● If you like this, try
Khachaturian's *Masquerade*
(300)

★

EMI CDC 555227 2
London Philharmonic Orchestra/
Mariss Jansons

Erato 4509 91717-2
Chicago Symphony Orchestra/
Daniel Barenboim

✔

RCA GD 60875
Chicago Symphony Orchestra/
Fritz Reiner

Rodrigo

CONCIERTO DE ARANJUEZ

Music of Spain
Rodrigo
Concierto de Aranjuez
Fantasía para un gentilhombre
Tres piezas españolas
Invocation et danse
John Eliot Gardiner • Leo Brouwer

Julian BREAM EDITION
VOLUME 28

This was Spanish composer Rodrigo's first concerto, completed in 1939 and very quickly a success the world over. The Aranjuez of the title is a Madrid palace that used to be the summer haunt of the old Bourbon kings in centuries past. This helps explain the grace and dignity of the music, as well as its liveliness. The first movement, given a 'Fandango' title, emphasises dance and evokes images of flamenco dancers and their accompanying troupes of guitars, strings and percussion. Rodrigo's careful balance between soloist and orchestra allows the smallest sound to come through clearly. The slow second movement has a hint of melancholy from its opening minor-key theme, played first by the woodwinds, then finally in its complete form by the solo guitar, which embellishes seemingly at will. It is this haunting movement which has kept the *Concierto* near the top of the classical popularity lists for decades. Certainly it is the work's emotional core, and one that places a burdensome spotlight on the guitarist, who must maintain forward momentum while not short-cutting the emotion.

All three guitarists listed on these recordings are capable of maintaining that balance. Alfonso Moreno and Enrique Batiz bring the required passion and character to the work, Moreno proving adequate to the task in the slow movement's unaccompanied section, but the real fireworks occur, predictably, with the other two star soloists. John Williams brings his beauty of tone and his deep understanding of phrase and gesture to his performance with Louis Frémaux on a mid-price Sony reissue. Julian Bream, however, sweeps away any thoughts of calm, dispassionate assessment with the torrents of emotion he unleashes in the slow movement during his 1982 performance with John Eliot Gardiner for RCA. This, plus his unerring plasticity of phrase and variance of tone, makes him, at mid-price, the natural choice.

● If you like this, try Tárrega's *Recuerdos de la Alhambra* (191)

EMI CES 568532 2
Alfonso Moreno (guitar)/
Mexico State Symphony Orchestra/
Enrique Batiz

✔

Sony SK 37848
John Williams (guitar)/
Philharmonia Orchestra/Louis Frémaux

★ ✔

RCA 09026 61611-2
Julian Bream (guitar)/
Chamber Orchestra of Europe/
John Eliot Gardiner

Mozart
30) REQUIEM

Perhaps the most famous thing about Mozart's Requiem is that he didn't finish it: the work had to be completed by his friend and fellow-composer Franz Sussmayr. This, and the fact that an already mortally ill Mozart was commissioned by a mysterious and anonymous patron (some said the Devil) to write the work, has given this famous piece the status of a last will and testament with supernatural overtones. The truth is, as ever, more prosaic. Mozart, like every other freelancer, accepted what commissions came his way, and undertook this one because it paid reasonably. The patron was a Viennese count and amateur musician who loved fooling his friends by passing off the work of professionals as his own: thus the anonymity.

The profundity of Mozart's music is, as ever, reached through refinement, balance and harmony, not through bombast. All three recordings of the work here reflect

that approach. William Christie's Les Arts Florissants take the authentic instruments approach, giving the orchestral playing a brightness and clarity often lacking in more conventional productions. His choir and soloists are not remotely operatic about things, and this is all for the good, giving back the music its purity and religious integrity. A similar story is told on the Harmonia Mundi recording under the baton of Philippe Herreweghe, where the keywords for the whole project might be grace and dignity.

George Guest takes the traditional path to musical salvation with the English Chamber Orchestra. His choir and soloists use techniques suited to the music but not especially inspired by 'authentic' practice. But Guest is careful not to make his forces too big or his sound unmanageable.

● If you like this, try Mozart's Mass in C Minor (242)

★

Erato 0630 10697-2
Anna Maria Panzarella (soprano)/Nathalie Stutzmann (contralto)/Christoph Prégardien (tenor)/Nathan Berg (baritone)/ Les Arts Florissants/William Christie

Harmonia Mundi HMC90 1620
Sibylla Rubens (soprano)/Annette Markert (contralto)/Ian Bostridge (tenor)/Hanno Muller-Brachmann (baritone)/Orchestre des Champs Elysées/Chorus of La Chapelle Royale/Collegium Vocale/Philippe Herreweghe

Chandos CHAN 7059
Yvonne Kenny (soprano)/Sarah Walker (mezzo-soprano)/William Kendall (tenor)/David Wilson-Johnson (baritone)/ Choir of St John's College/English Chamber Orchestra/George Guest

---

Beethoven
31) VIOLIN CONCERTO

Beethoven's only violin concerto was premièred in Vienna in 1806 during one of the most creatively active periods of his career. It was conceived on a scale not attempted before, its first movement alone being longer than most other concertos of his time. The ambitiousness of its design delayed its acceptance as a 'great' work, but today it is incontrovertibly regarded as one of the greatest concertos ever composed, regardless of instrument. Its overall mood is perhaps best described as a cross between pensive and apprehensive, as if the music were a consolation for a string of reverses in everyday life. Consolation it most definitely is to anyone with experience of the world.

All three violinists listed here are supreme virtuosi who long ago transcended the search for an individual stylistic voice and a technique with which to express it. Nigel Kennedy's recording comes from a live concert in 1992, and he is accompanied by a conductor of the first rank, Klaus Tennstedt. Their tempi are quite slow, allowing Kennedy plenty of room to establish his ruminative and dignified approach. He chooses the first-movement *cadenza* written by Fritz Kreisler. Two unaccompanied Bach violin pieces make up the rest of the programme. Tennstedt is also the conductor on our second choice, Kyung-Wha Chung's 1989 recording for EMI. Her bright, silvery tone is given weight by the refined gravitas of her approach, helped as she is by Tennstedt's complete understanding of the work's import. She also uses the Kreisler *cadenza*, and her CD coupling is the Bruch concerto. Finally, it is impossible to write of this concerto without praising the genius of Jascha Heifetz. His RCA recording with Charles Munch may date from the 1950s, and the sound may not be up to today's standards, but his playing is phenomenally accurate, his tone majestic and his phrasing a dream. He also plays his own *cadenza*. If you are not worried by non-digital sound, then don't miss Heifetz. If you're after something more up to date, Kennedy will do fine.

● If you like this, try Paganini's Violin Concerto No. 1 (137)

★

EMI CDC 754574 2
Kennedy (violin)/North German Radio Symphony Orchestra/Klaus Tennstedt

EMI CDC 7540722
Kyung-Wha Chung (violin)/ Concertgebouw Orchestra, Amsterdam/Klaus Tennstedt

✔

RCA 09026 61742-2
Jascha Heifetz (violin)/Boston Symphony Orchestra/Charles Munch

---

Beethoven

32) SYMPHONY NO. 5

For decades after World War II the first movement of this symphony was the most well-known piece of classical music in Britain, having been used in BBC broadcasts during the war itself as the 'victory' theme. These days it has slid down the popularity stakes somewhat, but its urgent message still rings out loud and clear. Beethoven was dealing with the ideas of fate and freedom, destiny and self-determination, and these qualities are at the heart of the musical struggles that galvanise every listener who follows Beethoven's design through to the end. In this symphony (as in most of Beethoven's major works) there is a positive outcome – freedom and good win over evil and suppression.

A lot of the time conductors are all too concerned with fashioning some image of themselves and Beethoven as superheroes struggling against the world in general and a cruel fate in particular. Thus the achievement of David Zinman and the Tonhalle Orchestra,

Zurich, is considerable. Zinman, the first to record using the new, corrected scholarly editions of Beethoven's symphonies, brings a stunning new sense of scale and scope to these works, which mostly disappear under the heavy weight of larger orchestras. He allows a proper ebb and flow of dynamics by not pressing for all-out white-hot intensity in every phrase. This beautifully played version becomes the top recommendation: sensational at budget price, too. For those who want the older approach with large forces, the most forceful argument is mounted by Carlos Kleiber and the Vienna Philharmonic from 1975, while the recent 1996 recording by Christian Thielemann with the Philharmonia shows how even good performances can lose their shape through the adoption of a late Romantic approach.

● If you like this, try Schubert's Symphony No. 9 (100)

★

Arte Nova 74321 49695-2
**Zurich Tonhalle Orchestra/
David Zinman**

Deutsche Grammophon DG 447 400-2
**Vienna Philharmonic Orchestra/
Carlos Kleiber**

Deutsche Grammophon DG 449 981-2
**Philharmonia Orchestra/
Christian Thielemann**

Schubert

33) 'TROUT' QUINTET

Chamber music is well known in the recording industry as a turn-off for most music-lovers – almost as much a turn-off as the average lieder recital. However, there are exceptions. With Schubert's 'Trout' Quintet, the exception is huge, for the work is one of the most popular in the repertoire and has been for over 100 years. Incredibly, this year it came above *La Bohème*, *Carmina Burana* and *Madama Butterfly*, to name three at random, in the Hall of Fame. And it is a beautiful and inspired piece of music, rather than a cynically calculated audience pleaser. What next!

There are three fine performances to choose from. In all piano-plus-chamber-strings recordings there is a problem of balance: the piano so easily overwhelms the strings. The Philips recording featuring Alfred Brendel with a quartet led by Thomas Zehetmair overcomes this obstacle with ease, the strings losing none of their natural body

while the piano, though clearly audible, is never predominant. This, plus sensitive readings which avoid sentimentality, places Brendel's rendition high on any list. Equal to it in terms of performance, but a poor second in terms of recording sound, is the famous 1958 Decca album by Clifford Curzon and the Vienna Octet members. No amount of digital fussing can conceal the basic inadequacy of the recording, so this is a 'must' performance for connoisseurs only. More truly recorded but something of an acquired taste is the Naxos performance featuring Jeno Jandó and the Kodaly Quartet. The music is played superbly but the recording is oddly distanced, as if the microphone were at the other end of a small hall. If you can get used to this, then Jandó's is a very enjoyable rendition.

● If you like this, try Schubert's String Quintet in C (67)

★
Philips 446 001-2
Thomas Zehetmair (violin)/
Tabea Zimmermann (viola)/
Richard Duven (cello)/
Peter Riegelbauer (double bass)/
Alfred Brendel (piano)

✔
Decca 417 459-2
Clifford Curzon (piano)/
Vienna Octet

✔
Naxos 8.550658
Jeno Jandó (piano)/
Kodaly Quartet

Sibelius

34) FINLANDIA

inlandia, appropriately given its title, was meant as a patriotic gesture towards Sibelius's homeland when, in 1899, Finland was under the Russian Czar's yoke and craving freedom. Its brooding, threatening opening paints a grim picture indeed of a dark land under the control of dark forces. Through highly skilful use of interlocking themes and gradually brightening harmony, Sibelius brings the work full circle to the point where, in the final measures, the orchestra calls out wordlessly in unison 'Finland awake!' Hearing this in a concert hall never fails to stir the emotions (and the patriotic sentiments, even for non-Finns). On record the detail can occasionally disappoint under a less than watchful conductor allowing the crescendo towards the end to lose its shape. It can also stall in the immediate aftermath of the dramatic opening, where strings and woodwinds move through a series of static chord progressions. But a watchful conductor negotiates these pitfalls without concern. This is the case with Neeme Järvi on his BIS collection of Sibelius concert favourites. This is a taut and seamless performance that carries the listener along through its hidden artistry, Järvi allowing the music the continuity it craves as one theme and section succeeds another. There are currently two versions on Chandos, both of them below full price. Leif Segerstam has a recital which is good value at mid-price, recorded in the 1990s and with intelligent direction from the conductor. A late 1970s production with Sir Alexander Gibson, now at budget price, is less well recorded and a little dull in places, but good value at its price point. The other mid-price recommendation for *Finlandia* comes from the eponymous label with Okko Kamu conducting. But Järvi is first choice.

★

BIS CD 610
**Gothenburg Symphony Orchestra/
Neeme Järvi**

✔

Chandos CHAN 7075
**Danish National Radio
Symphony Orchestra/
Leif Segerstam**

Finlandia 4509 95844-2
**Helsinki Philharmonic Orchestra/
Okko Kamu**

● If you like this, try Sibelius's *Valse Triste* (296)

Beethoven
35) SYMPHONY NO. 7

You'd be hard pressed to fall asleep in a concert hall during a half-decent performance of the first movement from the Seventh. Its remorseless concentration on rhythmic drive and its general excitement level leave most audiences on the edge of their seats, nicely poised for the shock of surprise delivered by the serenely beautiful melody which introduces the second movement: a melody that has become famous worldwide and is used in many other contexts. The final movement needs to be cast in bright colours, the fast rhythms shaded to distinguish them as they come and go, and the beauty of contrast must be uppermost in the conductor's mind.

Taking a typically extreme stance towards the work (albeit with a regular modern-day symphony orchestra in the Vienna Philharmonic) is Carlos Kleiber in his 1976 DGG recording. He manages the contrasts well and is always eager to push his orchestra, but there are points in the symphony, especially in the first movement, where bombast and volume overcome the natural ebullience of the writing. David Zinman finds more dynamic shade and precision through a less frantic tempo in the beginning of the opening movement, although his timings are generally shorter. His interpretation of the stately dance melody of the second movement is full of grace and charm. His is my first choice over Klemperer's 1956 EMI version, if only for the gulf in recording techniques between the two. Klemperer manages an equally sane and well-balanced recording (the word 'humane' keeps presenting itself), and those not bothered by non-digital sound will find it holds up brilliantly. But the Zinman gets the recommendation. And it is at budget price.

● If you like this, try Beethoven's Symphony No. 8 (323)

Deutsche Grammophon DG 447 400-2
**Vienna Philharmonic Orchestra/
Carlos Kleiber**

★ ✔

Arte Nova 74321 56341-2
**Zurich Tonhalle Orchestra/
David Zinman**

✔

EMI CDM 566795 2
**Philharmonia Orchestra/
Otto Klemperer**

Rachmaninov

36) PIANO CONCERTO NO. 3

Rachmaninov was already a major international star when he completed this concerto in 1909, fêted on both sides of the Atlantic as both composer and pianist, so it was no surprise to find his latest concerto the toughest yet from a technical point of view (some pianists still declare it the most difficult ever written). Yet the work was a failure on its New York début, and it took years of promotional toil by Rachmaninov and other virtuosi, especially Horowitz, to establish it as a popular favourite. Listening to it today, this seems strange. From the opening statement the music is warm and nostalgic, the minor introductory theme sounding folk-like and welcoming. True, there are some shattering climaxes, but Rachmaninov is careful to resolve these into romantic lyricism, however bittersweet.

For music like this, which is as exotically Russian-sounding as Borodin or Mussorgsky, it is appropriate to turn to Russian pianists. Evgeni Kissin is the youngest, being just 21 when he made his 1993 recording in Boston Symphony Hall with Seiji Ozawa. The sound is spacious, as befits this expansive music, but his reading is understated, as if for some reason the blood wasn't flowing fast and strong that night. No such problems with Lilya Zilberstein and Claudio Abbado, who keep the full bloom of colour on every pianistic and orchestral note, and who are also careful to point up the folk origins of some of the themes. Equally full of life and character is Ashkenazy with André Previn. His effortless technique and silvery sound illuminate Rachmaninov's essentially private, withdrawn, Romantic soul. At mid-price this has to be a first recommendation.

● If you like this, try Shostakovich's Piano Concerto No. 2 (88)

RCA 09026 61548-2
**Evgeni Kissin (piano)/
Boston Symphony Orchestra/
Seiji Ozawa**

Deutsche Grammophon DG 439 930-2
**Lilya Zilberstein (piano)/
Berlin Philharmonic Orchestra/
Claudio Abbado**

★ ✔

Decca 436 386-2
**Vladimir Ashkenazy (piano)/
London Symphony Orchestra/
André Previn**

Puccini
) LA BOHÈME

Puccini had been trying unsuccessfully to become the pre-eminent Italian opera composer after Verdi for the best part of a decade when things finally clicked – and sensationally so – with *La Bohème* in 1896. In this work Puccini unveiled a melodic gift uniquely his and an unerring ability to match his orchestral effects to his vocal line. This, and an understanding of rhythmic vitality second only to Verdi's, are the two qualities at the core of his best work.

Although a stickler for quick tempos, Sir Georg Solti had a tremendous instinct for drama and a genuine enjoyment of good singing. On this set, recorded in London in 1974, he must have been in heaven, for he had Domingo at an age close to that of his character, Rodolfo, and full of youthful ardour and humour, while Montserrat Caballé as Mimi would melt the hardest heart. Her miraculously pure, creamy voice is the essence of girlish purity.

Roberto Alagna and Angela

Gheorghiu are equally ardent in their 1990s recording under the baton of Riccardo Chailly, but oddly enough the extra clarity the improvement in recording technology brings diminishes the intimacy of the production. The voices are also a mite too prominent. Yet both Alagna and Gheorghiu are too intelligent and talented not to bring depth and beauty to their roles.

As pure as Caballé's is the glorious voice of Victoria de los Angeles in the famous EMI version by Sir Thomas Beecham in 1956. That quality is matched by tenor Jussi Bjoerling opposite her, and Beecham himself comes as near perfection in conducting this music as anyone on record. Yet it is impossible to ignore the boxy recording sound. This is a classic of 20th-century recording, but best left until you are familiar with the music from a modern recording. At that point it can be intoxicating.

● If you like this, try Verdi's *La Traviata* (73)

RCA 74321 39496-2
**Monserrat Caballé (soprano)/
Placido Domingo (tenor)/Wandsworth
School Boys' Choir/John Alldis
Choir/London Philharmonic Orchestra/
Sir Georg Solti**

Decca 466 070-2
**Angela Gheorghiu (soprano)/Roberto
Alagna (tenor)/Orchestra & Chorus of
La Scala, Milan/Riccardo Chailly**

EMI CDS 556236-2
**Victoria de los Angeles (soprano)/
Jussi Bjoerling (tenor)/Columbus Boys'
Choir/RCA Victor Chorus & Orchestra/
Sir Thomas Beecham**

Carl Orff

38) CARMINA BURANA

The whole point of a recording of this work is to blow the roof off the building and deliver a buzz of excitement rarely matched in choral music. The opening sequence, 'O fortuna' (heard in a million different media contexts around the world, from film soundtracks to advertisements), has such an impact with its thumping drums, explosive brass, jubilant singing and its sense of anticipation that it cannot fail to pull the unwary listener in. The rest of the work may be something of a foreign country for the average TV watcher or radio listener, but there is plenty more dramatic music and gripping melody to be found. It just comes in different guises, including solo singing and beautiful, transparent scoring for orchestra (something Orff would develop further with *Catulli Carmina*, his next work in this genre).

Given all this, a successful recording is going to have to knock your socks off from bar one. The performances listed here certainly manage that. Strangely enough, two of them are American: perhaps Americans' love of the spectacular allows them to let it all out better than others. Robert Shaw and the Atlanta Symphony deliver a hefty opening punch, their percussion and choir meshing nicely. With Judith Blegen and Hakan Hagegård as two stirring soloists, this 1981 odyssey in sound is not going to disappoint. But if you want your raw nerves really tweaked, then the blatant sensuality and almost violent percussive attack of Leonard Slatkin's 1994 version for RCA Red Seal is the clear choice, especially with soloists such as Sylvia McNair and John Aler (Hakan Hagegård is also on this one). At budget level, the recent Arte Nova version conducted by Ross Pople packs a punch for a small fiscal outlay on the part of the listener.

● If you like this, try Mussorgsky's *Pictures at an Exhibition* (103)

Telarc CD 80056
Judith Blegen (soprano)/William Brown (tenor)/Haken Hagegård (baritone)/ Atlanta Symphony Orchestra & Chorus/Robert Shaw

RCA 09026 61673-2
Sylvia McNair (soprano)/John Aler (tenor)/Haken Hagegård (baritone)/ St Louis Symphony Orchestra & Choir/Leonard Slatkin

Arte Nova 74321 34048-2
Anne Liebeck (soprano)/Martyn Hill (tenor)/David Barrell (baritone)/Tallis Chamber Choir/New London Children's Choir/London Festival Orchestra/Ross Pople

Puccini

39) **MADAMA BUTTERFLY**

Butterfly (regarded as a notorious failure on its Milan opening in 1904) was Puccini's own favourite among his operas: he fretted over it long after he'd abandoned *Tosca* and *La Bohème* to any impresario who wanted to produce them. It is easy to understand his concerns: the plot is very simple, the action sparse. The fragile character of the childlike Butterfly and the betrayal of her love and desires work only if the audience identifies completely with her. The atmosphere by which she is constantly cocooned has to be invoked and sustained by consistently inspired orchestral accompaniment. If one element fails, the whole work crumbles.

Consequently there are many recordings that don't quite work. The three versions here all have weaknesses, but there is enough good in them to make them recommendable. The newest recording is from James Conlon. It is one of a tiny handful which has attempted to use a Butterfly (Ying Huang) anywhere near the age of the character she is singing. Her voice is vibrantly youthful and innocent and she has amply expressive control in the big arias. Pinkerton is sung adequately by Richard Troxell, while the

orchestral accompaniment is deft without being revelatory.

The second recommendation, from 1974, is Herbert von Karajan conducting Mirella Freni and Luciano Pavarotti. Karajan is anxious to register every orchestral nuance, and in this he is successful: the orchestra sings as sweetly as the singers themselves. The bit parts are as vividly played as the central characters, while the two leads give convincing performances. Pavarotti reflects his character's impetuousness and chauvinism perfectly. The recorded sound is superb and well balanced.

The third version is from the early 1960s: it features some pretty rough orchestral playing and listless direction from Gabriele Santini, and the sound leaves something to be desired. But it has the incredible voice of Victoria de los Angeles as Butterfly in a role that suits her perfectly, plus outstanding tenor work from Jussi Bjoerling. Not a version to recommend as a first-time buy – try either of the above for that – but one to savour if you want to broaden your appreciation of this opera and its history.

● If you like this, try Puccini's *Tosca* (115)

★

Sony S2K 69258
Ying Huang (soprano)/Richard Troxell (tenor)/Radio France Chorus/Paris Orchestra/James Conlon

Decca 417 577-2
Mirella Freni (soprano)/Luciano Pavarotti (tenor)/Vienna State Opera Chorus/ Vienna Philharmonic Orchestra/ Herbert von Karajan

EMI CMS 763634 2
Victoria de los Angeles (soprano)/Jussi Bjoerling (tenor)/Rome Opera Orchestra & Chorus/Gabriele Santini

---

Prokofiev

40) ROMEO AND JULIET

When Prokofiev composed *Romeo and Juliet* in 1935, shortly after his return to Russia, both the subject-matter and the delicate, lyrical nature of much of the music came as something of a shock to his public. So much so, in fact, that the ballet remained unseen until 1938, and then its première was in Czechoslovakia, not Russia. His homeland had to wait until a Leningrad production in 1940. By then Prokofiev had already extracted his first orchestral suite from the stage work. In 1946 and again in 1947, two more suites of extracts were premièred, by which time the ballet and its concert versions had become the most widely loved new classical dance score since Tchaikovsky's death, *The Rite of Spring* included.

Given the work's background, it is apt that the first recommendation – for the entire ballet – comes from Valery Gergiev and the Kirov Orchestra, Leningrad. The conductor misses no nuance of humour, no twist in the simple plot of the doomed lovers, and brings tremendous vitality to what is a dance score full of compelling rhythms. The recorded sound is sonorous: this is a full-blooded love affair, although the portraits are never crude. The sound on Järvi's recording of the three suites for Chandos is, if anything, even more immediate. From the opening bars of 'Folk Dance', there is a spirit and attack which brings the electricity of the affair into stark relief. There is plenty of blood and fire here, but this ever-alert conductor is always at pains to bring out the smallest details of Prokofiev's brilliant scoring. Esa-Pekka Salonen's recording for Sony with the Berlin Philharmonic is equally as finely drawn as Järvi's. He uses the opulent sound of his orchestra to concentrate more on the romance of the tale and its setting – no bad thing, depending on where you position yourself on this classic love story.

● If you like this, try Tchaikovsky's *Romeo and Juliet* (72)

★

Philips 432 166-2
**Kirov Opera Orchestra/
Valery Gergiev**

Chandos CHAN 8940
**Royal Scottish National Opera/
Neeme Järvi**

Sony SK 42662
**Berlin Philharmonic Orchestra/
Esa-Pekka Salonen**

Tchaikovsky

41) PIANO CONCERTO NO. 1

MARTHA ARGERICH
Tchaikovsky · Piano Concerto No.1
Berliner Philharmoniker · Claudio Abbado
The Nutcracker-Suite
(for two pianos)
Nicolas Economou

Tchaikovsky the passionate melodist certainly stood up to be counted with this, his first piano concerto. From the glorious opening declamation by the brass, soon followed by those tremendous piano chords in slow 3/4 time chiming out over the orchestral melody, this work has everything in it writ large. The soloist is given plenty of opportunity to impose their personality on the piece, yet it is not solely about pulling out all the stops and making as much noise as possible in an orderly fashion. The slow second movement is full of calm, reflective passages, the melodies calculated to soothe the tempestuous feelings unleashed by the storms of the first movement. The last movement's energy has significantly less of the emotional turmoil of the first, concentrating instead on fleet pianistic fireworks against rolling triplet rhythms and a climax which, though noisy, is at least celebratory.

Pianists who successfully negotiate this concerto have big personalities of their own which they are not afraid to project. The earliest recording here, from 1963, features the quixotic Sviatoslav Richter at the piano with Herbert von Karajan and the Vienna Symphony. Richter is dynamite in this music, playing with incredible precision, a jewel-like sound and great expression. Karajan's accompanying is first-rate. Equal to Richter, and three decades newer, is the Martha Argerich performance with Claudio Abbado and the Berlin Philharmonic. Argerich has a tiger-like energy in this piece, accompanied by a seemingly limitless technique. It is debatable whether the BPO reach the Viennese levels of sensitivity and precision, but there is more depth in the sound registration. For a very different view of this music (and an amazing account of Scriabin's Piano Concerto), the curious should seek out Nikolai Demidenko's highly individual treatment on Hyperion.

● If you like this, try Tchaikovsky's *Capriccio Italien* (161)

✔
Deutsche Grammophon DG 447 420-2
Sviatoslav Richter (piano)/
Vienna Symphony Orchestra/
Herbert von Karajan

★
Deutsche Grammophon DG 449 816-2
Martha Argerich (piano)/
Berlin Philharmonic Orchestra/
Claudio Abbado

Hyperion CDA 66680
Nikolai Demidenko (piano)/
BBC Symphony Orchestra/
Alexander Lasarev

Vaughan Williams

42) FANTASIA ON A THEME OF THOMAS TALLIS

A collection of wonderful tracks from one of Britain's most popular composers

vaughan williams
the ultimate collection

includes The Lark Ascending, Fantasia on a Theme by Thomas Tallis, Greensleeves, The Wasps Overture, and many more

omposer Elizabeth Lutyens once dismissed the entire English Pastoral composers' output of the early 20th century as 'cowpat music'. While some of the lesser lights deserved such derision, Vaughan Williams did not: his music was never that narrowly based. Ample proof of this is the Tallis *Fantasia*, a remarkable and sombre meditation on an English Renaissance composer's original theme. No cows, trees and chirping birds here – the echoes are of austere variations on plainchant and religious fervour.

The version made for Teldec by the BBC Symphony Orchestra under the baton of Andrew Davis in 1991 is superb. This is meat-and-potatoes repertoire for Davis and his aggregation, music he has lived with and performed for many years. He judges the sombre mood of the piece to perfection but does not ignore the almost sensual delights of the slow-moving harmony as the piece unfolds. The recording quality helps tremendously, for the sound is transparent, allowing complete

and faithful reproduction of the entire orchestral sound.

Bryden Thomson makes an equally persuasive case for the piece on his Chandos disc of Vaughan Williams's shorter works. Thomson opts for a slightly faster tempo, moving the work away from the darker depths of meditation favoured by Davis, but he and the LPO retain the emotional intensity that is so important to any successful reading of the piece. Both Thomson and the famous 1960s Barbirolli disc offer attractive programmes of accompanying music and neither are at full price. The Barbirolli recording is justly famous, for it is an unabashedly romantic reading of the music, but the earlier recording date means that the sound is a little compressed compared with Teldec's 1991 sound. Still, if you need a Tallis *Fantasia* in a hurry and this is the only one available, it won't disappoint.

● If you like this, try Delius's *Walk to the Paradise Garden* (222)

★
Teldec 3984 22125-2
BBC Symphony Orchestra/ Andrew Davis

Chandos CHAN 9775
London Philharmonic Orchestra/ Bryden Thomson

EMI CDC 747537 2
Allegri String Quartet/ Sinfonia of London/ Sir John Barbirolli

Rachmaninov

43) SYMPHONY NO. 2

This symphony starts in a dark place, as if dawn is yet to arrive. The oppressive weight is gradually lifted as the strings are allowed to begin singing in typically Rachmaninovian vein, delineating a melody both beautiful and melancholic. The mood and the tempo continue to lift as if a morning mist is slowly being burned off by the winter sun, and we finally glimpse a landscape of inordinate beauty: a Russia which existed in Rachmaninov's imagination, perhaps. The elegiac mood develops and becomes almost Elgarian (the Englishman was completing his first symphony as Rachmaninov premièred his second) before plunging into more crises. The drama lasts until the end of the movement and a switch into a much more urbane, civilised *allegro*. The following *adagio* produces the most serene music of the symphony, a lazy and luxuriant melody which ranks as one of Rachmaninov's most pleasantly insinuating. In the final *allegro vivace* the orchestra plays bustling themes with brio before the peacefulness

of earlier descends once again. After moving between the various states aroused by the music he has created, Rachmaninov finally plumps for celebration and reassurance in a noisy and rousing coda.

Svetlanov tackles the work of his fellow Russian with spirit and insight: the occasional rawness and lack of finesse from his woodwinds and the generally over-spacious acoustic (a mid-1960s Melodiya trait) aside, he is a serious contender. His version certainly has the raw urgency the music needs. Mariss Jansons for Chandos makes a finely judged recording, but the orchestra suffers from a strange lack of presence: highly unusual from Chandos's normally impeccable team. With the Previn EMI recordings currently unavailable, this leaves the venerable 1959 Eugene Ormandy as a brilliant budget-priced bargain.

● If you like this, try Rachmaninov's *Vocalise* (351)

★ ✔
Melodiya 74321 40064-2
**Bolshoi Theatre Orchestra/
Evgeni Svetlanov**

Chandos CHAN8520
**Philharmonia Orchestra/
Mariss Jansons**

✔
Sony SB2K 63257
**Philadelphia Orchestra/
Eugene Ormandy**

Beethoven

44) SONATA NO. 14 OP. 27 NO. 2
'MOONLIGHT'

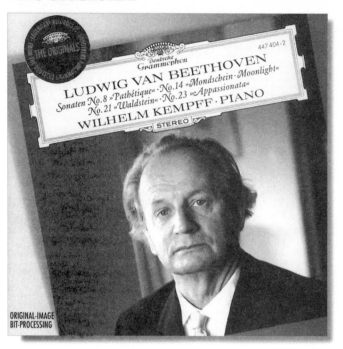

The soulful minor-key arpeggios that characterise the first movement of Beethoven's 'Moonlight' Sonata are some of the most brutalised bars of music ever played. So many pianists, through the use of leaden hands, funereal tempos and endless pressing of the sustain pedal, have taken their mystery and hidden drama as an excuse to make sure that not a whit of mystery or drama is left by the end of the movement. Yet when it is approached with no such preconceptions, when the pianist is content to let his ego come second to that of Beethoven's, then the magic begins. The piece regains its proportions.

Such a performance is that of Wilhelm Kempff. Kempff made two memorable complete sets of Beethoven sonata recordings for DGG, one in the 1950s in mono, one in the 1960s in stereo. The present recommendation is for the stereo version. A philosopher of music, Kempff goes for the music's core of meaning, judging the exact character of each phrase, each movement. Equally gifted and just as poetic, but a touch more mercurial in temperament, is Emil Gilels in another famous 1960s interpretation for the same record company. The fire of the third movement is awesome, but always appropriate. Both these versions are mid-price.

Alfred Brendel's Philips recording comes from 1984. He plays with complete authority and avoids any hint of bathos, although his is a deeply frowning moon-worshipper. Yet there is poetry in Brendel's playing, and his *allegretto* is poised if rather formal. The *presto finale* is a close-run thing which occasionally conjures thoughts of horse races rather than storm clouds, but the refinement of technique is always impressive. The recorded sound is resonant and clear.

● If you like this, try Beethoven's Piano Sonata No. 8 (Pathétique) (169)

✔
Deutsche Grammophon DG 400 036-2
Emil Gilels (piano)

★ ✔
Deutsche Grammophon DG 447 404-2
Wilhelm Kempff (piano)

Philips 438 863-2
Alfred Brendel (piano)

Tchaikovsky

45) SYMPHONY NO. 6
'PATHÉTIQUE'

One long, beautiful howl of anguish is one way of describing this brilliant but deeply neurotic symphonic masterpiece. It was the last major work completed by the composer, who conducted its première in St Petersburg in 1893. There is no mistaking the intensely personal nature of this music, which many observers have noted carries an autobiographical subtext. If to some ears it sounds like film music (and it has been used as such on a number of occasions) it accompanies the film of Tchaikovsky's life. Yet no matter how overheated the whole thing becomes, how insistent and explosive, the abiding memory is of heart-wrenching tunes scored to perfection. Tchaikovsky knew exactly how to give artistic shape to his sufferings.

An inspired (and inspiring) performance of the 'Pathétique' must be ready to plumb the deepest depressive depths (the opening of the last movement) and scale the heights of resolution and triumph (the close of the third movement), as well as meeting every challenge on the scale of emotions along the way. It must also keep its musicianly discipline. If all these concerns are met, then the listener is in for a very intense experience indeed. This is certainly the case with the Russian National Orchestra under Mikhail Pletnev. His 1991 recording is searing in its intensity but not at all bombastic in its rhetoric. The recording quality is first-rate and, at budget price, this is a bargain. Long famed for his Tchaikovsky interpretations is Herbert von Karajan. His is a dark and claustrophobic reading, the resonant studio sound adding to the oppressive weight in the music. This mid-price version is also highly recommendable. Most startling in their grim viewpoint are Mariss Jansons and the Oslo Philharmonic, who paint the work in the colours of mourning without resorting to crude orchestral effects. Jansons also manages the right level of cheer in the gayer movements. Full price it may be, but it is a winning interpretation.

● If you like this, try Tchaikovsky's *Serenade for Strings* (224)

✔
Virgin VBD 561636 2
Russian National Orchestra/
Mikhail Pletnev

Deutsche Grammophon DG 439 020-2
Vienna Philharmonic Orchestra/
Herbert von Karajan

★
Chandos CHAN 8446
Oslo Philharmonic Orchestra/
Mariss Jansons

J. S. Bach

46) BRANDENBURG CONCERTOS

Bach's series of masterful concertos, probably written during the 18th century's second decade, were never intended to form a coherent cycle, as were Vivaldi's *Four Seasons*. All six concertos were gathered together and dedicated to Christian Ludwig of Brandenburg as a selection of pieces for his court chamber orchestra. This explains why individual concertos are often performed or recorded separately, and why few people listen to all six concertos in a row, as one would a suite or symphony.

Still, it would be a foolhardy person who would decline to consider these six graceful and stimulating works in a collected CD edition. The first choice, from the Akademie Für Alte Musik, Berlin, dating from 1998, newly available at mid-price, presents the music as an exciting adventure, bursting with ideas and almost conversational in its relationship with the listener. It takes very little imagination to hear a whole series of convivial musical dialogues going on throughout the ensemble, from strings to horns to

woodwinds and back to strings, all with their distinct personalities. The use of 'authentic instruments' and a proper chamber size give the music excellent separation and lightness of texture, while the musicians are never afraid of giving proper vent to their enthusiams, bringing often surprising colour to Bach's music.

Jordi Savall's 1991 recording for Astree uses his own consort, Le Concert des Nations, and brings a similar clarity of line and profile to the music, his 'authentic instruments' blending buoyantly. There is less expressive range in the playing, but it is never less than lively.

A reliable version in the conventional manner is available on EMI by Yehudi Menuhin and the Bath Festival Orchestra, where the music is just as lovingly played as on any latter-day version. It may be old but it's good, especially given the low price.

● If you like this, try Bach's *Orchestral Suites* (105)

Harmonia Mundi HMX295 1634/5
Akademie Für Alte Musik, Berlin

Astree E8737
**Concert des Nations/
Capella Reial Instrumental Ensemble/
Jordi Savall**

EMI CES 568516 2
**Bath Festival Orchestra/
Yehudi Menuhin**

Smetana
47) MÁ VLAST

Nationalism enabled both Dvořák and Smetana to escape the smothering cultural influence of German and Austrian music-making and develop their own musical identities. Both men made the connection plain by the titles they chose for their works. Smetana's *Má Vlast* (literally meaning 'my country' or 'my fatherland') is a suite of tone poems depicting various aspects of Czech landscape, life and culture, dedicated by its composer to 'the city of Prague'.

The two most famous sections of the cycle are *Vltava* ('The Moldau'), musically depicting the journey of the river that runs swiftly by Prague itself, and *From Bohemian Woods and Fields*, another loving musical portrayal of the Czech countryside. Our first choice, with Neeme Järvi conducting the Detroit Symphony, conjures a changing stream of images from the musical score as the river moves downstream from its source. Järvi does not drive the music too hard, and does not resort to crude hammering at the climaxes,

allowing the natural swell of expectation in the music to do its own work through to the cheerful, upbeat conclusion. The equally vivid but more dramatic natural depictions in the latter movement allow Järvi to flex the orchestra's muscle, but its balance is never lost, the detail not obscured.

The second recommendation comes from the concert given by Rafael Kubelik on his return to Prague after the Velvet Revolution, and is teeming with the emotion of the occasion. It may not be the most polished of performances, but the circumstances make it treasurable. Our third choice, from Antoni Wit on the Naxos label, is orderly and disciplined, the Polish National Symphony orchestra playing with precision. A perfectly serviceable introduction to the composition at budget price, it is not, however, a recording to rival the others for inspiration.

● If you like this, try Kodály's *Háry János Suite* (384)

★
Chandos CHAN 9366
**Detroit Symphony Orchestra/
Neeme Järvi**

Supraphon 11 1208-2
**Czech Philharmonic Orchestra/
Rafael Kubelik**

✔
Naxos 8.550931
**Polish National Radio
Symphony Orchestra/
Antoni Wit**

Grieg

48) PEER GYNT SUITE NO. 1

Grieg's music for Ibsen's early drama is generally as incidental and meandering as the great playwright's plot. Although it contains a great many gems it is not often heard in its entirety for two reasons: the play itself is rarely staged, being very costly to mount and not one of Ibsen's masterworks; and the forces needed for a concert hall performance don't justify the ends. Grieg saw early on that his music would disappear without trace with no natural venue, so he fashioned two concert suites, taking the best and most characteristic music (and leaving the vocal pieces behind). The Suite No. 1 contains just four pieces. The famous 'Morning Mood', dominated by the four-note flute arpeggio, opens the suite. Second is 'Aase's Death', a mournful dirge from the strings; this is followed by the considerably more cheerful 'Anitra's Dance', a beautiful and exotic waltz which would have graced even a Tchaikovsky ballet. Lastly there is the creepy and malevolent 'In the Hall of the Mountain King',

which builds to a fevered and highly unpleasant climax.

There are many recordings of this music, but Herbert Blomstedt and the San Francisco Symphony, in their 1991 recording for Decca, manage a brilliantly clear and crisp recorded sound with an attentive reading which allows the full scope of Grieg's musical imagination to be appreciated. Equally convincing, but with an all-American cast, is Leonard Slatkin on Telarc. This is a selection from both suites, giving us all Suite 1 and two of the four pieces from Suite 2: the rest of the programme is the two suites from Bizet's *Carmen*. If your appetite is whetted by now, a fine modern recording of the complete incidental music from the play – vocals, choir and all – is available on DGG from Neeme Järvi and the Gothenburg Symphony. For the suite alone (he includes the second suite), stick with Blomstedt.

● If you like this, try Grieg's *Holberg Suite* (145)

★
Decca 425 857-2
**San Francisco Symphony Orchestra/
Herbert Blomstedt**

Telarc CD 80048
**St Louis Symphony Orchestra/
Leonard Slatkin**

Deutsche Grammophon DG 437 523-2
**Gothenburg Symphony Orchestra/
Neeme Järvi**

Rachmaninov

49) RHAPSODY
ON A THEME OF PAGANINI

RACHMANINOV

NAXOS

DDD
8.550809

Piano Concertos Nos. 1 and 4
Rhapsody on a Theme of Paganini

Bernd Glemser, Piano
Polish National Radio Symphony Orchestra
Antoni Wit

The Paganini Rhapsody (not so much a Rhapsody as a theme with a sequence of no less than 24 separate variations) was composed in 1934 when Rachmaninov was a worldwide celebrity. In a sense it was a salute from the great composer-virtuoso of one century to that of the previous century. Rachmaninov was not alone in his impulse, for other composers – Brahms included – had used Paganini's theme, which comes from his *24 Caprices for Violin*. Its jaunty, compact and symmetrical nature lends itself to artful new inventions limited only by each composer's imagination. Rachmaninov alternates brilliant explosions of piano technique and orchestral fireworks with quiet lyricism and romantic reflection: there is truly something here for everyone. What is more, Rachmaninov managed to come up with two themes – the initial arrangement of Paganini's melody and the rapturous 18th variation – which are two of the most famous passages of music in the world today.

Charisma is a key element in

bringing off an entrancing performance of this work. All three pianists in this list bring such a quality to their playing. Vladimir Ashkenazy and André Previn delivered a version for Decca which remains something of a benchmark. Ashkenazy, this time conducting the Cleveland Orchestra, with Jean-Yves Thibaudet at the piano, also produces a sparkling account of the variations in superb sound. Yet, considering that both recordings involving Ashkenazy have just the Piano Concerto No. 2 as a companion piece, with the 1972 Previn disc being mid-price and the other full price, we should not overlook the budget-priced delights of Bernd Glemser and Antoni Wit on Naxos. Resisting the temptation to grandstand which marred their interpretation of the Second Piano Concerto, these artists pull off a memorable set of variations and throw in the First and Fourth Concertos for a very full CD programme. Hard to top.

● If you like this, try Rachmaninov's Piano Concerto No. 1 (283)

✔
Decca 417 702-2
**Vladimir Ashkenazy (piano)/
London Symphony Orchestra/
André Previn**

Decca 440 653-2
**Jean-Yves Thibaudet (piano)/
Cleveland Orchestra/
Vladimir Ashkenazy**

★ ✔
Naxos 8.550809
**Bernd Glemser (piano)/
Polish National Radio Symphony
Orchestra/Antoni Wit**

50) CANTIQUE DE JEAN RACINE

DDD
8.550765

FAURÉ

Requiem

Messe basse
Cantique de Jean Racine

VIERNE: Andantino
de SÉVERAC: Tantum ergo

Lisa Beckley, Soprano
Nicholas Gedge, Bass-Baritone
Schola Cantorum of Oxford
Oxford Camerata
(Instrumental Ensemble)
Jeremy Summerly, Conductor

This simple, brief and flowingly melodic setting of a canticle written by the 17th-century poet Jean Racine won Fauré a prize for composition in 1865 while he was still a student at Paris's Ecole Niedermeyer. After that it languished unpublished for over a decade while Fauré got on with other, more pressing projects. What is so immediately attractive about this music is its utter lack of sentimentality. Fauré wrote this and his other choral music specifically for church usage, rather than as opportunities for concert-hall pose-striking. Its emotions are unvarnished yet readily accessible, its musical language uncomplicated although highly skilled.

Given this, the things to look for in a performance of the Cantique are a determination to stick to the sound it would naturally generate in a church or cathedral, a complete lack of artifice in the singing and playing, and a performance that does not exaggerate either the mood or the style of the piece. The Hyperion recording featuring the Westminster Cathedral Choir, Iain Simcock and James O'Donnell conjures a direct liturgical image: you really feel as if you're sitting in the cathedral pews listening to a powerful choir singing quietly. With the Naxos performance by Jeremy Summerly's Oxford-based group, the mood is even more church-based, the sound more intimate. The instrumental accompaniment, as with O'Donnell, comes from a pipe organ. With John Rutter's performance on his Collegium label this is expanded to violas, cellos, basses and harp, using an arrangement by Rutter himself, shifting the tone away from a church setting and more towards a concert stage. It is a beautiful performance but is perhaps a step or two away from where the music works its magic best. Given all this, perhaps the place to start is with the first-rate budget-priced performance on Naxos by Summerly's musicians and singers.

● If you like this, try Barber's *Agnus Dei* (210)

Hyperion CDA 66669
Iain Simcock (organ)/
Westminster Cathedral Choir/
James O'Donnell

★ ✔

Naxos 8.550765
Colm Carey (organ)/
Oxford Schola Cantorum/
Jeremy Summerly

Collegium CSCD 500
Cambridge Singers/City of London
Sinfonia/John Rutter

Tchaikovsky

51) 1812 OVERTURE

This work is one for which no amount of bombast could ever be described as too much. In making such a claim, I am reassured that the composer himself had a similar opinion. Tchaikovsky wrote the work in 1880 to a commission that called for as much pomp and patriotism as possible, and although he declared in a letter that the overture 'probably has no merit, as I wrote it without warmth or love', the general public have showered it with affection ever since. After all, who can resist a work calling not only for a massive orchestra but cathedral bells (real, not faked) and actual cannon shot? That plus the liberal usage of patriotic themes (including a number of despairing flashes of 'The Marseillaise' as Napoleon's troops figuratively meet their doom) is guaranteed to stir the heart.

So – who wins out in the battle of the large noise? Antal Dorati and the Minneapolis Symphony make a valiant effort,

all trumpets blazing, and their cannon sound like howitzers (although in fact they are 'authentic instruments'), but they get a little lost in their cathedral bells in the grand finale before the final rout. Erich Kunzel and his Cincinnati Pops boys weigh in with a bludgeoning campaign that will seriously test any audio equipment deployed at high volume (the CD cover comes with a warning, 'Caution – digital cannon', so you know you're in for a sustained assault). But if you want the job finished off for good, leave it to those peace-loving Swedes. The Gothenburg Symphony, Brass Band, Artillery Division and Church Bells all storm in under the direction of Neeme Järvi in one final push which delivers them full-on (and full-price) victory.

● If you like this, try Tchaikovsky's *Marche Slave* (345)

✔
Mercury 434 360-2
**Minneapolis Symphony Orchestra/
Antal Dorati**

Telarc CD 80041
**Cincinnati Symphony Orchestra/
Erich Kunzel**

★
Deutsche Grammophon DG 429 984-2
**Gothenburg Symphony Orchestra,
Chorus & Brass/
Neeme Järvi**

Massenet

52) MEDITATION FROM 'THAÏS'

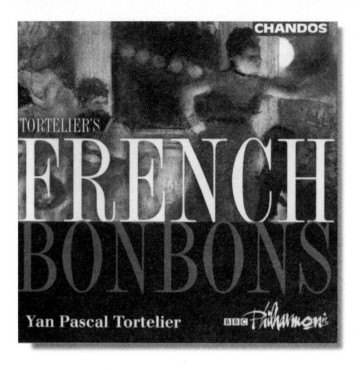

Thaïs is a Massenet opera more notorious than famous. It has never been a great success on stage or record, although it is occasionally recorded: its crude subject-matter (a rather vulgar story of venal sex and sensuality involving the eponymous courtesan) never really tallies with the generally ethereal music accompanying it. However, one piece has proved to be resilient in its ability to please the public. This is the 'Meditation', for violin, harp and orchestra, which accompanies Thaïs's thoughts as she contemplates her acceptance into the nunnery in which she will die. It starts with a harp arpeggio, then blossoms with the long-spun and slightly lugubrious melody from the violin which is the piece's reason for fame. It is typically French in its appeal to both the spiritual and the sentimental in the listener.

Violinists have recorded this short piece in their scores, and with just about every conceivable type of accompaniment. Here we have limited the choice to conventional formats: two versions for violin and orchestra (plus harp) and an arrangement for violin and piano. Anne-Sophie Mutter, being the big-league violinist that she is, tends to prefer a forward position in the mix, so the violin in her recording is an 'in your face' experience. Considering the operatic setting of the music, this is hardly ideal, although her playing is very convincing. Interestingly, her version lasts over six and a half minutes, while the version for Chandos by Yan-Pascal Tortelier with Yuri Torchinsky on violin finds a more natural opera-house balance between all the instruments and lasts just under five minutes. This recital is one of a group of 19th-century French 'bon-bons' from various sources, whereas Mutter's collation crosses various boundaries of time and space. Lastly, a violin-piano recital by Josef Suk emphasises grace and sentimentality in the salon and encore tradition.

● If you like this, try Fauré's *Pavane* (142)

Deutsche Grammophon DG 447 070-2
**Anne-Sophie Mutter (violin)/
Vienna Philharmonic Orchestra/
James Levine**

★

Chandos CHAN 9765
**Yuri Torchinsky (violin)/
BBC Philharmonic Orchestra/
Yan-Pascal Tortelier**

Supraphon 11 1311-2
Josef Suk (violin)/Josef Hála (piano)

Shostakovich

53) THE GADFLY

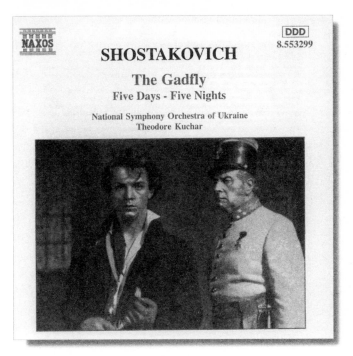

NAXOS

DDD
8.553299

SHOSTAKOVICH

The Gadfly
Five Days - Five Nights

National Symphony Orchestra of Ukraine
Theodore Kuchar

Shostakovich was nothing if not resourceful: during a long composing career he wrote music for just about every medium going, from concert hall to ballet, opera and film score, as well as for state occasions. The music for the film *The Gadfly* was completed in the mid-1950s and gave Shostakovich the opportunity to mimic a whole range of 19th-century Romantic composing styles. Snippets of Tchaikovsky, Massenet, Borodin and even Saint-Saëns continue to waft past the listener's ears as the music develops and the plot thickens. This was all highly appropriate for a pot-boiler of a novel that could easily have served as a plot for one of Verdi's more melodramatic swashbuckling operas. The famous love scene melody, played in bittersweet melancholic vein by a single violin against string section beats, could have come directly from Massenet. Other sections are extremely noisy and energetic: at any moment, you feel, Errol Flynn may come bursting into the fray.

With this in mind, the major ingredients in any successful recording of this music are lots of colour, lots of dramatic contrast and real red-blooded commitment from the orchestra. These are to be found in spades on the Riccardo Chailly version, where the Philadelphia Orchestra is happy to exaggerate every attitude in the excerpts they have chosen. They make this film score music sound like film score music, where heroes and villains, maidens and murderers all parade in front of your ears as you recall the context. Theodore Kuchar, in a Naxos release, makes an equally enthusiastic noise at budget price. This time we get the concert suite from the score, and in a version by the NSO of Ukraine which stresses its Russian media connections: this is Moscow Film Unit, not Hollywood, and very likable for that reason.

● If you like this, try Shostakovich's *Jazz Suite No. 1* (196)

Decca 452 597-2
**Philadelphia Orchestra/
Riccardo Chailly**

★

Naxos 8.553299
**Ukraine National Symphony Orchestra/
Theodore Kuchar**

Mozart

54) LE NOZZE DI FIGARO

It's all too easy to speak of the great Mozart operas as 'immortal', 'timeless' and other such gush. True, they are peerless in their realm, but it's important to remember what that realm was. Mozart undoubtedly saw an opera such as *The Marriage of Figaro* primarily as an entertainment. There is no harm in recognising the quality of the music or the unusual depth of characterisation, but the first thing here must be the sheer enjoyment of the thing. This is an 18th-century comedy with serious undertones, not an angst-ridden Romantic melodrama. If a production misses that, then it's missed everything.

Needless to say, the three performances chosen here have not forgotten the basics. Harnoncourt benefits from the latter-day drive for performing authenticity which he did so much to inspire 30 years ago. His *Figaro* suffers no cuts to the action and is happy to include all the recitative, ebulliently delivered by Tom Hampson, Barbara Bonney and the rest of the cast.

Fricsay's *Figaro* is a little more

★
Teldec 4509 90861-2
**Anton Scharinger (baritone)/
Barbara Bonney (soprano)/Thomas
Hampson (baritone)/Charlotte Margiono
(soprano)/ Netherlands Opera Chorus/
Royal Concertgebouw Orchestra/
Nikolaus Harnoncourt**

✔
Deutsche Grammophon DG 437 671-2
**Renato Capecchi (baritone)/Irmgard
Seefried (soprano)/Dietrich Fischer-Dieskau
(baritone)/Maria Stader (soprano)/
Berlin RIAS Chamber Choir/Berlin Radio
Symphony Orchestra/Ferenc Fricsay**

✔
Decca 466 369-2
**Cesare Siepi (bass)/Hilde Gueden
(soprano)/Alfred Poell (bass)/Lisa della Casa
(soprano)/Vienna Stata Opera Chorus/
Vienna Philharmonic Orchestra/Erich Kleiber**

mischievous than Harnoncourt's, his orchestral overture bursting with sly fun and a touch of bumptiousness, while the Figaro of the young Dietrich Fischer-Dieskau and the Susanna of Irmgard Seefried are perfectly matched and wonderfully cheeky. They (and Maria Stader as the Countess) are all in wonderful voice. The earliest recording here, from 1955 under the baton of Erich Kleiber, is every bit as lively as that of Fricsay but a deal more straight-faced, both in orchestral direction and in the approach of the singers. The humour is made more obvious, not so knowing and light. It's a matter of inter-pretation, however, for the level of performance is very high indeed, the singing wonderfully idiomatic. No superstar antics here to spoil things. The recording quality is not as good as the other two, despite the latest remastering process. All three versions have librettos with parallel English text.

● If you like this, try Mozart's *Cosi fan Tutte* (120)

Verdi

55) AIDA

*A*ida is one of the most spectacular of all grand operas: its première in 1871 took place at the foot of the Geza pyramids and used a cast of thousands. Its story is the usual one of love crossing socio-political boundaries. This time the heroic young man is a member of the Egyptian royalty, the heroic young girl a slave who turns out to be the daughter of the Ethiopian king. Eventually the two doomed lovers are sealed in a tomb together. Verdi's music is endlessly resourceful in its capacity to change scale, style and direction to suit each scene and make these stock characters come vividly alive. Aida gets the most famous aria ('Rittorno vincitor'), but the duets with Radames are equally affecting, while the part played by the chorus is key in giving the work its scope and historical context.

There have been many recordings, despite the prohibitive costs of mounting a new production: Verdi's masterpiece exerts an enduring fascination. The oldest of the three

---

✔

RCA (mono) GD 86652
Zinka Milanov (soprano)/Fedora Barbieri (mezzo-soprano)/Jussi Bjoerling (tenor)/ Rome Opera Orchestra & Chorus/ Jonel Perlea

★ ✔

Decca 460 978-2
Renata Tebaldi (soprano)/Giulietta Simionato (mezzo-soprano)/Carlo Bergonzi (tenor)/Vienna Singvereien/ Vienna Philharmonic Orchestra/ Herbert von Karajan

Deutsche Grammophon DG 410 092-2
Katia Ricciarelli (soprano)/Elena Obraztsova (mezzo-soprano)/Placido Domingo (tenor)/Orchestra & Chorus of La Scala, Milan/Claudio Abbado

---

recommended here is that of Jonel Perlea, from 1955, in good mono, and has Zinka Milanov as Aida. The great diva was no longer close to the age of the role she was playing, but her outsize vocal personality makes this a memorable interpretation. Jussi Bjoerling is a sweet-voiced Radames, Fedora Barbieri a stern Pharaoh. Perlea's conducting is a mite routine. This is a charge that could never be waged at von Karajan, whose classic 1959 recording for Decca with Tebaldi and Bergonzi in the lead roles concentrates on the grand scale and the lushness of the orchestral settings. Tebaldi, though, is magnificent. The sound and the conducting are even better with Abbado in 1982, and Domingo is a dashing Radames, but Katia Ricciarelli is too insecure technically as Aida for this to be a prime recommendation. In the Egyptian desert stick with Karajan.

● If you like this, try Verdi's *Il Trovatore* (220)

Handel

56) SOLOMON

Handel's 1749 oratorio *Solomon* may be a masterpiece equal in stature to his 1741 *Messiah*, but the complete work has never enjoyed the same sustained popularity, even though the text is in English. Yet it has never been entirely forgotten, for one of its orchestral passages has for many decades been one of the great British and European concert-hall favourites. This is 'The Arrival of the Queen of Sheba'. As the title suggests, the music combines the ceremony and dignity associated with royalty and the nervous, excited expectation usually associated with the long-anticipated fulfilment of a coming event. The music is also quintessential busy, elaborate, thrusting and colourful Handel and, in the context of the overall composition, works beautifully as a contrast to the more lyrical and genteel music found elsewhere in the piece.

Solomon is packed full of elegant solo melody and impressive choruses in the *Messiah* tradition, which makes it a work fully deserving of investigation at leisure. However, it is not often recorded (just two versions in the past two decades), so the version recommended here, directed by Paul McCreesh and featuring Andreas Scholl, is not only a superb achievement, it is virtually the sole choice. It is, McCreesh claims, the first really complete recording of the work, and it uses period instruments and singing techniques, so those who despair of such an approach will not be happy. Those of a less traditional cast of mind will enjoy the experience immensely.

When it comes to Sheba's arrival, there are many versions available as an excerpt on a range of baroque compilation CDs. The ASMF recording with Iona Brown on Hänssler preserves its vivaciousness and sense of occasion, while the budget-price Chandos collection of baroque classics uses a fast-paced and stimulating interpretation by Cantilena conducted by Adrian Shepherd.

● If you like this, try Gluck's *Orfeo ed Euridice* (87)

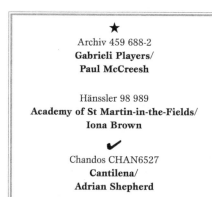

★
Archiv 459 688-2
**Gabrieli Players/
Paul McCreesh**

Hänssler 98 989
**Academy of St Martin-in-the-Fields/
Iona Brown**

✔
Chandos CHAN6527
**Cantilena/
Adrian Shepherd**

Brahms
57) VIOLIN CONCERTO

Do you take the traditional approach to Brahms, which sees him as a beacon of the conservative musical establishment, not too good at orchestral scoring and as unsmiling and correct as an over-zealous customs official? Or do you lean towards the idea of him being, at heart, a romantic revolutionary who liked nothing better than writing a huge-hearted and passionate piece of music? On the evidence of the best current recordings of his only violin concerto, opinion remains deeply divided.

The inspired virtuosity of Maxim Vengerov, accompanied on his 1999 Teldec recording by Daniel Barenboim and the Chicago Symphony, is certainly channelled towards passionate outpourings of the soul. He gives a performance bursting with every kind of ardour. Barenboim and his orchestra take a much more stolid approach, generally settling for slower-than-normal tempos and an absence of the grand orchestral gesture. This offsets Vengerov very effectively, but it makes the piece less of a dialogue between ensemble and soloist than it can be in others' hands.

Nikolaus Harnoncourt, with Gidon Kremer as the soloist, looks for quicker tempos and cleaner orchestral sonorities, giving the whole thing a much greater sense of urgency and tension. Kremer responds fully to this challenge. The recording is generously coupled with a version of the Double Concerto.

No one would dare argue with the third choice here as being a towering achievement. It's old, dating from 1955, but it is by arguably the greatest violinist of the century, Jascha Heifetz, accompanied by the Chicago Symphony conducted by Fritz Reiner. As with everything Heifetz did, this is a hard-driven, no-quarter-given reading. Heifetz's tone and phrasing cut through like a laser beam, and you'd need to be tone deaf not to get shivers down your spine, despite the inferior studio acoustics and balance of the day.

● If you like this, try Sibelius's Violin Concerto (91)

★
Teldec 0630 17144-2
Maxim Vengerov (violin)/
Chicago Symphony Orchestra/
Daniel Barenboim

Teldec 0630 13137-2
Gidon Kremer (violin)/
Royal Concertgebouw Orchestra/
Nikolaus Harnoncourt

✔
RCA 09026 61742-2
Jascha Heifetz (violin)/
Chicago Symphony Orchestra/
Fritz Reiner

Handel

58) ZADOK THE PRIEST

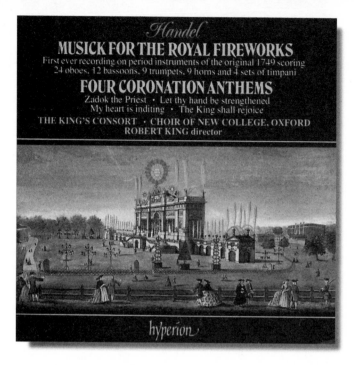

Handel
MUSICK FOR THE ROYAL FIREWORKS
First ever recording on period instruments of the original 1749 scoring
24 oboes, 12 bassoons, 9 trumpets, 9 horns and 4 sets of timpani
FOUR CORONATION ANTHEMS
Zadok the Priest · Let thy hand be strengthened
My heart is inditing · The King shall rejoice
THE KING'S CONSORT · CHOIR OF NEW COLLEGE, OXFORD
ROBERT KING director

hyperion

Zadok is one of four anthems composed by Handel on commission for the Royal Coronation of 1727 and used during the ceremony at Westminster Abbey. All four used texts extracted directly from or based on Bible passages, and all fulfilled specific functions during the official proceedings. *Zadok* was played during George II's anointing and is suitably triumphal and celebratory in spirit. The relatively small orchestral forces (strings with brass and woodwind accompaniment, plus a drum) provide bright support for the all-important chorus with its celebratory 'rejoice!' message. *Zadok* has been played in all sorts of contexts, with a wide range of instrumentation and vocal deployments. The three versions chosen here reflect that diversity.

Simon Preston and his English Consort use the Westminster Abbey choir to deliver the text for their Archiv CD. The Consort is an authentic instruments aggregation: their bright tone contributes substantially to the vivid musical colours evoked by the complete ensemble, while their small numbers keep the sound strictly under control. David Hill moves the proceedings to Winchester Cathedral, whose choir delivers the priest's message. Hill and the Brandenburg Consort once again are using authentic instruments, but the 1994 Argo recording is more distant and airy, the choir more prominent. This makes for a slight imbalance between choir and orchestra, favouring the choir, except this choir is not as smartly disciplined as the Abbey's, and the whole thing sounds a little too full of effort. This leaves the New College Oxford Choir, accompanied by The King's Consort and conducted by Robert King. This team are certainly intent on making it a celebratory occasion. There is a satisfying balance between choir and (once again authentic) instruments. That, plus a coupling of all four anthems with a convincing Royal Fireworks display by the Consort, makes this a happy first choice.

● If you like this, try Mozart's *Exsultate, jubilate* (207)

✔

Archiv 447 280-2
**Westminster Abbey Choir/
English Consort/
Simon Preston**

Argo 440 946-2
**Winchester Cathedral Choir/
Brandenburg Consort/
David Hill**

★
Hyperion CDA 66350
**Choir of New College, Oxford/
King's Consort/Robert King**

Mozart

59) SERENADE K525
'EINE KLEINE NACHTMUSIK'

S erenades during Mozart's time usually took the form of a collection of movements (most typically five) imitating popular dance patterns. Mozart was one of many composers who took this loosely organised form and developed it into an entertainment that could be presented to a rather more rarefied stratum of society, whether at court or for a private gathering. *Eine kleine Nachtmusik* is his own subtitle for the work, relating it to its street-serenading origins. The music, written in 1787, is backward-looking rather than adventurous, taking a fond glance at an old tradition Mozart knew and enjoyed, and is a combination of formal correctness and delicious, rather archaic melodies. The melody of the third movement *menuetto*, a slow-stepping, rising line which crosses between triple and common metre, is one of his most famous, but also appears in Haydn's music, so is quite possibly a well-known common tune of the time.

Many recordings of this work are stodgy, too full of protocol and self-importance for their own good. The music needs to be as light as a soufflé and as bewitching as a far-off voice serenading the moon on a still summer night. This is certainly the case with the six-piece Drottningholm Baroque Ensemble on BIS: they give rapt delivery to every movement, from the tearaway opening *allegro* to the stately *rondo* of the finale. Bruno Weil and Tafelmusik manage a similar clarity and freedom of expression, their ensemble work quite incredible. But Sony's acoustics make it sound as if the concert hall is the venue, not the courtly music room. Both ensembles use authentic instruments to great effect. A more traditional approach is taken by Willi Boskovsky for Decca on a budget-price release. This gives none of the music's secrets away but a good time is had by all.

● If you like this, try Mozart's *Sinfonia Concertante* (209)

★
BIS CD 506
Drottningholm Baroque Ensemble

Sony SK 46695
Tafelmusik/
Bruno Weil

✔

Decca 443 458-2
Vienna Mozart Ensemble/
Willi Boskovsky

Verdi

60) **REQUIEM**

Verdi's *Requiem* has often been called an opera in disguise, and for good reason. The work pulsates with energy, passion and an overall concern with telling a story. This is nowhere more exemplified than in the famous 'Dies Irae', the work's second section and the first to be created. Often performed separately, this piece bursts upon the listener after a reverential 'Kyrie' with full orchestra, full choir and drums thundering as if the Last Judgement were upon us all. If the unbound terror of this section is one extreme, then the lyric beauty of the 'Agnus Dei' or the magnificence of the concluding 'Libera Me' show other less anguished extremes, ones calculated to reassure and console.

The *Requiem*, a work requiring vast forces – choir, orchestra and the rest – has been blessed by more than a few good recorded interpretations. The three here are no exception. The 1964 Giulini set for EMI is justly famous for its drama as well as the sheer beauty of the solo singing. This is no surprise, given that soloists such as Elisabeth Schwarzkopf, Christa Ludwig and

Nicolai Gedda are involved. An added bonus is the inclusion of the last music Verdi wrote, the *Four Sacred Pieces*. The sound stands up well and there is a libretto and commentary. The only problem is that it is still full price. The Telarc recording by Robert Shaw is also full price, but it is much younger, dating from 1987. His soloists acquit themselves well, and the Atlanta Orchestra and Choir give their all. The recording quality is very clear and powerful; the closing section really packs a punch. Finally, there is a very worthy effort on Naxos, with speeds that often threaten to match Toscanini's and a massive sound to equal Telarc's. This has the Hungarian State Opera Chorus and Orchestra conducted by Pier Giorgio Morandi. His soloists include Elena Filipova but are not generally known. They cannot match the quality available to Giulini, but at budget price it is a very fine alternative. The *Four Sacred Pieces* are also included, as is a libretto.

● If you like this, try Brahms's *German Requiem* (127)

★

EMI CDS 556250 2

Elisabeth Schwarzkopf (soprano)/Christa Ludwig (mezzo-soprano)/Nicolai Gedda (tenor)/ Nicolai Ghiaurov (bass)/ Philharmonia Choir & Orchestra/C. M. Giulini

Telarc CD 80152

Susan Dunn (soprano)/Diane Curry (contralto)/Jerry Hadley (tenor)/Paul Plishka (bass)/Atlanta Symphony Orchestra & Choir/Robert Shaw

✔

Naxos 8.550944 5

Elena Filipova (soprano)/Gloria Scalchi (mezzo-soprano)/ Cesar Hernandez (tenor)/ Carlo Colombara (bass)/Hungarian State Opera Chorus & Orchestra/P. G. Morandi

---

J. S. Bach

61) TOCCATA & FUGUE
IN D MIN BWV 565

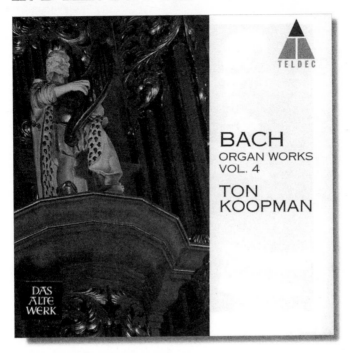

BACH
ORGAN WORKS
VOL. 4

TON KOOPMAN

TELDEC

DAS ALTE WERK

Bach's most famous organ work has suffered the fate of most universally known classical music: it has appeared in countless films, TV shows and more than a few adverts; it has been arranged for virtually every combination of instruments; and it has been arranged in a wide variety of musical styles. The cinema-goer most probably associates it with the Gothic thrills of horror films ancient and new. It is sometimes difficult to recall that the young Bach wrote this as a free fantasia, designed to explore the capabilities of the organ – and of the player as well. Though it is cast in a minor key, its exuberance is irresistible, the forward momentum of the piece never faltering for a moment as the drama of the music unfolds.

The recordings chosen here reflect the view of the piece taken by Bach. None of the three players is treating the music as a competition to see who can finish first, play loudest, camp it up to the highest degree or in any other way distort its purpose. Ton Koopman, playing an organ dating from 1688 and situated in St Jacob's, Hamburg, stresses the magnificent brightness and clarity of sound the piece can produce when the right stops (rather than all the stops) are pulled out. He is also very careful in his keyboard phrasing. Simon Preston produces a cool, measured technique and carillon-like tone on his DGG recording, while Wolfgang Rubsam, a Bach interpreter with a lifetime of experience behind him, finds something quite spiritual as well as earth-shaking in the organ at Oberlin College, northern Ohio. His is a budget-price effort and probably the place to start.

● If you like this, try Widor's Symphony No. 5 (75)

★
Teldec 4509 98443-2
Ton Koopman (organ)

Deutsche Grammophon DG 427 668-2
Simon Preston (organ)

✔
Naxos 8.553859
Wolfgang Rubsam (organ)

Delibes

62) LAKMÉ

One thing Léo Delibes knew how to do was take a threadbare romantic plot (exotic young beauty meets soldier, falls in love and sacrifices herself for him) and make it something an audience could identify with through the power and beauty of his score. Lakmé is the daughter of a Hindu savant who is up to all sorts of nasty practices (including revenge killings). She is capable of fine feelings; he isn't. When the European officer has to choose between honouring his regiment and love, he chooses love and survives. She dies. Before this unfortunate development, she manages a couple of memorable moments, however – the 'bell song' and the 'flower duet'. These two exquisite vocal scenes guarantee the opera's survival, whatever changes of taste may come along.

There are numerous versions of the famous bits, but not many of the complete opera – only a handful currently in the catalogue. The oldest – dating from 1968 – is that of Joan Sutherland, Alain Vanzo and Richard Bonynge on

Decca. It is currently available at mid-price and has as its strongest point the creamy, beautifully controlled soprano of Sutherland. As is usual with her singing, the text is largely indecipherable (and there's no libretto in this slimline edition). But it's a beautiful noise, although the sound is not state-of-the-art. Second-oldest is the 1971 Alain Lombard production for EMI. This features Mady Mesple in the lead role: she is a prim and poised Lakmé, and Lombard supports her with agile strength, but she doesn't have the eager innocence the part demands. That is supplied by Natalie Dessay in the newest recording, again for EMI and from 1998, with Gregory Kunde as the soldier, and with Michel Plasson conducting. Dessay brings such sweetness to the role (and Plasson such attention to the score's detail) that this must now be the first choice for anyone interested in the whole story.

● If you like this, try Bizet's *Pearl Fishers* (12)

✔

Decca 460 741-2
Dame Joan Sutherland (soprano)/Alain Vanzo (tenor)/Gabriel Bacquier (baritone)/ Jane Berbie (mezzo-soprano)/ Monte Carlo Opera Orchestra & Chorus/ Richard Bonynge

EMI CDS 749430 2
Mady Mesple (soprano)/Charles Burles (tenor)/Roger Soyer (bass)/Danielle Millet (mezzo-soprano)/Paris Opéra-Comique Chorus & Orchestra/Alain Lombard

★

EMI CDS 556569 2
Natalie Dessay (soprano)/Gregory Kunde (tenor)/José van Dam (bass baritone)/ Delphine Haidan (mezzo-soprano)/ Toulouse Capitole Orchestra & Chorus/ Michel Plasson

63) SYMPHONY NO. 2 OP. 43

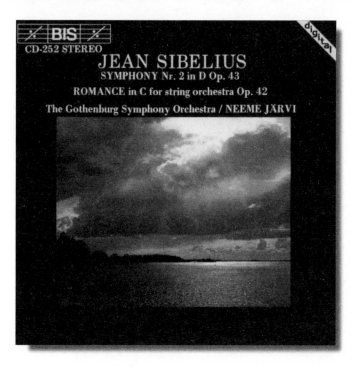

BIS
CD-252 STEREO
JEAN SIBELIUS
SYMPHONY Nr. 2 in D Op. 43
ROMANCE in C for string orchestra Op. 42
The Gothenburg Symphony Orchestra / NEEME JÄRVI

Sibelius is often referred to as the composer who most closely captures the sense of 'the frozen north', the vast expanses and landscapes of his northerly country. If that is so, then the Second Symphony is perhaps one of the works where this sense of vastness, of the tyranny of the huge sky, is most dominant. The symphony is unusual in that it is cast in just three movements, with a two-part last movement; even so, it lasts for around 40 minutes, so its scope is substantial. As ever with Sibelius, his handling of instrumental combinations – brass with strings, woodwinds and brass, drums and strings – brings about completely personal sounds and stamps his instantly recognisable identity on the music, just as a great painter's own personal choice of palette gives him a unique hue.

The colour of his work being so important, Sibelius needs outstanding recording quality and a conductor who knows the right way to mix the instrumental sonorities to get the perfect blend of musical colours. This is certainly achieved by Neeme Järvi and the Gothenburg Symphony on their 1984 BIS recording. The CD is completed by the beautiful *Romance in C* for string orchestra, Op. 42. Vladimir Ashkenazy completed an excellent Sibelius symphonies cycle for Decca during the 1980s and 1990s. His Second is available separately at mid-price; the fillers are *Karelia* and *Finlandia*. Finally, the mid-1970s Colin Davis cycle with the Boston Symphony for Philips was important at the time and remains a reliable guide to the music.

● If you like this, try Sibelius's *Karelia Suite* (102)

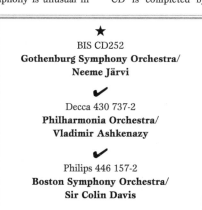

★
BIS CD252
**Gothenburg Symphony Orchestra/
Neeme Järvi**

✔

Decca 430 737-2
**Philharmonia Orchestra/
Vladimir Ashkenazy**

✔

Philips 446 157-2
**Boston Symphony Orchestra/
Sir Colin Davis**

Chopin

64) PIANO CONCERTO NO. 1
IN E MINOR

The odd thing about the two Chopin piano concertos is that No. 2 in F minor was composed first and No. 1 in E minor second. They were composed within months of each other in 1830 when Chopin was a 20-year-old attempting to make an impression on the sophisticated Parisian audiences he was convinced would give him fame and success. This they certainly did in quick measure. The first concerto is famous for its meltingly beautiful second movement, titled 'Romanze. Larghetto'. In it Chopin weaves a tracery of bewitching melody at the piano while the orchestra accompanies sympathetically. It is one of his supreme moments, certainly in the genre of music for piano and orchestra. The last movement is equally blessed, this time with a jaunty tune over a polka-like rhythm that moves between piano and orchestra to a satisfying climax.

Needless to say, pianists of merely normal calibre need not apply when it comes to recording this concerto. The three listed here all possess exceptional abilities.

Murray Perahia's beautiful touch and effortless sense of phrasing make his 1990 version with Zubin Mehta a thing of joy: he also injects a real sense of the Polish background into his playing. The only demerit is a rather recessed sound for the orchestra, which needs all the help it can get owing to Chopin's uninspired scoring. A similar problem occurs on the Demidenko disc for Hyperion. The pianist has astonishing presence and assurance, his tone jewel-like through both the power of his hands and the use of an 1880 piano which had a more brilliant tone than those of today. But Schiff's orchestra is even more lost. Krystian Zimerman's 1979 performance for DGG, still at full price, also brings high artistry to the work, his fluid playing a particular attraction. Giulini's conducting is exact and caring, but the LA Philharmonic, although more brightly recorded than the others, are not as delicate in their phrasing. A decision? Perahia by a whisker.

● If you like this, try Beethoven's Piano Concerto No. 3 (171)

★

Sony SK 44922
Murray Perahia (piano)/
Israel Philharmonic Orchestra/
Zubin Mehta

Hyperion CDA 66647
Nikolai Demidenko (piano)/
Philharmonia Orchestra/
Heinrich Schiff

Deutsche Grammophon DG 415 970-2
Krystian Zimerman (piano)/
Los Angeles Philharmonic Orchestra/
Carlo Maria Giulini

Sibelius

65) SYMPHONY NO. 5

There is an intense love of – and a kind of awe towards – the natural world embedded in every sound of this symphony, as well as a long and ultimately fruitful struggle to triumph over individual doubts and limitations: something which had often preoccupied Sibelius in earlier works, and would again, later in his career. Each movement works through sections of introspection before exploding into ringing affirmations: nowhere more so than in the electrifying horn fanfare which announces the work's last movement, or the full-force staccato ending. The sense of space, of distance and vastness, is occasionally almost overwhelming, achieved by masterful scoring by Sibelius, stretching the music across as wide a natural palette as possible.

The choice of performances here is an intriguing one. The same record company, BIS, offers a spectacular realisation by Neeme Järvi and the Gothenburg Symphony of the score finally published and authorised by Sibelius. It also offers a brilliant and substantially different recording of Symphony No. 5 by the Lahti Symphony under Osmo Vänskä. How different? Well, for a start, the wonderful horn call that opens the published Fifth is missing entirely. The work is also cast in four movements instead of three, and has a substantially longer finale. The scoring of the symphony also gives it a markedly darker emotional hue. It is clear why Sibelius kept working at it and eventually recast it entirely, but this early version is fascinating listening for those who love the finished item. Both BIS recordings are masterful and in brilliant sound, but are also full price. For those after a fine mid-price performance, the old Davis on Philips is still serviceable, though the sound cannot hold up against the BIS releases.

● If you like this, try Sibelius's *Swan of Tuonela* (202)

★

BIS CD 222
**Gothenburg Symphony Orchestra/
Neeme Järvi**

BIS CD 800
**Lahti Symphony Orchestra/
Osmo Vänskä**

✔

Philips 446 157-2
**Boston Symphony Orchestra/
Sir Colin Davis**

Mozart

66) FLUTE AND HARP CONCERTO
K299

In Mozart's concertos there are fantastic conversations going on between all the instruments as they help each other towards the conclusion of the piece and therefore the resolution of the musical story being unfolded. Think of the movements as acts of a short play, and the instruments as characters, and suddenly, as in his operas, the poetry, the naked humanity at the music's heart, is revealed. With the Flute and Harp Concerto the dialogue between the two is the doorway to the rest: the harp becomes the orchestra and then becomes a companion to the flute, just as the orchestra has been prior to their unaccompanied passages. Then the orchestra comments on their progress.

All this is made very clear in an authentic instruments version recorded by Frans Brüggen on transverse flute in 1971 and reissued on Sony Vivarte. The cumbersome timbre of the older type of flute explains Mozart's aversion to the instrument, but also shows why it was important

for it to work in concert with the other instruments around it, and how vital the harp's supporting role really was. This is not so clear in other versions, where everything is so beautifully polished and perfectly executed. In the Orpheus Chamber Orchestra version on DGG, recorded in 1989, we hear a Mozart brimming with confidence and brilliant by-play between instruments. But the vulnerability is no longer there. It is exceedingly beautiful, but it is a different dimension, and the harp struggles to be an equal partner. Halfway house? Perhaps the 1996 rerun by Brüggen, this time as conductor, with Konrad Hünteler on flute (not transverse flute). The instruments may be authentic still, but they nod in the direction of the modern age.

● If you like this, try Glière's Harp Concerto (380)

Sony SB2K 60381
Frans Vester (flute)/
Edward Witsenburg (harp)/
Mozart-Ensemble/
Frans Brüggen

★

Philips 442 148-2
Konrad Hünteler (flute)/
Helga Storck (harp)/
Eighteenth Century Orchestra/
Frans Brüggen

Deutsche Grammophon DG 427 677-2
Susan Palma (flute)/
Nancy Allen (harp)/
Orpheus Chamber Orchestra

Schubert

67) STRING QUINTET IN C
D956

SCHUBERT · Quintett C-dur
MELOS QUARTETT · Wolfgang Boettcher

harmonia mundi
FRANCE
901494

The Quintet was written in the last year of Schubert's life, after his C major Symphony, and perhaps surprisingly contains a good deal of resolute music. It is tempting to say that it also contains music of good cheer, but the smile is in the face of poor fortune and fends off tears. Yet Schubert's artistic ambition, even at this extreme point in his life, is not dimmed: this quintet lasts close on one hour, the first movement itself being over twenty minutes long. During that time Schubert more than once reveals the torment that will not leave him alone, especially in the pain of the long *adagio*. Only the well-known *scherzo*, with its cavalry-call theme, revives the flagging spirits, while the graceful final *allegretto* renews all the ambiguities.

Of the versions currently available on CD, the 1994 one by the Melos Quartett with Wolfgang Boettcher adding the second cello is a clear leader. Their overwhelming commitment is tangible in every bar, their peeling back of the layers of understanding for us to appreciate is faultless. They bring the music grace when it needs it, and fire at the right moments. A fine 1992 version by the Emerson Quartet with Rostropovich on second cello is only available in a three-CD set of Schubert's late quartets, while the Brandis on Nimbus also give a committed and praiseworthy rendition with its own special insights.

● If you like this, try Boccherini's String Quintet (294)

★

Harmonia Mundi HMC90 1494
Melos Quartett/
Wolfgang Boettcher (cello)

Deutsche Grammophon DG 459 151-2
Emerson Quartet/
Mstislav Rostropovich (cello)

Nimbus NI 5313
Brandis Quintet/
Wen-Sinn (cello)

Richard Strauss

68) VIER LETZTE LIEDER

These four orchestral songs (originally intended to be five) were heard publicly for the first time in 1950, two years after the composer's death. Since then they have been favoured with some of the most glorious interpretations of any vocal music committed to disc, sung by the greatest sopranos of each succeeding generation. Probably the most famous interpreter of these songs of resignation and the acceptance of life's end has been Elisabeth Schwarzkopf. She has made two equally distinguished recordings of the songs, both for EMI, one in mono and one in stereo. Hers became the voice and the interpretation which for decades were synonymous with the music, her perfect diction, beauty of tone and fabulous musicianship seemingly 'beyond category', as Duke Ellington called the true greats in any walk of life.

Her recordings hold up today as masterpieces, but it cannot be claimed that the recording quality from the 1950s and 1960s is comparable to that of the last two decades or so. If such things bother you, then there are other places to go. For example, there is a feelingly sung and superbly conducted 1982 recording by Lucia Popp and Klaus Tennstedt which, although some commentators have found fault with Popp's upper-register work, communicates all the subtleties of the text and the music. Popp's beautiful voice may have a frailty to it, but it a most becoming one. Tennstedt and the LPO are astonishingly empathetic. At the other end of the spectrum is the radiant, overwhelmingly beautiful singing of Gundula Janowitz on her 1972 recording with Herbert von Karajan. If there is a fault with this recording, it is that the orchestra is occasionally a little too far back in the recording balance, thus failing to wrap Janowitz's voice in quite as sumptuous an accompaniment as Strauss intended. That aside, this is still the one to get.

● If you like this, try Elgar's *Sea Pictures* (290)

✔

EMI CDM 566908 2
**Dame Elisabeth Schwarzkopf
(soprano)/Berlin Radio Symphony
Orchestra/George Szell**

✔

EMI CDR 569840 2
**Lucia Popp (soprano)/
London Philharmonic Orchestra/
Klaus Tennstedt**

★ ✔

Deutsche Grammophon DG 447 422-2
**Gundula Janowitz (soprano)/
Berlin Philharmonic Orchestra/
Herbert von Karajan**

Ravel

69) BOLÉRO

This famous piece of music was once described by its creator as quite probably not music at all. Ravel was fond of his little jokes, but as always with him there was an element of truth in what he was claiming. The most fastidious composer and orchestrator in living memory, Ravel greatly enjoyed setting challenges for himself; the more unlikely, the better he enjoyed the fun of beating expectations. Considering what he was capable of in terms of orchestral tone poems, stage works and compositions of pure extravagant fantasy, the idea of limiting himself to a single theme for the entire duration of a piece must have been immense perverse fun. Of course the biggest fun of all was to pull it off in such a spectacular way. There is no doubt that the slow progression of *Boléro* from incidental background tune to overwhelming orchestral climax, all on the same remorseless idea, becomes mesmerising long before its end.

As for performances of this monstrous beauty, the bigger the sound and the sharper the presence, the more imposing it finally becomes. It is highly reliant on faithful reproduction of the orchestra's colours to carry it off. Telarc have long been masters of such things, so their extravaganza with Jesús López-Cobos (a conductor with an instinctive feel for the Spanish edge to the piece) is hard to top. Charles Dutoit, in brilliant, splashy sound, keeps the pressure on in Montreal while Adrian Leaper registers high on the Richter scale on a worthy Naxos compilation of spectacular pieces. But Telarc's sonic boom does the trick and will have the walls of Jericho down before the end, should you be antisocial enough to turn it up too loud.

● If you like this, try Dukas's *Sorcerer's Apprentice* (326)

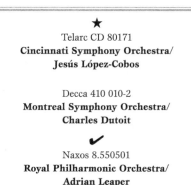

★
Telarc CD 80171
Cincinnati Symphony Orchestra/
Jesús López-Cobos

Decca 410 010-2
Montreal Symphony Orchestra/
Charles Dutoit

✔
Naxos 8.550501
Royal Philharmonic Orchestra/
Adrian Leaper

Tchaikovsky
70) VIOLIN CONCERTO

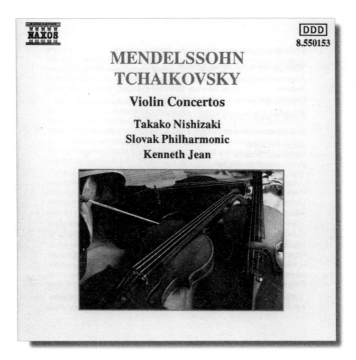

The great Russian composer's only violin concerto was designed as a good old-fashioned showcase for a superlatively gifted virtuoso, and it has been embraced by every great violinist since as exactly that. Influenced by the French tradition for combining technical wizardry with elegance and memorable melody, Tchaikovsky gives the soloist ample opportunity to show greatness of soul as well as fleetness of fingers. The soaring melodies so typical of the Russian romantic dominate each movement and are the principal reason why the listening public are as ardent in their love of the piece as are the virtuosi who continue to play it with such enthusiasm.

Tchaikovsky didn't exactly give the orchestra a great deal to do apart from offer loud and continuous support to the soloist in the outer movements, while in the slow *canzonetta* it is expected to give a cushion of romantic sound on which the soloist can rapturously float. This may not seem a very large task, but it is still important in achieving the best possible recorded version. It is also one of the main reasons why Decca's Kyung-Wha Chung noses ahead of Xue Wei in the Classic FM recommendations, for Chung has André Previn and the London Symphony giving impeccable support, while Xue Wei occasionally finds himself being less than perfectly accompanied by the Philharmonia under the baton of Salvatore Accardo. Perhaps the best buy, however, is the well-recorded and spirited performance of Takako Nishizaki with the Slovak Philharmonic under Kenneth Jean on Naxos. Her playing is clean and expressive, the orchestra is disciplined and responsive, the price just about right. You also get a fine version of the Mendelssohn concerto included in the package.

● If you like this, try Sibelius's Violin Concerto (91)

✔
Decca 425 080-2
Kyung-Wha Chung (violin)/
London Symphony Orchestra/
André Previn

ASV CDDCA 713
Xue Wei (violin)/
Philharmonia Orchestra/
Salvatore Accardo

★ ✔
Naxos 8.550153
Takako Nishizaki (violin)/
Slovak Philharmonic Orchestra/
Kenneth Jean

Mendelssohn

71) HEBRIDES OVERTURE

MENDELSSOHN
DDD
8.554433
A Midsummer Night's Dream
Overtures: Ruy Blas • Hebrides
Calm Sea and Prosperous Voyage
Slovak Philharmonic Orchestra
Anthony Bramall • Oliver Dohnányi

This famous overture is one of Mendelssohn's most memorable portraits from nature. He experienced the Hebrides (and Fingal's Cave) at first hand during a foray north to Scotland in 1829. At that time Scotland was perceived by the German cultural élite (influenced by the enormously popular novels of Sir Walter Scott) as a land of high romance and bracing, harsh beauty. Mendelssohn's overture underlines this idea through its drama, romance and flashing melodies. As with all the composer's works, the noble theme and the gradual musical filling in of the seascape, seemingly natural, spontaneous and artless, are in fact the result of deftly concealed artistry and industry. He brings the listener through his tour of the Hebrides and face to face with Fingal's Cave through a superb economy of means, dressing each new twist of his basic material in such a way as to make it freshly appealing. Sometimes this is as simple as moving themes around the instruments of the orchestra; at other times he changes the

harmony or sets up a counter-theme to change the context. Lastly, he makes tiny modifications to the original theme itself: it always remains instantly recognisable but its character shifts.

Two of the three versions listed here come as cameos on CD programmes mostly dedicated to Mendelssohn's music from *A Midsummer Night's Dream*. Philippe Herreweghe keeps a brisk tempo and his band of players show exemplary discipline, while Olivier Dohnányi and the Slovak Philharmonic take a slower pace around the islands. Also at budget price is a version by Dmitri Sitkovetsky that is paired with Mendelssohn's Third and Fourth Symphonies. Considering that the Overture is around 10 minutes long and consequently doomed to be a filler on a larger work's disc, it may be best to go for a budget-price performance to extract full value for your minutes.

● If you like this, try Brahms's *Academic Festival Overture* (262)

Harmonia Mundi HMC90 1502
**Champs-Elysées Orchestra/
Philippe Herreweghe**

★ ✔

Naxos 8.554433
**Slovak Philharmonic Orchestra/
Oliver Dohnányi**

✔

Classic FM 75605 57013-2
**Ulster Orchestra/
Dmitri Sitkovetsky**

Tchaikovsky

72) ROMEO AND JULIET
OVERTURE

This telling profile of a great Shakespearean play was never conceived to be given during a performance of the drama: it was composed as a subjective reaction to Shakespeare's work. It does not attempt to trace the convolutions of the plot, but it does go to considerable trouble to tell the psychological story of the doomed young lovers. Tchaikovsky did this by a combination of masterly atmospherics (as in the dark and troubled opening chords) and a series of set pieces whereby the themes he has assigned to the main groups and characters intertwine, fight for supremacy and look for peaceful resolution. No melody in the overture is more famous or better loved than the great, soaring love theme between Romeo and Juliet that occurs for the first time around halfway through the score. Scored for high woodwinds and strings, it signifies the strength of their love and its eventual futility. Tchaikovsky's immensely skilful weaving of his different themes together at the end makes this a

hectic, memorable and often very moving piece of concert music. Clearly it was one close to his own heart as well.

Blazing passion and a flair for the dramatic are the essential ingredients in making an above-average recording of this work. Orchestral discipline must also be first-rate if the lightning-quick shifts of mood and scene are not to be blunted by poor ensemble playing. No such problems with Daniel Barenboim's outing on DGG, a 1982 recording that is now available at mid-price and features the rich sonorities of the Chicago Symphony. Geoffrey Simon gives us something interestingly different by recording the original 1869 version of the score (Tchaikovsky heavily revised it twice later). Lastly, a new Naxos recording by Adrian Leaper is a very good place to start if your budget is tight.

● If you like this, try Khachaturian's *Spartacus* (122)

★
Deutsche Grammophon DG 445 523-2
**Chicago Symphony Orchestra/
Daniel Barenboim**

Chandos CHAN 9191
**London Symphony Orchestra/
Geoffrey Simon**

✔
Naxos 8.550500
**Royal Philharmonic Orchestra/
Adrian Leaper**

Verdi

73) LA TRAVIATA

Verdi's famous setting of Alexandre Dumas's novel *La Dame aux camélias* has been a perennial favourite since its first triumphal year on-stage in 1853. This is absolutely prime mid-career Verdi, the melodies spilling out of his leads' mouths in thrilling fashion whether they be a subtle lament for lost youth and health or an all-out drinking song. Being a 'domestic' opera, too, the scale of the drama is intimate, the music correspondingly warm and oddly delicate.

Most of the focus in a *Traviata* production usually falls on the soprano lead, Violetta, although the tenor, Alfredo, is also important, as is his father, Germont. For this reason most commentators have valued Maria Callas's recordings of the work as something quite special. Her interpretations undoubtedly are, but unfortunately they are both recorded live (1955 and 1958) and suffer from what must honestly be described as sound quality that only Callas fans or opera devotees would be prepared to put up with. If you fall into these two categories, then make sure the 1955 La Scala performance on EMI CMS 566450 2 (mono) is added to your collection

immediately. For the rest of us, the 1979 DGG recording led by Carlos Kleiber has just about everything going for it: a wonderfully complex and beautifully sung Violetta in Ileana Cotrubas, an ardent Alfredo in young Placido Domingo, and a sage Germont in Sherrill Milnes. The only trouble is the speed with which everything happens. The recording was the first made specifically to fit onto two vinyl LPs rather than three, and the rush to cram it all in becomes simply too distracting. We reach back to 1967 for the most consistently successful current release, that of Georges Prêtre with Montserrat Caballé, Carlo Bergonzi and a younger Sherrill Milnes. For a third recommendation, which could have been a first if not for the fact that it's sung in English, you can happily turn to Sir Charles Mackerras's 1980 version on Chandos featuring Valerie Masterson as Violetta, although her many fans will want to buy Angela Gheorghiu's recent version on Decca 448 119-2.

● If you like this, try Verdi's *Rigoletto* (129)

Deutsche Grammophon DG 415 132-2
**Ileana Cotrubas (soprano)/
Placido Domingo (tenor)/
Bavarian State Opera Orchestra
& Chorus/Carlos Kleiber**

★

RCA RD86180(2)
**Monserrat Caballé (soprano)/Carlo
Bergonzi(tenor)/RCA Italiana Opera
Chorus & Orchestra/ Georges Prêtre**

Chandos CHAN 3023
**Valerie Masterson (soprano)/
John Brecknock (tenor)/ Christian du
Plessis (baritone)/Orchestra & Chorus
of the English National Opera/
Sir Charles Mackerras**

Mahler

74) SYMPHONY NO. 2
(RESURRECTION)

EMI CLASSICS

MAHLER
Sinfonie · Symphony
No. 2
'Auferstehungs-Sinfonie'
'Resurrection'

ARLEEN AUGÉR
JANET BAKER

CBSO Chorus
City of Birmingham Symphony Orchestra
SIMON RATTLE

Mahler was nothing if not ambitious. Not the most modest of men, he often said to friends that his symphonies were whole worlds which were supposed to give hope and enlightenment to his fellow-men. Certainly they are nearly all long enough to be whole worlds, while the idea of death and salvation through resurrection, which is Mahler's theme for this massive symphony, is hardly a trifling one. The second symphony took over six years of thought and labour for him to complete: it remains a work that occasionally struggles to come together as a whole, its disparate movements sitting uneasily together. Technical aspects aside, what repeatedly comes to its rescue from a listener's point of view is the contrast between fierce, unblinking musical looks into the hellfires of death and damnation and the sweetest of orchestral melodies. The most famous lyrical passage fills the entire short fourth movement, where, against a hushed background, an alto soloist

sings one of the most heavenly melodies ever heard.

Making sense of all this is not easy, as many conductors have found to their cost. Claudio Abbado and the Vienna Philharmonic get a great deal of it right on their 1994 effort, especially the sudden shifts in mood and texture, between storm and calm, joy and despair. But their fourth movement is ponderous and overly operatic, the gap between vocalist and orchestra much too noticeable. Simon Rattle and the CBSO avoid this trap, their dignified and experienced soloist Dame Janet Baker also singing with great sensitivity, while the 1987 studio acoustic is natural and true. All that aside, had it not been for the technical advances in studio sound between 1958 and 1987 I would be recommending Bruno Walter's once-in-a-lifetime recording for Columbia/Sony with the New York Philharmonic and Maureen Forrester. A towering interpretation.

● If you like this, try Mahler's Symphony No. 4 (176)

Deutsche Grammophon DG 439 953-2
Cheryl Studer (soprano)/Waltraud Meier (mezzo-soprano)/Arnold Schoenberg Choir/Vienna Philharmonic Orchestra/Claudio Abbado

EMI CDS7 47962-8
Arleen Augér (soprano)/Dame Janet Baker (mezzo-soprano)/City of Birmingham Symphony Orchestra & Chorus/ Sir Simon Rattle

Sony SM2K 64447
Emilia Cundari (soprano)/Maureen Forrester (contralto)/Westminster Choir/New York Philharmonic Orchestra/Bruno Walter

Widor

75) SYMPHONY NO. 5

In an age of symphony writers Charles-Marie Widor stands alone. He composed ten, all for the organ only. This has tended to limit their appeal outside a relatively small band of organ enthusiasts. However, one movement of his Fifth Symphony, the *toccata* (itself the finale of the composition), has caught the imagination of a wider public. The reason is not hard to fathom, for it contains some of the most spectacular and triumphal organ music ever composed. Suitable for any grand or celebratory occasion, it bursts with pride and joy, sounding for all the world like the musical equivalent of the *Queen Mary* leaving port while everybody cheers on the quay.

Given this key characteristic, the most successful and popular recordings are going to stress magnificence. In the battle of the big sounds, David Hill's recital on the Westminster Cathedral instrument comes marginally ahead: he takes the symphony's finale at a considerable trot and delivers some gargantuan instrumental sounds. No one could fail to be impressed. The rest of the recital on this Hyperion CD is also from Widor's pen, and includes the impressive *March Pontificale* from Symphony No. 1. Equal to Hill in the sonics stakes is Ian Tracey on a Chandos disc that includes Guilmant's noisome Symphony No. 1 for organ and orchestra and Poulenc's Concerto for Organ Strings and Trumpet. However, Tracey's electing for a slower pace tends to let the momentum slip a little too far, giving the sensation of an ocean liner trapped in heavy seas. Not for the squeamish. It may surprise those unfamiliar with the rest of the work to discover, however, that it is generally peaceful and reflective, as both organists make a point of demonstrating. If this aspect is not to your taste, then a selections disc of French organ music highlights on Naxos with Simon Lindley may be just the job.

● If you like this, try Bach's Toccata and Fugue in D minor (61)

★

Hyperion CDA 66181
David Hill (organ)

Chandos CHAN 9271
Ian Tracey (organ)

✔

Naxos 8.550581
Simon Lindley (organ)

---

76) CARMEN

Soon after its unsuccessful 1875 première, *Carmen* was rearranged so that it could be presented, not at Paris's Opéra Comique, where it belonged, but as an example of French *grand opéra*. Instead of having spoken dialogue between musical numbers, there was new (and inferior) text, set as recitative with orchestral accompaniment. A ballet was also added. It is only since the 1960s that productions and recordings have returned to Bizet's original concept, only to find no definitive version remains. Bearing this in mind, the recording of arguably the most popular opera in the world is something of a minefield. There is no doubt that Bizet's original libretto and setting are vastly superior, but some of the greatest performances on record used the old, corrupt text with the recitatives.

This is certainly the case with the 1959 Sir Thomas Beecham recording on EMI, featuring Victoria de los Angeles as Carmen and Nicolai Gedda as Don José. Beecham's spirit and lightness of touch are infallible, the two principals are wholly believable, and the recorded sound is very acceptable. But the opera is cut according to tradition and uses the recitatives. Sir Georg Solti confronted this situation head-on in 1975 for his Decca recording featuring Tatiana Troyanos and Placido Domingo, going back to the newly available original sources and coming as close as he thought possible to Bizet's own intentions. This delivers an opera that is wonderfully paced, dramatic, exciting, and light as a feather. The only problem is that Troyanos and Domingo are undistinguished (Domingo would make a better fist of Don José for Maazel a decade or so later). More red-blooded are Jennifer Larmore and Thomas Moser for Giuseppi Sinopoli in 1996. This Teldec recording also benefits from having Angela Gheorghiu as Michaela and Samuel Ramey as Escamillo. Sinopoli chooses an even more inclusive version of the original than Solti, but lets himself down through his erratic tempo choices, especially in some of the big arias. So what does a poor listener do? If you're starting out, begin with the Beecham. Once your appetite is whetted, move on to the Sinopoli and Solti for the complete experience, pitfalls and all.

● If you like this, try Bizet's *L'Arlésienne* Suite No. 1 (293)

★

EMI CDS 556214 2
Petits Chanteurs de Versailles/French Radio Chorus/French Radio National Orchestra/Sir Thomas Beecham

Decca 414 489-2
John Alldis Choir/Haberdashers' Aske's School Choir/ London Philharmonic Orchestra/ Sir Georg Solti

Teldec 0630 12672-2
Bavarian State Opera Children's Choir/Bavarian State Opera Orchestra & Chorus/Giuseppe Sinopoli

77) DIE ZAUBERFLÖTE

Often cited as Mozart's last opera (it wasn't – *La Clemenza di Tito* had its première later), *The Magic Flute* is a triumph of musical ingenuity and inspiration over what is generally conceded to be a confused and none too consistent libretto.

A wholly successful recording of this work, then, is not exactly a straightforward proposition. You have to have a cast capable of executing some of the most technically demanding roles in all opera but also showing that same fully rounded humanity and fallibility of character so central to Mozartean opera. All three of the recordings listed here have an open-hearted approach, typified by how the comic figure of bird-catcher Papageno and his eventual lover Papagena are delivered from their trials of separation.

The most recent recording, from William Christie's Les Arts Florissants, uses instrumentation from Mozart's own period and vocal practices more in tune with the time of Napoleon than with our own. What that gives the listener is a near-ideal balance between singer and orchestra and complete transparency of sound. Anton Scharinger's Papageno has a Shakespearean humour about him and the earnest Prince Tamino, sung by Hans-Peter Blochwitz, the right combination of ardent passion and thoughtfulness. Natalie Dessay is a convincing Queen of the Night, but it is only when you hear Sumi Jo in the same role for our second choice, the Drottningholm Court ensemble under Arnold Ostman, that you realise how heart-stopping this role can be. This recording also features so-called 'authentic' instruments.

The oldest recording here, Karl Böhm's 1964 effort for DGG, features Fritz Wunderlich (a truly heavenly toned Tamino), Dietrich Fischer-Dieskau as Papageno and Roberta Peters as the Queen of the Night. Now at mid-price (and the only recording of the three to use modern instruments), its lightness of touch and impeccable production standards make it an unmissable choice for those testing the water in Mozart opera.

● If you like this, try Mozart's *Don Giovanni* (138)

★
Erato 0630 12705-2
Rosa Mannion (soprano)/Natalie Dessay (soprano)/Hans-Peter Blochwitz (tenor)/ Reinhard Hagen (bass)/Les Arts Florissants Orchestra & Chorus/William Christie

L'Oiseau-Lyre 440 085-2
Barbara Bonney (soprano)/Sumi Jo (soprano)/Kurt Streit (tenor)/Gilles Cachermaille (baritone)/Drottningholm Court Theatre Chorus & Orchestra/Arnold Ostman

✔
Deutsche Grammophon DG 449 749-2
Evelyn Lear (soprano)/Roberta Peters (soprano)/Lisa Otto (soprano)/Fritz Wunderlich (tenor)/Berlin Radio Chamber Orchestra/Berlin Philharmonic Orchestra/ Karl Böhm

Tchaikovsky

78) THE NUTCRACKER SUITE
OP. 71A

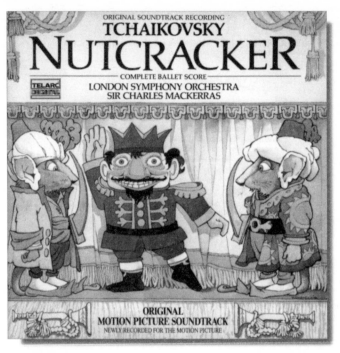

It is certain that Tchaikovsky's best-known music is that written for his three great ballets. Of those, *The Nutcracker*, composed in 1892, has become the favourite owing to the glorious concert suite Op. 71a, which Tchaikovsky himself extracted from it. Set to a tale from the collection of E. T. A. Hoffmann (a prolific source for 19th-century composers of operas and ballets), it is a simple tale of a girl's adventures with her favourite toy, a nutcracker, and her ultimate reward of being granted entry to the land of sweets. This is a little thin as a plot for a full-length score, so Tchaikovsky padded it out with a series of the most delectable dances in Act 2. They add nothing at all to the plot development but they entertain royally and are also the centrepiece of the Suite. Tchaikovsky delivers scintillating, exciting music for the dancers and audience, conjuring whole scenes into the imagination through his skills. Whether it is the 'March', the 'Arabian Dance',

the 'Chinese Dance' or the brittle perfection of the 'Sugar Plum Fairy', each one is utterly distinct and carved in high relief.

There are many versions of this special work. The Suite is quite short and is therefore usually to be found accompanied by other ballet music, sometimes other Tchaikovsky suites, sometimes those by other composers. Two fine recordings of the complete ballet are listed here, the Russian containing an intoxicating atmosphere as well as the occasional orchestral blemish. Mackerras's orchestra avoids pratfalls and is sumptuously recorded, making it the pick of the complete works. For a suitable disc of the suite, the budget-price CD by Eugene Ormandy from the 1960s, which includes ballet excerpts from Delibes and Chopin as well, is excellent value.

● If you like this, try Tchaikovsky's *Swan Lake* (84)

★
Telarc CD 80137
**Tiffin Boys School Choir/
London Symphony Orchestra/
Sir Charles Mackerras**

✔
Sony SBK 46550
**Philadelphia Orchestra/
Eugene Ormandy**

Melodiya 74321 17081-2
**State Symphony Orchestra/
Evgeni Svetlanov**

Chopin

79) PIANO CONCERTO NO. 2
IN F MINOR

Chopin delayed the publication of the F minor concerto owing to concerns over the orchestration, and you don't have to be an expert to note that he didn't fully resolve these problems: the scoring for the orchestra is conventional and unimaginative, rarely breaking away from an entirely piano-based conception of what an orchestra can do. Yet all is forgiven as soon as the piano starts playing, for the freshness and creativity in his ideas for the instrument are as startling today as when they were first heard in 1830. Although both his concertos were in minor keys, this F minor work is generally more sombre in mood than the E minor concerto (entry 64), which has sustained passages in related major tonalities to brighten the overall mood. Still, this one has its compensations, including a very beautiful *larghetto* for the second movement full of graceful turns and runs from the soloist.

The results of the play-off between the three recordings are not significantly different from those for the first concerto. All three pianists play with breathtaking assurance and rapt poetry in all the right places, with Zimerman and Perahia very close in their ability to project an uncanny fluidity and grace of line, especially to the *larghetto*. Based on the age-old idea of a change being as good as a holiday, with three such outstanding interpretations it would be beneficial to shift our vote to the hard-edged brilliance of Demidenko for this concerto. Bearing in mind, of course, that either of the others will do just as well, for all three double up on Chopin concertos on the one disc and it may be prudent to opt for just a single purchase.

● If you like this, try Brahms's Piano Concerto No. 2 (111)

Sony SK 44922
Murray Perahia (piano)/
London Symphony Orchestra/
Antal Dorati

Deutsche Grammophon DG 415 970-2
Krystian Zimerman (piano)/
Los Angeles Philharmonic Orchestra/
Carlo Maria Giulini

★

Hyperion CDA 66647
Nikolai Demidenko (piano)/
Philharmonia Orchestra/
Heinrich Schiff

J. S. Bach

80) ST MATTHEW PASSION

O f the five Passions Bach is recorded as having written to gospel texts, only two survive today, the St John and the St Matthew. Of these, the Matthew Passion is by far the more popular. Bach may occasionally be thought of as daunting in his complexity or austere in his intellectualism, but the major facet of his religious music is his undisguised delight in creating beautiful melodies by which his singers deliver the message of the text.

As with any other Bach work on record today, there are plentiful representatives of both schools of performance, those that favour 'authentic' instruments and vocal styles, and those that prefer to stick with the traditional methods which have their roots in the Romantic revival of interest in Bach initiated in the last century by Felix Mendelssohn. Two of the recordings recommended here take the 'authentic' approach. The latest is from Philippe Herreweghe and

Harmonia Mundi HMC95 1676/8
Ian Bostridge (tenor)/Franz-Josef Selig (bass)/Andreas Scholl (alto)/Sibylla Rubens (soprano)/Collegium Vocale Gent Orchestra & Chorus/Philippe Herreweghe

Hänssler 98 925
Christiane Oelze (soprano)/Ingeborg Danz (mezzo-soprano)/Michael Schade (tenor)/ Matthias Görne (baritone)/Thomas Quasthoff (baritone)/Stuttgart Gäschiner Kantorei/Stuttgart Bach Collegium/Helmuth Rilling

Naxos 8.550832/4
Ibolya Verebits (soprano)/Rózsa Kiss (soprano)/Judit Németh (mezzo-soprano)/Agnes Csenki (contralto)/Jósef Mukk (tenor)/Istvan Gáti (baritone)/Péter Cser (baritone)/Péter Köves (bass)/Ferenc Korpás (bass)/Hungarian Festival Chorus/ Hungarian Radio Children's Choir/ Hungarian State Philharmonic Orchestra/Géza Oberfrank

was released in the closing weeks of 1999, so it is very recent. Its 'period' style is impeccable, and the different sense of scale Herreweghe achieves makes it a much more approachable, humble work than usual. Helmuth Rilling features an all-German cast of singers and a finely judged sense of proportion, along with the required gravitas, to make his 1994 Hänssler recording a very persuasive one.

On the traditional side, the Naxos recording with Hungarian State Symphony Orchestra, Choir and soloists directed by Géza Oberfrank retains a sense of intimacy many others lose on the way to Gethsemane, but there is no doubting the effect a symphony orchestra's sound has on the overall character of the work. We are definitely in the formal surroundings of a concert hall, though the performing standards are high.

● If you like this, try Bach's Mass in B minor (99)

Beethoven

81) SYMPHONY NO. 3 'EROICA'

Beethoven's third symphony, completed in 1803 and premièred the next year, has long been regarded as the work in which the young composer began to make substantial changes to the very idea of what a symphony constituted, both in terms of orchestration and design. For a start, the work is a good deal longer than any symphony by Mozart, Haydn or any other of his contemporaries. It also has a new idea of orchestral coloration, and introduces the idea of symphonic music with a theme. The work is subtitled 'Eroica', and Beethoven long toyed with the idea of dedicating it to Napoleon in the name of freedom, before realising that Napoleon had a very different definition of the word.

Yet the best performances on record have not ignored Beethoven's insistence on this music being an ode to freedom and the spirit of man. The 1961 recording by Otto Klemperer and the Philharmonia confirms that a

sense of proportion, a denial of excess, is crucial here. Klemperer coaxes a singing, vibrant sense of exultation from his orchestra rather than a desire to flatten the listener by sheer weight of sound. The detail is always delicate, always sweetly phrased. David Zinman and the Zurich Tonhalle follow Klemperer's general policy, though their tempos are faster and their dynamic range stretched to the limit of what this music can stand. But at budget price, they are hard to resist. Yet the most interesting and refreshing version available on a single CD at present is that from 1994 by Jordi Savall and the Concert des Nations on Auvidis. On authentic instruments, Savall brings an extraordinary degree of life and vivacity to the music while keeping its feet on the ground.

● If you like this, try Beethoven's *Egmont* Overture (205)

✔
EMI CDM 566793 2
**Philharmonia Orchestra/
Otto Klemperer**

✔
Arte Nova 74321 49695-2
**Tonhalle Zurich/
David Zinman**

★
Auvidis Astree ES 8557
**Concert des Nations/
Jordi Savall**

82) TRISTAN UND ISOLDE

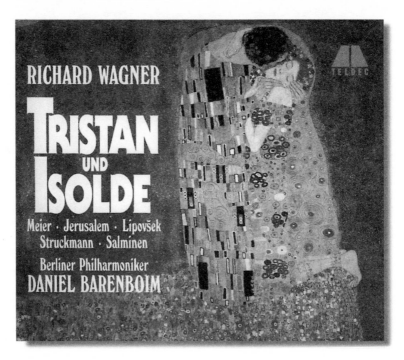

If any one musical work sums up the late 19th century's artistic obsession with love and death and the whole damned thing, it is *Tristan und Isolde*. Wagner wrote the opera in the late 1850s, breaking off work on his four-opera cycle, *The Ring*. The catalyst was his doomed love affair with the married Mathilde Wesendonck. As usual he tells his story through the means of a medieval legend, but there is no mistaking the personal nature of the tale. The lush, all-consuming orchestration, the epic length (not far short of four hours), the fever pitch of emotional intensity, and the constant stretching of the singers' capacities, all point to someone working at the limit of their powers.

A successful performance needs a conductor with a very firm grasp of the work's colossal proportions, as well as its emotional ambitions. It also needs a very responsive orchestra and singers with massive stamina and technique. There have been many distinguished recordings, including a mono 1950s version by Wilhelm Furtwängler and a brilliant mid-1960s Bayreuth recording by Karl Böhm, but the music begs for state-of-the-art recording techniques and sound. For that reason, these are ruled out here. The 1982 Dresden production under Carlos Kleiber was for many years regarded as the best digital recording of the work, with René Kollo and Margaret Price convincing as the two doomed lovers. But in 1995 Daniel Barenboim made a new recording for Teldec which has set new standards in recorded sound for the opera, revealing as never before the orchestral tapestry and giving a real depth of sound to the soloists, Siegfried Jerusalem and Waltraud Meier. So whether it's the whole work, just the *liebestod* or the orchestral interludes and introductions you want, this really is the best place to start. If you want the 'bleeding chunks', as Wagner called excerpts, the pickings are currently slim. The full-price Cheryl Studer/Giuseppi Sinopoli recital on DGG 439 865-2, having the most complete 'bits' plus the Wesendonck lieder, is a good bet.

● If you like this, try Wagner's *Götterdämmerung* (118)

Deutsche Grammophon DG 413 315-2
René Kollo (tenor)/Dame Margaret Price (soprano)/Leipzig Radio Chorus/ Staatskapelle Dresden/Carlos Kleiber

★

Teldec 4509 94568-2
Siegfried Jerusalem (tenor)/Waltraud Meier (mezzo-soprano)/Berlin State Opera Chorus/Berlin Philharmonic Orchestra/ Daniel Barenboim

Handel
83) WATER MUSIC SUITE 1

Handel's *Water Music* continues to entertain, centuries after the Thames spectacular that occasioned its writing. It was composed for relatively modest orchestral forces and runs through a gamut of moods and tempos, although the emphasis is on bright colours and happy tunes. This is typified by the third movement's famous double horn trill, which is echoed by the strings and harpsichord: a big, bright and portentous sound in keeping with royal entertainment and courtly pleasures. The music evokes such strong images of 18th-century pleasure-grounds and summer activities, dances and leisure time for the rich and important that it is like a musical key to a lost world.

Performances of this music need a lightness of touch in keeping with the discretion and brilliant artifice it was intended to display to its original patrons. They also need to be sunny and full of good cheer, though not to the point where the needs of the musicians outweigh the pleasure of the listener: after all, this music is intended to accompany a public occasion, though it is not ceremonial in mood or form. All three recordings manage this. Tafelmusik and Jeanne Lamon for Sony keep their tones bright and their instruments in superb balance: they present all three suites from *Water Music*, though in an undifferentiated form which may confuse some incautious purchasers. Ton Koopman avoids this by having his CD clearly demarcated, suite by suite, so that listeners can choose the exact tracks they want to hear. His ensemble's sound is also beautifully crystalline and full of colour, his horns burnished and golden. This is also mostly the case with Collegium Aureum, who include the *Music for the Royal Fireworks* as a bonus on a mid-price reissue. There are moments when inspiration fails them (the Minuet, for example, which is rather dull), but it is good value for money, if expenditure is a prime consideration.

● If you like this, try Handel's *Music for the Royal Fireworks* (166)

Sony SK 68257
Tafelmusik/
Jeanne Lamon

Erato 4509 91716-2
Amsterdam Baroque Orchestra/
Ton Koopman

Deutsche Harmonia Mundi 05472 77414-2
Collegium Aureum

Tchaikovsky

84) SWAN LAKE

Swan Lake was Tchaikovsky's first ballet, composed in 1875 when he was in his mid-30s and beginning to make his mark in Russian music circles. It was not a success in his lifetime, only receiving its due during the extended lamentations following his death in 1893. Since then it has been a perennial worldwide favourite: his public had caught up with him too late on this occasion. Considering the delicious scoring, the bewitching rhythms and the inspired melodies (including the perky 'Dance of the Swans' and one of his most famous, the dirge known as 'The Dying Swan'), it is baffling what anyone could have objected to. Of course the complete experience is only to be gained by watching the ballet while simultaneously listening to its music, but the armchair listener has plenty to be seduced by in the music alone. Tchaikovsky consistently shows the lightest of gossamer touches when it comes to choosing the instrumentation for any one scene: everything is vivid, varied and fresh, nothing simply mundane.

As is to be expected with Tchaikovsky, the work wears its heart on its sleeve, so the orchestra must be ready to do so as well, while keeping precision and clarity at the forefront of their aims. Both Charles Dutoit and the Montreal Symphony, in their complete recording for Decca, and Charles Mackerras with the RPO, in his suite for Telarc, manage this balance and also benefit from outstanding recording quality. Dutoit dates from 1992, Mackerras from 1987. Each takes a flexible, supple and discreet line, but is not afraid to make the dynamics count when it comes to a climax. The full score is over two hours long, so those after the highlights only would be advised to stick with Mackerras.

● If you like this, try Tchaikovsky's *Sleeping Beauty* (141)

Telarc CD 80151
**Royal Philharmonic Orchestra/
Sir Charles Mackerras**

★

Decca 436 212-2
**Montreal Symphony Orchestra/
Charles Dutoit**

Berlioz
85) SYMPHONIE FANTASTIQUE

At its première in 1830 Berlioz publicly declared this to be a symphony that traced the emotional travails of an intoxicating love affair. This was a mad passion he developed for a sylph-like Irish actress, Harriet Smithson, whom he met in Paris while she was acting in Shakespeare. The elements of the *Symphonie Fantastique* – drugs, mad love, witches, the guillotine, murder and orgies – all make this one of the defining works of the Romantic period. The music is cast in new, open and unresolved forms and tied together with what Berlioz called his '*idée fixe*', a motif which runs through all five movements, representing both his tormented love and the artistic unity of the music. Although there are respites from the madness of unfulfilled desire which dominates the whole work, this is a symphony that thrives on its own turbulent and distorted reality.

Predictably, the music needs someone with a huge imagination and a firm grip on practicalities to bring off a successful performance. The large forces Berlioz deploys, the complexity of the score and its sheer capriciousness mean the conductor is always having to exert a strong influence. Mariss Jansons manages this with the Royal Concertgebouw in a 1992 EMI recording. A perfectly serviceable budget-price recording from 1996 features the Grand Canaria Philharmonic Orchestra under Adrian Leaper, while Philips still have available what was regarded in 1968 as a ground-breaking version. Once again this is with the Concertgebouw, this time with Colin Davis, that early champion of Berlioz's work who did so much to bring him to prominence and make this work a perennial favourite. The 1960s sound is unexpectedly vigorous, just a touch thin, but very presentable. At mid-price it is still a valid alternative.

● If you like this, try Mendelssohn's *A Midsummer Night's Dream* (135)

★
EMI CDC 754479 2
Concertgebouw Orchestra, Amsterdam/ Mariss Jansons

✔
Arte Nova 74321 46492-2
Gran Canaria Philharmonic Orchestra/Adrian Leaper

✔
Philips 446 202-2
Concertgebouw Orchestra, Amsterdam/ Sir Colin Davis

Mozart

86) AVE VERUM CORPUS

Mozart's K618 is a simple and affecting little thing lasting just under four minutes. It has none of the pomp and splendour of his more extended choral compositions but is a concentrated dose of sincere religious desire. Its short text deals with a plea to the crucified Christ to accept imperfect humanity into Heaven, and an honouring of the sacrifice Christ made for mankind. The mood is largely subdued, the tempo barely reaching *lento* in many performances.

The two main recommendations have important differences. Ton Koopman uses the Amsterdam Baroque Choir as well as its Orchestra, achieving a less stark and bleak setting than that heard on the recital by the Westminster Cathedral Choir, directed by James O'Donnell and with Iain Simcock accompanying on organ. It must be said, too, that although there are only two years separating the two recordings (the O'Donnell in 1993, the Koopman in 1995), the Erato recording has much the cleaner and richer acoustics, the

Westminster performance being rather indistinct and lacking in presence in comparison. Still, both performances succeed in their very different ways in providing highly individual moods. Both discs are at full price. The Koopman is an all-Mozart recital, combined with *The Coronation Mass*, the *Vesperae* K339 and *Exsultate, jubilate* K165, making it a desirable collection of much of Mozart's most popular choral music. The O'Donnell is a very different collation, combining works by a wide range of composers including Franck, Gounod, Mendelssohn, Holst, Fauré and Elgar. The budget-price Davis rendition on Belart is also a compilation of a range of choral music, this time mixing performers as well as composers. Not comparable to the discs above, it is still an entry-point disc with the benefit of being a cheap way to acquire a number of well-known small choral works.

● If you like this, try Mozart's *Vesperae Solennes* (112)

★
Erato 0630 10705-2
**Amsterdam Baroque Choir & Orchestra/
Ton Koopman**

Hyperion CDA 66669
**Iain Simcock (organ)/
Westminster Cathedral Choir/
James O'Donnell**

✔
Belart 450 048-2
**London Symphony Orchestra & Chorus/
Sir Colin Davis**

Gluck

87) ORFEO ED EURIDICE

This was a revolutionary opera in the Vienna of 1762. With it Gluck and his librettist, Calzabigi, cut out all the excesses that had become mandatory in 18th-century opera and returned to basics: a strong story properly observed by performers and audience alike and real characters for singers to portray. Today it seems incredible, but without Gluck the glory of Mozart's operas just twenty years later would have been inconceivable. On top of that, *Orfeo*, through the sustained lyricism of its melodies, whether these are from the singers or from the instrumental ensemble, remains a beautiful operatic masterpiece. The famous 'Dance of the Blessed Spirits' which initiates Scene 2 of Act 2, or Orfeo's heartfelt set of arias in Act 3 prior to his recovery of Euridice, are all examples of this rare and timeless talent.

The oldest of the three recommended recordings comes from France and was made for Astree in 1984 by Jean-Claude Malgoire. It is on authentic instruments and features moving performances from counter-tenor James Bowman and soprano Lynne Dawson. The sound is just a little dull and distant, but the most annoying thing is a complete lack of page or index references in the libretto. The 1992 recording by Frieder Bernius for Sony Vivarte features Nancy Argenta and Michael Chance: it is again on authentic instruments and possesses grace in abundance, although Michael Chance's counter-tenor can be a little ungainly at times. The 1993 recording by John Eliot Gardiner for Philips has a counter-tenor the equal of James Bowman in Derek Lee Ragin and a fine Euridice in Sylvia McNair. His authentic instruments ensemble has an immediacy denied Malgoire owing to Astree's distant recording sound. The performance may not be artistically better than Malgoire's, but the overall package is superior.

● If you like this, try Handel's *Serse* (144)

Astree E8538
**Namur Chamber Choir/
Grande Ecurie/
Jean-Claude Malgoire**

Sony Vivarte SX2K 48040
**Stuttgart Chamber Choir/
Tafelmusik/
Frieder Bernius**

★

Philips 434 093-2
**Monteverdi Choir/
English Baroque Soloists/
John Eliot Gardiner**

Shostakovich
88) PIANO CONCERTO NO. 2

Shostakovich is often regarded as someone incapable of raising a smile. This concerto, written for his pianist son Maxim in the 1950s, gives the lie to such ideas. Shostakovich constantly works childlike themes and ideas into the piano part in the pleasantly romping first movement, while the slow second, which touches on melancholy, is clear in its homage to Chopin. The third and final movement brings us full circle back into the warmth and high spirits of the opening.

We listeners are doubly blessed in the recording stakes by having not only Shostakovich's own recording of this music (made in Paris in 1958), but that of Maxim himself, this time conducting while his own son (and the composer's grandson), Dmitri, takes the piano role. The composer stresses the mischievous side of the high spirits in the first movement, allowing things to become a little manic at the climax. His *andante* is tender and loving, stressing the seriousness of intent underlying the Chopin pastiche, while the finale is full of optimism and fun.

Maxim and son quite rightly make the high jinks of the first movement sound decidedly more innocent, while the *andante* is reverent, a touch of boyish awe emerging. The first-rate recording sound and careful balance of soloist and orchestra make this a natural first choice apart from the fact that the concerto's pairing is the orchestral arrangement of String Quartet No. 10 – a dark and troubled work which quite dissipates the goodwill and warmth generated by the star attraction. Father Dmitri's companion piece is the 1933 First Piano Concerto, a more natural CD partner.

● If you like this, try Shostakovich's Symphony No. 5 (213)

✔
EMI CDC 754606 2
Dmitri Shostakovich (piano)/
French Radio National Orchestra/
André Cluytens

★
Chandos CHAN 8443
Dmitri Shostakovich Jr (piano)/
Musici de Montreal/
Montreal Symphony Orchestra/
Maxim Shostakovich

Debussy
89) # SUITE BERGAMASQUE

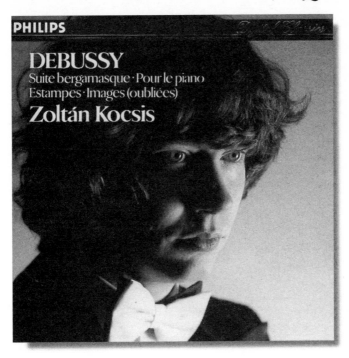

Debussy's piano music sounds simple to play but is devilishly difficult to get right. Debussy himself detested most of the playing of his own work that he heard, accusing pianists of 'murdering' it. They continue to do so today, for few concert pianists can suppress their performing egos to the extent Debussy demands. All four parts of *Suite Bergamasque*, an early piano work from the 1890s, are creations of exquisite charm and delicacy, with a sense of French music history. All but the famous 'Clair de lune' ('Moonlight') have titles taken directly from old dance forms.

Fine modern performances of this music are few and far between, and do not come from the obvious virtuosos. The most celebrated interpreters of the past (Gieseking, Casadesus, François) are all victims of the limited recorded sound of their time. Today the benchmark for pianistic scruples and vivid imagination is made by Zoltán Kocsis in a 1984 recording for Philips. Although the sound is a little too reverberant, the piano touch is incredible, the phrasing and nuance perfectly judged, the scholarship rigorous. Suffering in the sound stakes (it is a 1978 recording) but equally true to his performing scruples is Pascal Rogé on a mid-price Decca recital. Pre-digital recording makes for some tape hiss, but these are very worthy performances. At budget price there is a proliferation of CDs but not a massive amount of true quality. Pick of the bunch (although a very full CD programme only admits 'Clair de lune' of the *Suite Bergamasque*) is the late 1960s recital by Philippe Entremont which, though not electrifying, is at least refined and avoids exaggeration.

★
Philips 412 118-2
Zoltán Kocsis (piano)

✔
Decca 443 021-2
Pascal Rogé (piano)

✔
Sony SBK 48174
Philippe Entremont (piano)

● If you like this, try Debussy's *Arabesques* (365)

Mozart

90) SYMPHONY NO. 40 K550

In the summer of 1788, his fortunes on the slide, Mozart composed three symphonies which he hoped would be heard at a subscription concert, thus raising some desperately needed cash. These were Symphonies 39, 40 and 41, and they turned out to be the last he composed, though he still had three years to live. The hoped-for subscription concerts failed to materialise and Mozart abandoned any attempt to place them elsewhere.

As with any of the great works of his maturity, a modern listener is astounded that Mozart could have had such a hard time getting these sublime and graceful works played. In fact, the 'dark' D minor 40th remained a work regarded with suspicion as a difficult proposal well into the 19th century. Today, as the Classic FM Hall of Fame list shows, it is his most popular symphony. The first choice in recordings of the work is that of Nikolaus Harnoncourt and the Royal Concertgebouw Orchestra on Teldec. Not an authentic instruments performance, it nonetheless has the crispness and coherence of authentic practice.

Harnoncourt consistently teases out the nuances and hidden dramas in the music. He makes the symphony fairly crackle with electricity, from its famous quasi-operatic minor-key opening theme to its stirring conclusion.

Ironically, Trevor Pinnock's English Concert recording, using period instruments, has less attack and brightness of tone than the Concertgebouw, with a rather over-polished and over-ambient quality that robs the music of some of its immediacy. The actual playing is commendable: the end-result just misses the mark. This is not the case with the final recommendation, the latter-day recording of Symphonies 40 and 41 by Karl Böhm with the Vienna Philharmonic. Böhm's unique mixture of urbanity and unerring attention to detail makes this one to seek out.

● If you like this, try Haydn's Symphony No. 101 (350)

★
Teldec 4509 97490-2
**Concertgebouw Orchestra, Amsterdam/
Nikolaus Harnoncourt**

✔
Archiv 447 048-2
**English Concert/
Trevor Pinnock**

Deutsche Grammophon DG 413 547-2
**Vienna Philharmonic Orchestra/
Karl Böhm**

Sibelius

91 **VIOLIN CONCERTO**

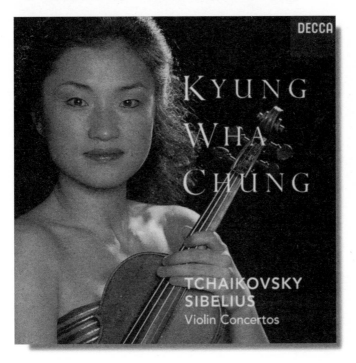

Sibelius wrote just one concerto, and this is it. He completed it in 1903 and then thoroughly revised it in 1905. It is the 1905 version which is regularly given today. This is full of appropriate rhapsody from the violin and emotional response from the orchestra. It is also full of stunning technical challenges for the soloist, from the first to the last movement, with the violin often left unsupported by the orchestra in a cruel spotlight where any technical slip or lack of projection will deeply mar the overall impression of the piece. As always with Sibelius, there is a definite emotional climate being worked through, often dark, quite regularly threatening in the shape of orchestral interpolations, and always intense. Even in the sweet lyricism of the *adagio* there is a sense of starkness which is perhaps as much a result of Sibelius's Finnish background as of any other factor.

The violinist who conquers this work must have an indomitable spirit and a direct honesty of expression which surpass the technical questions being asked of them. An early recording by Kyung-Wha Chung, from 1970, accompanied by André Previn with the London Symphony, sustains its tautness and emotional tension throughout the three movements. This is also the case with Julian Rachlin and Lorin Maazel on Sony, though Rachlin sounds less implacable in his pursuance of the music's essence than does Chung. Chung is also at mid-price. A fascinating alternative to these two is the BIS recording from 1990 which programmes both the original 1903 and the customary 1905 versions in sequence. Leonidas Kavacos is the impressive soloist, with Osmo Vänskä conducting the Lahti Symphony.

● If you like this, try Sibelius's *Valse Triste* (296)

★ ✔

Decca 425 080-2
Kyung-Wha Chung (violin)/
London Symphony Orchestra/
André Previn

Sony SK 53272
Julian Rachlin (violin)/
Pittsburgh Symphony Orchestra/
Lorin Maazel

BIS CD 500
Leonidas Kavacos (violin)/
Lahti Symphony Orchestra/
Osmo Vänskä

Tchaikovsky
92) SYMPHONY NO. 5

Tchaikovsky's fifth and penultimate symphony, written when he was 47, finds the composer balanced between the confusions and uncertainties of his past and the hope of a happy accommodation with his own nature as the basis for his future. This accommodation was twofold: he finally felt confident in his ability to write a successful symphony, and was also reconciled to his homosexuality. Thus he may have written about 'fate' governing this work, but there is also a tangible sense of relief. The music may pass through dark and stormy passages in all four of its movements, but it also glories in the serenity of the second-movement string melody that at times touches bliss.

Both the Karajan and the Jansons recordings of this symphony are mid-price and available separately or as part of boxed sets of complete Tchaikovsky symphony cycles (the Jansons includes 'Manfred'; the Karajan doesn't). Both have 'special' boxed set prices, though the Karajan has three CDs fewer: this has an obvious cost advantage but inconveniently breaks both Symphonies 2 and 5 over two CDs in the set to cram as much onto each as possible. Chandos have taken the luxurious route of having one symphony per disc (the second symphony CD is filled out by *Capriccio Italien*), which is infinitely preferable if you can afford the extra CDs. Both Karajan and Jansons give intense and disciplined performances, with the 1979 Karajan perhaps shading it on his ability to phrase Tchaikovsky's melodies 'just so'. If you want an even cheaper bargain, then Kurt Masur and the Leipzig Gewandhaus offer the 4th, 5th and 6th Symphonies in good modern sound with respectable performances at budget price across two discs.

● If you like this, try Tchaikovsky's Symphony No. 4 (152)

★
Deutsche Grammophon DG 439 019-2
**Vienna Philharmonic Orchestra/
Herbert von Karajan**

Chandos CHAN 8351
**Oslo Philharmonic Orchestra/
Mariss Jansons**

✔
Teldec 0630 18966-2
**Leipzig Gewandhaus Orchestra/
Kurt Masur**

Gershwin
93) RHAPSODY IN BLUE

GERSHWIN

PIANO CONCERTO IN F

RHAPSODY IN BLUE

SECOND RHAPSODY

Howard Shelley
piano

Philharmonia Orchestra

Yan Pascal Tortelier
conductor

DIGITAL

CHANDOS

Rhapsody in Blue bears the character of the age and the country that spawned it: young, brattish, flashy and full of rakish charm. Not many people know that there are two versions. The original was scored specifically for Paul Whiteman's curious hodge-podge line-up of part dance-band, part orchestra, while the later concert version substituted a conventional symphony orchestra. Another little-known fact is that Gershwin imported the rhythms, not of jazz, but of ragtime: the authentic 'folk' touch came from the blues and spirituals (that famous opening clarinet glissando, for example). With that in mind, Wayne Marshall brings us plenty of youthful bravado and a healthy lack of interest in being 'cute', and the Aalborg generally seems to agree with him. Marshall's rhythmic flair and aggressive touch are on display through the rest of the CD on pieces such as *American in Paris* and the *I Got Rhythm Variations*.

Pianist Howard Shelley and conductor Yan-Pascal Tortelier take a more traditional approach, going for symphonic niceties, well-turned phrases and an orchestra that is dignified rather than raucous. A very sensible CD programme sees the concerto coupled with the Second Rhapsody and the Piano Concerto in F, both logical successors to the Rhapsody. The real surprises, however, are sprung on the Tilson-Thomas disc. He not only uses the original Whiteman scoring, but also calls upon the services of George Gershwin himself, via the medium of a piano roll the composer cut back in 1925. This leads to many fascinating contrasts with other recordings, including some insanely fast tempos, but it sure is exciting. Not a performance to doze off to, but it recaptures the ferment of the composer's own times. For that alone it deserves recommendation. Add first-rate sound and it becomes highly collectable.

● If you like this, try Copland's *Appalachian Spring* (126)

✔
Virgin VM 561247 2
Wayne Marshall (piano)/
Aalborg Symphony Orchestra

★
Chandos CHAN 9092
Howard Shelley (piano)/
Philharmonia Orchestra/
Yan-Pascal Tortelier

✔
Sony SMK 42240
George Gershwin (piano)/
Columbia Jazz Band/
Michael Tilson-Thomas

Dvořák

94) CELLO CONCERTO

Dvořák's passionate concerto was written in New York after the completion of his famous Symphony No. 9 , *From the New World*, but rather than looking more closely at the musical inspirations found for the symphony in this new land, Dvořák finds his inspiration in homesickness and fond nostalgia for the sounds of his native Czechoslovakia. The urgency of these feelings is communicated in the initial theme statement by the orchestra. The cello's entry is no less fraught, the soloist required to bow the same phrases with strength and passion before the composer allows the initial alarm and tension to subside in more flowing, mellifluous phrases from soloist and orchestra combined. Nostalgia of a more dewy-eyed type dominates the peaceful *adagio* of the second movement, its broad, sweeping cello theme possessing dignity and wonderful inner passion. The piece ends with a finale which combines the energy of the first with the gentleness of the second movement.

Recordings of this remarkable music abound: all the great cellists have made their mark with it. Yo-Yo Ma is one of the most recent, his recording with Kurt Masur and the New York Philharmonic dating from 1995. Ma brings tremendous passion and consummate skill to his reading, thus making a memorable recording, but he is not best supported by an orchestra that seems to strain to make its impact and is dully recorded. Raphael Wallfisch in 1989 has the inestimable advantage of having Czech music specialist Sir Charles Mackerras conducting the LSO for his performance. He also enjoys brilliant sound from the Chandos engineers. A thinner, more compressed sound is again present on a famous recording from 1969, that of Rostropovich with von Karajan and the Berlin Philharmonic, but this must be weighed against its mid-price availability and the urgent, committed readings from soloist and conductor.

● If you like this, try Haydn's Cello Concerto No. 1 in C (320)

Sony SK 67173
Yo-Yo Ma (cello)/
New York Philharmonic Orchestra/
Kurt Masur

★

Chandos 8662
Raphael Wallfisch (cello)/
London Symphony Orchestra/
Sir Charles Mackerras

✔

Deutsche Grammophon DG 447 413-2
Mstislav Rostropovich (cello)/
Berlin Philharmonic Orchestra/
Herbert von Karajan

Bruch

95) SCOTTISH FANTASY

Bruch may have termed this a fantasy, and indeed it plays upon material from a number of genuine Scottish themes, but it could as surely be titled a concerto with a novel introduction. In the work Bruch continues the pattern set in his first violin concerto by feeding the violin soloist a stream of beautiful – and often quite elegiac – melodies perfectly suited to the sweep and sustain characteristic of a bowed string instrument. This brings the violin very close to the human voice and allows it both to speak and sing like no other in this type of repertoire, and here in this highly charged work you can almost hear the words behind the violin's melody while the orchestra often acts like a chorus in support. There is plenty of room for the soloist to impress through technical brilliance, and few capable violinists resist the temptation to pull out all the stops.

Few first-class violinists have not made a recording of this work, so the choice is inevitably subjective, according to taste: how do you like your Scottish reels played? The three violinists chosen here have a very clear idea of their approach to the music. Both Midori and Kyung-Wha have tremendous attack in the lively passages and a very vocalised lyricism that suits the material perfectly. Kyung-Wha from 1972 has marvellous support from Rudolf Kempe while Midori in 1993 benefits from Zubin Mehta's attentions and better recorded sound. Kyung-Wha is at mid-price. If you are after terrific violin-playing, even though the sound is not comparable with Midori (or Chung, for that matter), then Alfredo Campoli's 1965 performance for Decca, now on Belart, is hard to beat.

● If you like this, try Bruch's *Kol Nidrei* (241)

★
Sony SK 58967
**Midori (violin)/
Israel Philharmonic Orchestra/
Zubin Mehta**

Decca 448 976-2
**Kyung-Wha Chung (violin)/
Royal Philharmonic Orchestra/
Rudolf Kempe**

✔

Belart 461 142-2
**Alfredo Campoli (violin)/
London Symphony Orchestra/
Sir Adrian Boult**

Beethoven

96) ROMANCE FOR VIOLIN & ORCHESTRA NO. 2 IN F MAJOR OP. 50

BEETHOVEN
VIOLIN CONCERTO
ROMANCES FOR VIOLIN AND ORCHESTRA
LA SCALA PHILHARMONIC ORCHESTRA
SALVATORE ACCARDO
CARLO MARIA GIULINI

G ood tunes usually win out. This short Romance (it runs for less than ten minutes) from 1798 starts with a great melody and keeps it up in various guises for its entire duration. The work sounds a little like the slow movement of a violin concerto, and there is a reason for this. Musicologists are fairly sure that this and its companion piece, the Romance No. 1, were early exercises in a second movement for the violin concerto which Beethoven long planned to write, and which finally saw the light of day in December 1806. This perhaps explains the immediate onrush of melody from the piece's first note, without any introductory formalities. In this piece Beethoven is emphasising grace and his ability to write sustained, singing melody. This, of course, is facilitated by the fact that he is writing for the violin, an instrument to which a sustained note comes naturally, rather than the piano with its immediate decay.

Deutsche Grammophon DG 458 488-2
Kyung-Wha Chung (violin)/
Philharmonia Orchestra/
Myung-Whun Chung

★

Sony SK 53287
Salvatore Accardo (violin)/
Philharmonic Orchestra of
La Scala, Milan/
Carlo Maria Giulini

✔

EMI CDM 764324 2
Sir Yehudi Menuhin (violin)/
Philharmonia Orchestra/
Sir John Pritchard

All three recorded versions come from unchallenged violin greats. Kyung-Wha Chung and Salvatore Accardo are both at full price and are wholly at home with Beethoven's violin music. They attack the sweet melody as if they have been playing it all their lives – which they undoubtedly have been – with Accardo perhaps showing the greater poise. The orchestra doesn't have a great deal to do apart from stay out of the way and add discreet rhythmic and harmonic support. Both Giulini for Accardo and Myung-Whun Chung for his sister Kyung-Wha manage this with accomplished finesse. The mid-price choice offers wonderful playing but a lesser degree of recorded violin tone, being from 1962.

● If you like this, try Franck's Violin Sonata No. 1 (261)

Puccini

97) TURANDOT

Puccini's great unfinished masterpiece may contain two of the most famous arias in all opera ('Nessun dorma' and 'Signora, ascolta') but this is an opera framed by the actions and singing of the Peking crowd, as represented by the opera chorus. It is as flat as non-gaseous mineral water without a great chorus. Similarly, the support cast such as Ping, Pang and Pong and the exquisite Liu have to be well above the ordinary. There are many recordings of the work where the chorus is recorded as if an afterthought. Those recommended here contain great male and female leads securely nestled in the right musical environment.

The 1972 version conducted by Zubin Mehta and featuring Joan Sutherland, Luciano Pavarotti and Montserrat Caballé comes fractionally ahead of the 1960 set conducted in Rome for RCA by Erich Leinsdorf and starring Birgit Nilsson, Jussi Bjoerling and Renata Tebaldi. Mehta's leads are beyond reproach, Sutherland managing in her tone the essential steely cruelty the part demands. Puccini's own favourite character, the all-suffering Liu, could have no better advocate than Montserrat Caballé. In contrast, Birgit Nilsson has for many years been lauded as the greatest postwar Turandot, her incredible vocal control always at the service of the music. Bjoerling is convincing as the Calaf, his 'Nessun dorma' a thing of beauty, while Renata Tebaldi as Liu brings all her great experience to the role.

The third choice listed here, recorded for Decca in 1955 and featuring Inge Borkh as Turandot, is a viable cheaper alternative, though there is no libretto on offer.

● If you like this, try Dvořák's *Rusalka* (110)

★
Decca 414 274-2
**Dame Joan Sutherland (soprano)/
Luciano Pavarotti (tenor)/
Monserrat Caballé (soprano)/
Wandsworth School Boys' Choir/
John Alldis Choir/London Philharmonic
Orchestra/Zubin Mehta**

✔
RCA 09026 62687-2
**Birgit Nilsson (soprano)/Jussi Bjoerling
(tenor)/Renata Tebaldi (soprano)/
Rome Opera Orchestra & Chorus/
Erich Leinsdorf**

✔
Decca 433 761-2
**Inge Borkh (soprano)/Mario Del Monaco
(tenor)/Renata Tebaldi (soprano)/
Santa Cecilia Academy Orchestra &
Chorus, Rome/Alberto Erede**

Johann Strauss II

98) THE BLUE DANUBE

Strauss's great friend Johannes Brahms openly acknowledged that he envied his colleague's gift for melody. Nowhere is that gift more immediately felt than in the waltz called *An der schönen, blauern Donau*, or, to us, *The Blue Danube*. From the first bars we are in sunny weather and carefree mood. It is quite impossible to listen to this piece with any form of sympathy and not be cheered. What is strange to recall now is that the waltz, that quintessential Viennese form of dance entertainment, was originally a folk dance and looked upon as too coarse and sensual for civilised people.

The three performances of this famous, delightfully bright waltz are all recorded in brilliant sound and by orchestras with real flair as well as a proper belief in the worth of the music. The oldest comes from a mid-price Fritz Reiner set and dates from the 1960s. Reiner was conducting in Vienna in 1915, so he had his own reasons for feeling close to this music. His version is lush and surprisingly tender, bringing a warm sense of nostalgia to the bright fabric of the piece. Erich Kunzel and the Cincinnati Pops have a glorious and detailed studio ambience and go for the sheer beauty of Strauss's melodic and rhythmic lines. Theirs is a cloudless Austrian sky, full of hope, their step light and quick. The Naxos performance comes from a set of no less than ten CDs of Strauss compositions with a variety of conductors; the *Danube* is with Johannes Wildner. It is a spirited rendition and quite faithfully idiomatic. At budget price it is a good buy, but for me the Reiner has that something extra which makes it very special.

● If you like this, try Strauss's *Die Fledermaus* (229)

★ ✔
RCA 09026 68160-2
**Chicago Symphony Orchestra/
Fritz Reiner**

Telarc CD 80098
**Cincinnati Pops Orchestra/
Erich Kunzel**

✔
Naxos 8.554520
**Slovak State Philharmonic Orchestra/
Johannes Wildner**

Bach

99) MASS IN B MINOR BWV232

Experts remain divided as to the musical unity of this Mass – it was written by Bach at two distinct times some 15 years apart, and in fact occupied him right up to his death. He certainly used some pre-existing musical material in an effort to complete it, but this need not overly concern us, for the standard of creativity is unusually high. Bach's setting of the Mass concentrates not on the horrors and hellfire of man's relationship to his maker, but on the serenity of the human being who walks beside his or her God. The 'Kyrie', 'Lord, have mercy', is an instance of this: the mood is serene, meditative, not turbulent; the soloists in the first section are given elegant interlocking lines with which to deliver their simple plea. The emotional heat is turned up by the choir's rendition next, but it is still given with complete decorum. Immediately after the 'Kyrie', the 'Gloria' leaves one in no doubt about Bach's state of mind, the fanfare and chorus

being overwhelmingly positive, the singing adjoining it affirmative.

Accentuating the positive is Peter Schreier in his 1992 project for Philips. His cast exercise restraint in their approach to the music. Soloists include such experienced Bach singers as Arleen Augér and Ann Murray, while Marjana Lipovšek and Anton Scharinger deliver finely wrought performances. Frans Brüggen uses authentic instruments but the production values are so good that it would be difficult to fault the playing or the tones being produced, so rich are they. Soloists include Jennifer Smith, Michael Chance and Harry van der Kamp. For a good mid-price alternative, Eugen Jochum's 1980 effort for EMI with Helen Donath and Brigitte Fassbinder will do nicely.

● If you like this, try Mozart's Mass in C minor (Great) (242)

Philips 432 972-2
Arleen Augér (soprano)/Ann Murray (mezzo-soprano)/Marjana Lipovšek (mezzo-soprano)/Anton Scharinger (baritone)/Leipzig Radio Chorus/Staatskapelle Dresden/Peter Schreier

 ★

Philips 426 238-2
Jennifer Smith (soprano)/Michael Chance (alto)/Nico van der Meel (tenor)/Harry van der Kamp (bass)/Netherlands Chamber Choir/Eighteenth Century Orchestra/Frans Brüggen

 ✔

EMI CZS 568640 2
Helen Donath (soprano)/Brigitte Fassbinder (contralto)/Roland Hermann (baritone)/Bavarian Radio Symphony Orchestra & Choir/Eugen Jochum

Schubert

100) SYMPHONY NO. 9 IN C (GREAT)

This work has fared well for a piece of music never heard in performance by its composer and which had to wait decades for its première; even longer for its publication. Now one of the best loved of all symphonies, it seems a model of musical architecture and a testament to Schubert's unending creativity. Each movement has its most remarkable features, but the overall impression is one of scale: this really is 'big' music. That is not to say it is merely loud: plenty of little pieces are that alone. No – this is music thought up on a large design and given room by its creator to develop into a huge, interlocking musical canvas. Its first movement has one of those flowing Schubertian themes which immediately make you feel better about the world, while the second plumbs the inner recesses of Schubert's lyrical soul. The finale is long and musically complex, but its main ideas are crystal clear and easy to follow. Its mood is upbeat, its colours

bold as Schubert resolves the outstanding issues. A noisy celebratory climax is apposite and justly exciting.

Neville Marriner, in his boxed set of all the Schubert symphonies plus all the known fragments, delivers a coherent and flowing interpretation of the Ninth. He may not possess the same keenness for the distinguishing trait which Harnoncourt manages, bringing a very Viennese feeling to the music, but his observations are insightful and germane. Harnoncourt uses newly edited versions of the symphony that allow him something of a head start as far as authenticity goes, and he maintains this lead in an authoritative performance. At mid-price, the 1971 New York Philharmonic recording under Leonard Bernstein gives excellent value.

● If you like this, try Haydn's Symphony No. 94 (348)

Philips 442 646-2
**Academy of St Martin-in-the-Fields/
Sir Neville Marriner**

★

Teldec 4509 97512-2
**Concertgebouw Orchestra, Amsterdam/
Nikolaus Harnoncourt**

Sony SMK 61842
**New York Philharmonic Orchestra/
Leonard Bernstein**

Saint-Saëns
101) CARNIVAL OF THE ANIMALS

So conservative and mindful of his reputation was Saint-Saëns that he forbade any public performance of this delightful set of miniatures during his lifetime. Written quickly in 1886 and played to a private party of friends, it then laid unheard until 1922, after the composer's will had been read, permitting its performance. It is always a hit with children, who immediately recognise the animals portrayed.

Charm and a light touch are essential ingredients of any performance of these delicate morsels. The Chandos recital with I Musici de Montréal conducted by Yuli Turovsky (who also solos on 'The Swan') and with David Owen Norris on piano is a top-draw current release. It also benefits from imaginative CD coupling, being paired with Saint-Saëns's own *Wedding Cake* and Mozart's *A Musical Joke*. For a budget-priced bargain, the ensemble under Philippe Entremont's leadership with Gaby Casadesus as second pianist and Yo-Yo Ma on cello is witty and tasteful. The rest of the Sony disc features Eugene Ormandy conducting the Third Symphony and the *Danse Macabre*.

Chandos CHAN 9246
David Owen Norris (piano)/Gregory Shaverdian (piano)/Constantino Greco (double bass)/Timothy Hutchins (flute)/Musici de Montréal/Yuli Turovsky

✔

Sony SBK 47655
Yo-Yo Ma (cello)/Gaby Casadesus (piano)/Philippe Entremont (piano/conductor)/Instrumental Ensemble

● If you like this, try Mussorgsky's *Pictures at an Exhibition* (103)

Sibelius
102) KARELIA SUITE

The Karelia Suite derived from incidental music Sibelius wrote in 1891 for a patriotic tableau of scenes from Karelian history devised by Finnish students eager to assert Finnish identity in the face of Russian intervention. Within a short space of time Sibelius had extracted three of the most impressive musical numbers and fashioned them into a suite echoing the simple and dignified melodies and actions of these people.

★

Finlandia 4509 95844-2
Helsinki Philharmonic Orchestra/ Okko Kamu

BIS CD 915
Lahti Symphony Orchestra/ Osmo Vänskä

With music such as this it is wise to select recordings with strong connections with Finland to capture the right flavour. This, combined with outstanding section playing and insightful conducting, makes the Finlandia recording by Okko Kamu and the Helsinki Philharmonic hard to top. The fact that it is combined with other Sibelius favourites, including *Finlandia*, makes it a clear front-runner. For the more curious listener, a very fine performance of the complete incidental music from the original tableaux is available on BIS, conducted by Osmo Vänskä and played by the Lahti Symphony. This also includes the incidental music from *Kuolema* and *Valse Triste*.

● If you like this, try Grieg's *Holberg* Suite (145)

Mussorgsky
103) PICTURES AT AN EXHIBITION

Mussorgsky dashed off these ten sparklingly imaginative portraits in less than a month in 1874. His inspiration had been the posthumous exhibition of paintings by a close friend, Viktor Hartmann. Each piece here bears a title taken from paintings in that exhibition, but they seem more closely to indicate the composer's states of mind than any pictures being 'portrayed' in music.

★
Deutsche Grammophon
DG 437 805-2
Lilya Zilberstein (piano)

Deutsche Grammophon
DG 445 238-2
**Berlin Philharmonic
Orchestra/Claudio Abbado**

Alfred Brendel made a considered and faithful recording of them for Philips in 1987 (442 650-2). His speeds are correct, his touch varied, but he lacks the capricious and almost cruel twists of mood and attack needed to transfix the listener as this work can. This is something Lilya Zilberstein does on her DGG recording from 1994. Zilberstein continually matches her imagination to the composer's, thereby stretching ours. The recorded sound is also outstanding.

Maurice Ravel scored Mussorgsky's work for full orchestra, and this version has become equally as popular as the original. The companion piece on the Brendel disc is a performance of this arrangement by the Vienna Philharmonic with André Previn. On an all-orchestral Mussorgsky disc, Claudio Abbado and the Berlin Philharmonic on DGG stretch the listener's imagination with an electric performance of Ravel's setting, alongside rare original Mussorgsky orchestral pieces. Zilberstein for piano, then, and Abbado for orchestra.

● If you like this, try Mussorgsky's *Night on the Bare Mountain* (237)

Elgar
104) CORONATION ODE

Elgar's 'occasional' and ceremonial music has become some of the most popular classical music of the twentieth or any century. The half-hour-long *Coronation Ode*, written for the accession of Edward VII in 1902, included a final selection which, in its original purely instrumental version, would later be incorporated into the *Pomp & Circumstance* marches. At King Edward's own suggestion, Elgar had words set to the stirring melody, which from then on became world famous as 'Land of Hope and Glory'.

✔
EMI CDM 565586 2
**London Symphony Choir/
Northern Sinfonia/
Richard Hickox**

★
Chandos CHAN 6574
**Scottish Orchestra
Chorus/Royal Scottish
National Orchestra/
Alexander Gibson**

The complete *Ode* is rarely recorded, unlike 'Land of Hope and Glory', which has been recorded innumerable times in an arrangement by Arthur Fagge sanctioned by Elgar. The 1977 recording of the *Ode* by Alexander Gibson is not only masterful and assured, but at mid-price: one could want no more. If just the Fagge arrangement of the famous finale is what you desire, then that is available, conducted by Hickox for EMI in 1988, in a programme of shorter Elgar occasional works.

● If you like this, try Elgar's *Pomp & Circumstance* March No. 4 (254)

J. S. Bach

105) ORCHESTRAL SUITES

Bach wrote four orchestral suites, composing them in the decades after his Brandenburg Concertos. The most famous by a long way is the third, featuring the famous *Air* (on a G String). The variety of colour, mood and invention makes this set of suites a welcoming and friendly experience, however little music by Bach the listener has previously heard.

The two outstanding CD buys in this repertoire are both performed on authentic instruments and both offer some sort of bargain deal. The energetic and committed playing of the Suites by Akademie für Alte Musik Berlin on Harmonia Mundi comes accompanied by two CDs of the group's Brandenburg Concertos recordings (recommended separately on page 64). Similarly, an excursion into the Suites by The Brandenburg Consort directed by Roy Goodman is on Hyperion's cheaper Dyad line and comes in a slimline two-CD case. This version has the added attraction of the instrumental overtures from relevant cantatas inserted between each suite. A musical treat that is never hard to digest.

> Harmonia Mundi
> HMC2908074/7
> **Berlin Akademie für**
> **Alte Musik**
>
> ★
>
> Hyperion CDD 22002
> **Brandenburg Consort/**
> **Roy Goodman**

● If you like this, try Vivaldi's Chamber Concerto RV93 (151)

Wagner

106) TANNHÄUSER

Wagner's early opera (1845) has fallen on hard times these days, rarely being recorded. It calls for heroic tenors, stentorian baritones and well-equipped sopranos, but fails to provide the subtlety and complexity of characterisation that make Wagner's later work so fascinating. Hence the lack of many modern productions. However, the Overture has remained consistently popular.

For this reason, the Overture is what we concentrate on here. There is a famous 1984 von Karajan recording with the Berlin Philharmonic which includes it, but it gives short shrift on playing time and is still full-price. Rather, a mid-price effort from Antal Dorati and the London Symphony that includes a host of non-*Ring* Wagner overtures is a more sensible buy, giving over twenty minutes from *Tannhäuser* in excellent 1960s sound. If you hanker after a complete version, then Bernard Haitink's 1986 recording for EMI featuring Klaus Konig, Waltraud Meier and Lucia Popp is as good a place as any to start.

> ★ ✔
> Mercury 434 342-2
> **London Symphony**
> **Orchestra/**
> **Antal Dorati**
>
> EMI CDS 747296 8
> **Bavarian Radio**
> **Symphony Orchestra/**
> **Bernard Haitink**

● If you like this, try Wagner's *Lohengrin* (189)

Schubert

107) SYMPHONY NO. 8 (UNFINISHED)

It is common knowledge today that Schubert left more than one symphony unfinished at his death; so much so that some music historians have revised the numbering of the symphonies, leaving everyone in confusion. However, this is the famous unfinished one which has two glorious movements and a rarely recorded fragment of a third. The music is thrilling and beautifully formed, full of dignity and stress, nobility and sadness.

Nikolaus Harnoncourt names this the Seventh Symphony in his recording of the Schubert cycle. It is the only 'unfinished' one he includes (others include more). His approach is by turns sweet and euphonious, vivid and well turned, tidy and mindful of Schubert's intentions. Leonard Bernstein recorded the work twice: his earlier recording, with the New York Philharmonic, is a confident and sensitive appraisal and thoroughly recommendable at mid-price, especially as its companion is a good Schubert Ninth.

Teldec 4509 97511-2
Concertgebouw Orchestra, Amsterdam/ Nikolaus Harnoncourt

★ ✔

Sony SMK 61842
New York Philharmonic Orchestra/ Leonard Bernstein

● If you like this, try Schubert's *Rosamunde* (233)

Bach

108) CANTATA BWV147
HERZ UND MUND UND TAT UND LEBEN

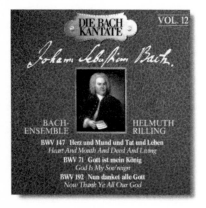

Cantata BWV147 is scored for soloists, choir and small orchestra. It is made up of two sections containing ten constituent parts between them – three choral sections, four arias and three recitatives. The piece was written to be performed on the fourth Advent Sunday, and the text deals with the joy of man's salvation through Jesus.

The two versions recommended here take slightly different approaches. That of the Bach Ensemble under Helmuth Rilling uses authentic instrumentation and ensemble size, while the singers, being German, have no problem with correct pronunciation. The Naxos version will satisfy the traditionalist, using a larger vocal ensemble while its instruments have the authentic 'edge' to them, and the Hungarian vocalists have

★
Hänssler 98 863
Arleen Augér (soprano)/ Helen Watts (contralto)/Kurt Equiluz (tenor)/Wolfgang Schöne (bass)/Frankfurt Kantorei/Stuttgart Bach Ensemble/Helmuth Rilling

✔

Naxos 8.550642
Ingrid Kertesi (soprano)/ Judit Németh (mezzo- soprano)/Josef Mukk (tenor)/ Istvan Gáti (baritone)/ Hungarian Radio Chorus/Failoni Chamber Orchestra/Mátyás Antál

an inflected but respectable German accent. It's at budget price, of course, but lacks a libretto, which is supplied by Hänssler for all three cantatas on its disc.

● If you like this, try Bach's Cantata No. 140 (243)

Mendelssohn

109) SYMPHONY NO. 4 (ITALIAN)

This symphony is said to be based on Mendelssohn's fond recollections of Goethe's famous travel book, *Italian Journey*. The second movement has a walking motive that takes us through a questioning, curious melody and perhaps has echoes of a Mendelssohn favourite, J. S. Bach. The raging inventiveness and high spirits of the opening visit us again from the outset of the finale, where a mad campfire dance seems to be taking place as the music starts up.

★ ✔
RCA 74321 20286-2
**Leipzig Gewandhaus
Orchestra/
Kurt Masur**

★ ✔
Classic FM 75605 57013-2
**Ulster Orchestra/
Dmitri Sitkovetsky**

Kurt Masur and the Leipzig Orchestra have this music in their blood, for Leipzig was Mendelssohn's home city. Their energy and spirit bring this work to life with added brio. The recording, from 1971, is a little scratchy in its upper reaches, but well balanced and clear. The Ulster Orchestra under Dmitri Sitkovetsky deliver a 1998 performance full of fire but with an extra helping of urbanity that makes it a good choice, especially at its budget price. Its companions are the *Scottish Symphony* and the *Hebrides Overture*.

● If you like this, try Brahms's Symphony No. 3 (149)

Dvořák

110) RUSALKA

Dvořák has long been regarded as one of the supreme symphonic composers, but his operas have generally struggled for an audience outside his native Bohemia. This is a shame, for many of them are outstanding. *Rusalka* itself is a national institution in Czech.

There are three complete recordings currently available. One is on Supraphon, from 1961, and features a very strong all-Czech cast, but the recording quality is not comparable to later efforts. A second on Supraphon (SU 3641-2), dating from 1983, features a terrific cast, with Václav Neumann conducting the Czech

★ ✔
Supraphon 11 2252-2
**Gabriela Benacková
(soprano)/Prague
Philharmonic Chorus/
Czech Philharmonic
Orchestra/Václav Neumann**

Decca 460 568-2
**Renée Fleming
(soprano)/Kühn Mixed
Choir/Czech Philharmonic
Orchestra/Sir Charles
Mackerras**

Philharmonic. The most recent, from 1999, features international leads in Renée Fleming and Ben Heppner: Sir Charles Mackerras directs the Czech Philharmonic. Fleming sings superbly, but her interpretation is that of a woman, not a young water-sprite. Heppner's Czech accent is unconvincing. Mackerras works miracles with the orchestral score. The choice, depends on what you want from the opera: a credible story from an all-Czech cast or a superb vocal display from experienced international leads. A final get-out: the Neumann version is available as a highlights disc (see box), saving the hard-pressed listener much money and time.

● If you like this, try Bellini's *Norma* (187)

Brahms

111) PIANO CONCERTO NO. 2

Brahms's second concerto is unusual in having four movements, its third being a hugely noble, extended *adagio* where the orchestra has quite as much as the pianist to do. The finale, an *allegro grazioso*, has a typically rushed, breathless Brahmsian melody and builds to an affirmative climax.

There are two excellent versions available for less than full price. The Russian pianist Emil Gilels made his reputation with this concerto in the 1950s and recorded it more than once. This version was made in 1972 with Jochum as guest conductor. The sound stands up well, with only the occasional string climax sounding a touch thin, and it has an especially warm piano tone. The concerto comes with a companion recording of the first concerto, a piece of music Gilels was not keen on (it shows). This is a mid-price reissue. At budget price is a slimline two-CD pack of both concertos from Elisabeth Leonskaja and Kurt Masur which is not far from being Gilels's equal.

★
Deutsche Grammophon
DG 447 446-2
Emil Gilels (piano)/
Berlin Philharmonic
Orchestra/
Eugen Jochum

✔
Teldec 0630 18948-2
Elisabeth Leonskaja
(piano)/
Leipzig Gewandhaus
Orchestra/
Kurt Masur

● If you like this, try Schumann's Piano Concerto in A minor (182)

Mozart

112) VESPERAE SOLENNES DE CONFESSORE K339

Mozart wrote church music on just about every conceivable scale, from full-blown requiems and a variety of ceremonial Masses through to very brief devotional pieces. This Vespers, dating from 1981, is a collection of psalms composed for use in Salzburg Cathedral and lasts just a little less than 30 minutes.

The two recordings both reflect a desire to keep the proper dimensions of the work: neither features bloated chorus sizes or augmented orchestras. Koopman's featured singers include a radiant soprano in Barbara Schlick and a big-toned bass in Matthijs Mesdag. Hogwood uses larger choir numbers and achieves a more opulent sound, but less definition. His soprano is the superb Emma Kirkby, his bass Michael George. Kirkby is the jewel here, but overall Koopman's musicians and singers have more to offer and are more faithfully rendered by the recording engineers. Both recitals are appendages to performances of the *Coronation Mass*.

★
Erato 0630 10705-2
Barbara Schlick
(soprano)/Elisabeth von
Magnus (mezzo-soprano)/
Paul Agnew (tenor)/Matthijs
Mesdag (bass)/Amsterdam
Baroque Choir &
Orchestra/Ton Koopman

L'Oiseau-Lyre 436 585-2
Emma Kirkby (soprano)/
Catherine Robbin (mezzo-
soprano)/John Mark Ainsley
(tenor)/Michael George
(bass)/Winchester Cathedral
Choir/Winchester Quiristers/
Academy of Ancient
Music/Christopher Hogwood

● If you like this, try Vivaldi's *Nulla in Mundo Pax Sincera* (188)

Górecki

113) SYMPHONY NO. 3

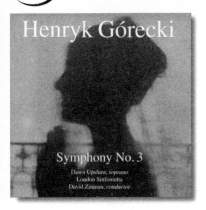

Today few classical music lovers will not have experienced the unique atmosphere of this, the most popular symphony written in the past 50 years. It is a three-movement work of transparent simplicity but great depth, subtitled 'Symphony of Sorrowful Songs' and designed to give eloquent voice to the sufferings of ordinary people victimised and tortured, often to death, during the course of the Nazi German occupation of much of Europe.

> ★
> Nonesuch 7559 79282-2
> **Dawn Upshaw (soprano)/**
> **London Sinfonietta/**
> **David Zinman**
>
> ✔
> Naxos 8.550822
> **Zofia Kilanowicz (soprano)/**
> **Polish National Radio**
> **Symphony Orchestra/**
> **Antoni Wit**

The 1992 recording by David Zinman and the London Sinfonietta featuring soprano Dawn Upshaw brought this music to hundreds of thousands of people throughout the world who had previously never heard of Górecki. It remains the single most incandescent version. Dawn Upshaw simply takes the music to another level when she sings: Górecki himself described her as his 'special angel'. However, there are other recordings, including a fine one by Antoni Wit on Naxos which is at budget price and therefore very competitive, though it misses that inspired spark of the Zinman version.

● If you like this, try Tavener's *Song for Athene* (168)

Mozart

114) HORN CONCERTO NO. 4 IN E FLAT, K495

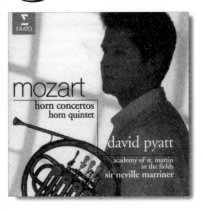

Mozart loved the natural horn and enjoyed toying with the technical limits of its expressivity. The gifted horn players of today enjoy the other challenges he makes. Ab Koster, with Bruno Weil and Tafelmusik, makes great play of his false-note technique to generate notes that do not lie in the natural scale, and the effect is charming once the ear has become accustomed. David Pyatt uses a conventional instrument and so does not have to 'reach' for notes as does Koster. This means a smoother, more

> Sony SK 53369
> **Ab Koster (horn)/**
> **Tafelmusik/**
> **Bruno Weil**
>
> ★
> Erato 0630 17074-2
> **David Pyatt (horn)/**
> **Academy of St Martin-**
> **in-the-Fields/**
> **Sir Neville Marriner**

seamless performance which is also enhanced by Neville Marriner's assured conducting, but Mozart has slipped farther away. This once again becomes 'pure' music. If you are prepared to take just a small risk outside the world of digital recording and experience a little analogue roughage in your audio diet, then please do make sure you hear Dennis Brain's wonderful performances for EMI, made over 40 years ago and unsurpassed for artistry and naturalness.

● If you like this, try Haydn's Trumpet Concerto (153)

Puccini
115) TOSCA

*T*osca has one of the most complex and operatically gift-laden soprano lead roles in all Italian opera. So who makes the most of it?

A generation ago there would have been no hesitation: Maria Callas. Listening to her performance on record today (a mono recording from 1953), one hears a voice which, while never greatly beautiful, is full of character, subtlety and vulnerability. The rest of the cast is equally committed and the orchestra, under Victor de Sabata, is fully engaged. But the sound is not up to 1990s standards, although it is surprisingly good. So this is a number-one recommendation with a large caveat. Callas recorded the role again for EMI, but while the stereo sound is an improvement, the deterioration in her voice is marked. A safe bet is to be found in the Decca version from 1988 featuring Pavarotti, with Nicola Rescigno conducting. But if you're ready for a thrill, stick your neck out and go for Callas.

★
EMI CDS 556304 2
Maria Callas (soprano)/Giuseppe di Steffano (tenor)/La Scala Orchestra & Chorus, Milan/Victor de Sabata

Decca 414 036-2
Mirella Freni (soprano)/Luciano Pavarotti (tenor)/Wandsworth School Boys' Choir/London Opera Chorus/National Philharmonic Orchestra/ Nicola Rescigno

● If you like this, try Puccini's *Gianni Schicchi* (190)

Elgar
116) THE DREAM OF GERONTIUS

*D*uring the 19th century Britain was one of the most enthusiastic nations when it came to embracing the oratorio form. It took a few decades, however, for this enthusiasm to overflow into the creation of British works. Predictably it was Elgar who came up with the first real masterpiece in this form, in the last months of 1899, when *The Dream of Gerontius* was first performed. Since then it has been a permanent part of the musical landscape.

Elgar's most famous choral work has been recorded often. The most persuasive versions currently available are naturally from British casts and orchestras. Richard Hickox assembled a superb cast for his 1988 Chandos recording with the LSO, with Felicity Palmer and Arthur Davies in outstanding form. This performance glows with commitment and passion, yet retains the restraint and dignity at the heart of Elgar's appeal. A 1972 recording on Decca by the composer Benjamin Britten (now at mid-price) is also worth visiting, though the soloists are not quite as unified as on the Hickox recording.

★
Chandos CHAN 8641/2
Felicity Palmer (soprano)/ Arthur Davies (tenor)/ Gwynne Howell (bass)/ London Symphony Orchestra & Choir/Richard Hickox

Decca 448 170-2
Yvonne Minton (mezzo-soprano)/Sir Peter Pears (tenor)/John Shirley-Quirk (baritone)/Choir of King's College, Cambridge/London Symphony Orchestra & Choir/Benjamin Britten

● If you like this, try Berlioz's *L'Enfance du Christ* (232)

Wagner
117) DIE WALKÜRE

Of the four massive operas that make up Wagner's *Ring* cycle, this is the second instalment. It tells of the immoral goings-on between a mythological family of proto-Teutonics. Among the incest, adultery and other acts of violence, disgrace and cruelty, there is a large amount of music which inspires and – occasionally – transfixes the audience. In fact, the opening of Act 3, when the Walküres, Brünnhilde's sisters, ride into the opera, transfixes everybody. It is quite probably the most famous single piece of music Wagner ever wrote.

★
Teldec 4509 91186-2
**Bayreuth Festival Orchestra/
Daniel Barenboim**

✔
Decca 466 261-2
**Vienna Philharmonic
Orchestra/
Sir Georg Solti**

Daniel Barenboim's *Ring* cycle for Teldec, recorded 'live' at Bayreuth in the 1990s, sets the standard for modern-day interpretations. His singers are equal to the demands made upon their voices and the orchestra is endlessly supple and responsive. The arrival of the Walküres is a thrilling event in his hands. If you want the ride without the chat, then it is available in a mid-price compilation of *Ring* highlights from Georg Solti's ground-breaking Decca sets of 40 years ago.

● If you like this, try Wagner's *Siegfried* (215)

Wagner
118) GÖTTERDÄMMERUNG

This, the fourth and last opera in Wagner's *Ring* cycle, is a four-hour resolution of the tangled web which makes up this huge, sprawling and massively influential 'music drama', as Wagner termed it. It is resolved in the most apocalyptic terms imaginable, with Brünnhilde bringing down Alberich's curse and condemning the gods to their own doom, leading directly to the destruction of Valhalla,

★
Teldec 4509 94194-2
**Bayreuth Festival Orchestra
& Chorus/Daniel Barenboim**

✔
Decca 466 261-2
**Vienna Philharmonic
Orchestra/Sir Georg Solti**

while Brünnhilde herself expires on the flames as the Rhinemaidens look on.

As with *Die Walküre*, there is little need to look farther than Barenboim and the Bayreuth Festival cast and orchestra for a compelling up-to-date version of the complete work: a strong cast, firm and imaginative conducting and good atmosphere. Siegfried Jerusalem sings the part of his namesake, Philip Konig is Hagen, Anne Evans Brünnhilde and Waltraud Meier plays, logically enough, Waltraute. For highlights, Solti's collection on Decca makes excellent sense and also includes an excerpt from the famous *Siegfried Idyll* for chamber orchestra.

● If you like this, try Wagner's *Die Meistersinger von Nürnberg* (192)

Beethoven

119) PIANO CONCERTO NO. 4

With this work, Beethoven moved the piano concerto on a long way from where it had been in the time of Mozart, and indeed from where he had left it with his own Third Concerto. He takes enormous risks in the use of space and silence. He succeeds owing to the sheer beauty of his writing and the steel-hard grip he has on the composition's form. Any performance that ignores these two key elements is lost. The great Japanese pianist Mitsuko Uchida brings wonderful touch and great sensitivity to her playing, while Kurt Sanderling and the Concertgebouw give her exemplary support. The only possible quibble here is that the recording occasionally gives an unfocused, indistinct piano sound. This is not so on the 1962 Wilhelm Kempff recording with Ferdinand Leitner, but on this DGG disc we swap transparent piano sound for a rather washed-out orchestral palette. The Uchida wins by a whisker.

★
Philips 446082-2
Mitsuko Uchida (piano)/
Concertgebouw Orchestra,
Amsterdam/
Kurt Sanderling

✔
Deutsche Grammophon
DG 447 402-2
Wilhelm Kempff (piano)/
Berlin Philharmonic
Orchestra/
Ferdinand Leitner

● If you like this, try Brahms's Piano Concerto No. 1 (223)

Mozart

120) COSÌ FAN TUTTE

Così is one of the three great operas resulting from the collaboration between Mozart and his best librettist, Lorenzo da Ponte. Inspired by having a witty and intriguing script to work from, Mozart consistently composed at his best: the delight is palpable in the music's sparkle. His arias, especially for the female leads, are unfailingly elegant and moving, the accompaniment apt and never overpowering.

The 1962 EMI recording by Karl Böhm, with a cast including Elisabeth Schwarzkopf and Christa Ludwig, has long been acknowledged as the finest Così ever given in a recording studio. It still sounds that way, nearly 40 years later, and it is now at mid-price. A latter-day companion for it is that by Sir Charles Mackerras for Telarc in 1994, its approach being similar in that orchestra and soloists are in perfect balance and harmony, although the singers are not quite up to Böhm's cast. Finally, a new Così from France, conducted by René Jacobs for Harmonia Mundi (HMC95 1663/5), gives an exciting authentic-instruments performance.

★ ✔
EMI CMS 769330 2
Elisabeth Schwarzkopf
(soprano)/Christa Ludwig
(mezzo-soprano)/
Philharmonia Orchestra
& Chorus/Karl Böhm

Telarc CD 80360
Felicity Lott
(soprano)/Marie McLaughlin
(soprano)/Edinburgh
Festival Chorus/Scottish
Chamber Orchestra/
Sir Charles Mackerras

● If you like this, try Mozart's Don Giovanni (138)

Prokofiev

121) SYMPHONY NO. 1 ('CLASSICAL')

Prokofiev wrote this short work in 1917 and heard it premièred in 1918, after the Revolution that swept away the old Russian power structure. He deliberately took old models for his work, looking to the classical period and the symphonies of Joseph Haydn for both form and inspiration. The wonder is that he managed to inject so much of himself into it while preserving the clear outline of a Haydn-type symphony.

Both performances here are given by conductors with vast experience in conducting Prokofiev. Neeme Järvi and the Scottish National give a bright, almost mischievous reading of the work, noting its undertow of irony. The sound is beautifully balanced. Dmitri Kitaenko and the Moscow Philharmonic, recorded in 1987, suffer from poor studio sound, the strings being very thin, but the balance is good and the playing spirited and true to Prokofiev's intentions. On balance, however, the first choice has to be Järvi, which is available both as a separate CD and as part of a complete Järvi Prokofiev symphonies cycle.

★
Chandos CHAN 8400
**Royal Scottish
National Orchestra/
Neeme Järvi**

RCA 74321 32042-2
**Moscow Philharmonic
Orchestra/
Dmitri Kitaenko**

● If you like this, try Prokofiev's *Lieutenant Kijé* (227)

Khachaturian

122) SPARTACUS

Even though Khachaturian's formal music – symphonies, concertos and the like – is rarely heard today, his stage works are still popular with the general public. *Spartacus* is in this list because it has great melodies, wonderful atmosphere and the ability to communicate directly with its audience. Its great *adagio* has also been used in television programmes and commercials.

Neeme Järvi and the Scottish National Orchestra preserve this directness in their Chandos recital of all three suites. Their treatment of the popular love theme from the second suite is tender and tasteful, preserving its folk origins. The St Petersburg recording under André Anichanov is cleanly executed and thoroughly in character, though the slower pieces are taken a little more sentimentally. The Naxos acoustic is a little over-reverberant, though not distractingly so.

★
Chandos CHAN 8927
**Royal Scottish National
Orchestra/Neeme Järvi**

✔
Naxos 8.550801
**St Petersburg State
Symphony Orchestra/
André Anichanov**

● If you like this, try Rimsky-Korsakov's *Capriccio espagnole* (279)

Borodin

123) PRINCE IGOR

P*rince Igor* owes its popularity to the efforts of Rimsky-Korsakov and Glazunov, both close friends of Borodin who volunteered to save the chaotic and incomplete mass of manuscripts for the opera Borodin left at the time of his abrupt death. They not only organised the material and reconstructed the plot, but Glazunov also composed a great deal of music, including the entire Overture, so that a performing version could be published.

People are now exploring what Borodin actually wrote before Rimsky-Korsakov and Glazunov became involved. The end result is Valery Gergiev's wonderful Kirov Opera recording of the complete opera in a version incorporating original Borodin material omitted by the collaborators. Immensely exciting, and with a real Russian spice to it, this version is essential for all those wanting the complete picture. If you're after just the Dances, then a stirring version is available on an Adrian Leaper Naxos disc with the Royal Philharmonic. This includes other spectacular music by Chabrier, Mussorgsky and Ravel, all in bright digital sound and at the right price.

★
Philips 442 537-2
Kirov Opera Orchestra & Chorus/
Valery Gergiev

✔
Naxos 8.550501
Royal Philharmonic Orchestra/
Adrian Leaper

● If you like this, try Borodin's *In the Steppes of Central Asia* (181)

Mozart

124) CLARINET QUINTET

M*ozart had discovered the special charm of the clarinet while in his early 20s and always wrote above his usual level when composing for it. This, plus a close friendship with Anton Stadler, the premier Viennese clarinettist of the day, provided ample motivation for something supreme when the Clarinet Quintet was begun in 1789.

The number of recordings of the work where the clarinet is simply out of tune is embarrassingly high. No such problems with Charles Neidlich and L'Archibudelli. These players are using 'period' instruments, Neidlich playing a modern copy of a late 18th-century basset clarinet. The CD coupling is particularly intelligent, the other works being the Clarinet Quartet K378 and the Kegelstatt Trio K498. If 'authentic' instruments unsettle you, then the famous 1964 Decca recording with Jack Brymer and the Allegri Quartet is currently available at budget price on Belart, coupled with Schubert's Trout Quintet.

★
Sony SK 53366
Charles Neidlich (clarinet)/
L'Archibudelli

✔
Belart 450 056-2
Jack Brymer (clarinet)/
Allegri Quartet

● If you like this, try Mozart's Serenade No. 10 in B flat (340)

Karl Jenkins
125) ADIEMUS

Jenkins is a highly successful composer who has enjoyed smash hits both in film soundtracks and in recordings, such as this one. *Adiemus* takes classical composing techniques and marries them to decidedly unclassical genres and styles of singing and music-making. It also uses recording techniques more associated with film and pop music than with classical, such as fading the music while it sustains an *ostinato* rhythm or pattern, or cross-fading between groups and themes.

> ★
> Virgin CDVE 925
> **Miriam Stockley (soprano)/**
> **Mary Carewe (soprano)/**
> **Pamela Thorby (recorder)/**
> **London Philharmonic**
> **Orchestra/**
> **Karl Jenkins**

The music is insinuating and enjoyable, melodic and rhythmic in turn, and very tasteful. In some circles it could well be described as an extension of 'new age' rather than classical music, but each to his own definition. If you enjoy it, why worry?

● If you like this, try Canteloube's *Songs of the Auvergne* (143)

Copland
126) APPALACHIAN SPRING

The original ballet, commissioned by Martha Graham, lasted well over 30 minutes. The concert suite Copland later arranged for symphony orchestra was shortened by around 10 minutes, the music more obviously concentrating on the stream of old Appalachian tunes at its source, especially the Shaker song 'Simple Gifts'. The suite is the most frequently recorded version, which is a pity, because there are certain moments in the uncut score which are spine-

> ✔
> Sony SMK 60133
> **London Symphony**
> **Orchestra/**
> **Aaron Copland**
>
> ★ ✔
> Sony SMK 63082
> **New York Philharmonic**
> **Orchestra/**
> **Leonard Bernstein**

tinglingly beautiful and which are not found in the suite. The best modern version is of the long score: this is Leonard Slatkin's for EMI. Unfortunately, this is at present on the budget HMV label, so unless you have an HMV store near you, it will not be available locally. There is an attractive performance of the full scoring of the suite on Nimbus NI 5246 by Williams Boughton. The most flamboyant and likable current orchestral version of the suite is Leonard Bernstein's 1960s effort, now mid-price on Sony Classical, while Copland's own is a model of balance and clarity.

● If you like this, try Stravinsky's *Rite of Spring* (160)

Brahms
127) EIN DEUTSCHES REQUIEM

Brahms had no great inclination towards organised religion, preferring to come to an individual *rapprochement* with his Creator. For this Requiem he himself compiled the texts from his own copy of the Bible, avoiding any contact with the traditional Latin texts used over centuries in the liturgical Mass for the Dead. This freed him to express his own thoughts and feelings on the ultimate fate of mankind and the specific loss of Robert Schumann and his own mother, two people absolutely central to his development as a man and musician. The resultant music is deeply moving and, properly performed, completely involves the listener in its inner dramas and convictions. An excellent modern-day recording comes from Philippe Herreweghe on Harmonia Mundi. Recorded in 1996, it features Christiane Oelze and Gerald Finley as soloists. For a first-rate older version at mid-price, the Klemperer from 1961 with Fischer-Diskau and Schwarzkopf is unbeatable.

> ★
> Harmonia Mundi HMC90 1608
> **Christiane Oelze (soprano)/
> Gerald Finley (baritone)/
> Collegium Vocale/Choir of
> the Chapelle Royale/Champs-
> Elysées Orchestra/Philippe
> Herreweghe**
>
> ✔
> EMI CDM 566903 2
> **Elizabeth Schwarzkopf
> (soprano)/Dietrich Fischer-
> Diskau (baritone)/
> Philharmonia Orchestra
> & Chorus/Otto Klemperer**

● If you like this, try Gounod's *St Cecilia Mass* (218)

Mozart
128) PIANO CONCERTO NO. 23 K488

The overall sense of gentleness is never dispelled in this concerto: Mozart is not looking for drama – he is content to take pleasure in the inordinate amount of beautiful, unforced melody he creates. This becomes a mite pensive in the *adagio*, cast in a minor key, but the extraordinary beauty of the melody retains a glow which saves it from ever becoming tragic or dispirited. The final movement, with its rhythmic patterns and generally gay character, entirely dispels the second thoughts of the *adagio* and brings a congenial resolution to the dialogue between soloist and orchestra.

> ★
> Sony SK 39064
> **Murray Perahia (piano)/
> English Chamber Orchestra**
>
> Philips 420 187-2
> **Mitsuko Uchida (piano)/
> English Chamber Orchestra/
> Jeffrey Tate**

Both Perahia and Uchida are supremely poised and confident in their playing here, relishing the clarity and beauty of Mozart's writing. The greater clarity of the Sony recording, and the special relationship between Perahia and the conductorless ECO, gives him the palm. Both performances are available on single CDs or as part of complete cycles.

● If you like this, try Beethoven's Piano Concerto No. 1 (206)

Verdi

129) RIGOLETTO

For a work that has produced some of the most singable melodies in all opera, this is a very dark and disturbing piece of music theatre. In 1851 there was little doubt that it was also Verdi's best up to that time, a verdict no one today would seriously argue with. For those wanting to try it, it is rich enough in music and plot to sustain taking in the whole work, however inexperienced they may be. The best modern full version is from Riccardo Chailly, with Pavarotti, Nucci and June Anderson in the three key roles. Pavarotti is superbly licentious and uncaring in his delineation of the Duke, though it must be said that the voices tend to be too forward in comparison to the orchestra. This is not quite so pronounced on the budget-price version by Alexander Rahbari on Naxos. A better voice/orchestra balance altogether is available on the meticulous but rather lacklustre full-price Carlo Rizzi recording on Teldec 450990851-2.

★
Decca 425 864-2
Luciano Pavarotti (tenor)/Leo Nucci (tenor)/June Anderson (soprano)/Bologna Teatro Comunale Orchestra & Chorus/Riccardo Chailly

✔
Naxos 8.660013-14
Eduard Tumagian (baritone)/Alida Ferrarini (soprano)/Slovak Philharmonic Chorus/ Bratislava Radio Symphony Orchestra/ Alexander Rahbari

● If you like this, try Verdi's *La forza del destino* (193)

Rossini

130) LA GAZZA LADRA

La gazza ladra (The Thieving Magpie) has languished in obscurity for many decades, the antiquities of its plot hindering its acceptance by the more sophisticated audiences of the post-Wagnerian period. But it has much good music to offer, and the luxury of a complete recording has now been afforded us by the kind offices of Sony Classical, by means of their 'live' recording with the Prague Philharmonic Chorus and the Turin Radio Symphony Orchestra under the direction of Gianluigi Gelmetti. The two-act opera is a long one by the standards of the day, spreading over three CDs, but the performance is full of spirit, the cast clearly relishing the chance to air a rarely heard and memorable score. There are plenty of recordings of the famous overture by itself. Riccardo Chailly, a Rossini champion, has made an outstanding CD of Rossini overtures in great modern sound (much better sound than the fabled old Fritz Reiner RCA disc of overtures). This is the obvious place to start today.

★
Sony S3K45850
Prague Philharmonic Chorus/Turin Radio Symphony Orchestra/ Gianluigi Gelmetti

Decca 448 218-2
Orchestra of La Scala, Milan/ Riccardo Chailly

● If you like this, try Offenbach's *Gaité Parisienne* (327)

Erik Satie
131) GYMNOPÉDIES

Agreat eccentric among a highly eccentric generation of Parisian *fin de siècle* musicians, Erik Satie was also something of a musical primitive. A contemporary of Debussy's at the Conservatoire, he failed to come to grips with what he was studying, but did manage slowly to put together his own approach to music. In this he was encouraged by Debussy, who took the trouble to orchestrate two of Satie's three *Gymnopédies*.

Satie was a mischievous composer of miniatures and liked nothing more than poking fun at pompous people. Any recital which fails to point this up does him a disservice. Michel Legrand plays the three *Gymnopédies* beautifully, but also takes huge delight in delivering some of Satie's most amusing musical jokes in the rest of his Erato recital disc. If you hanker after the orchestrated *Gymnopédies*, then Naxos (8.554279) has a well-judged 1997 set of orchestral Satie from all parts of his career conducted with panache by Jérome Kaltenbach, while BIS, on a diverse programme conducted beautifully by James Depriest, include the two *Gymnopédies* orchestrated by Debussy.

★
Erato 4509 92857-2
Michel Legrand (piano)

BIS CD 570
Malmö Symphony Orchestra/ James Depriest

● If you like this, try Satie's *Gnossienne* No. 1 (368)

Richard Strauss
132) DER ROSENKAVALIER

Up until this 1911 production, Strauss had been concentrating his efforts on shocking the bourgeoisie and upsetting the censor with such alternately amoral and bloodthirsty subjects as *Salome* and *Elektra*. With *Rosenkavalier* his subject matter, although still a touch risqué, was greatly toned down and given an impenetrable gloss of high-class manners and sophistication. *Der Rosenkavalier*, although a very long opera, is unfailingly polite and elegant, giving its audience as infallible a sense of what it should have been like to live in luxury in a bygone age of elegance as anything from Johann Strauss and his peers.

The immortal 1956 von Karajan recording for EMI features Elisabeth Schwarzkopf, Christa Ludwig and Teresa Stich-Randall. Recently refurbished from the original tapes, it is currently available in both stereo and mono versions. If the whole thing is too much for you, a brilliant single CD set of highlights was made by Silvio Varviso in 1965 featuring Elisabeth Söderström with Régine Crespin and Hilde Gueden.

★
EMI CDS 556242 2 (also mono)
Elisabeth Schwarzkopf (soprano)/Christa Ludwig (soprano)/Teresa Stich-Randall (soprano)/Eberhard Wächter (baritone)/ Philharmonia Orchestra & Chorus/ Herbert von Karajan

Decca 452 730-2
Régine Crespin (soprano)/ Elisabeth Söderström (soprano)/Hilde Gueden (soprano)/Heinz Holecek (baritone)/Vienna State Opera Chorus/Vienna Philharmonic Orchestra/Silvio Varviso

● If you like this, try Tchaikovsky's *Eugene Onegin* (244)

Vivaldi

133) MANDOLIN CONCERTO RV425

ANTONIO VIVALDI
CONCERTI PER LIUTO
E MANDOLINO
IL GIARDINO
ARMONICO

If ever a theory was disproved by the evidence, this mandolin concerto conclusively gives the lie to the idea that Vivaldi wrote 500 concertos that all sound the same. The Venetian master certainly had his own recognisable concerto style, but this is something he shared with all great composers. The fact is that he understood the unique characteristics of each instrument and composed so as to bring those qualities to the fore.

★
Teldec 4509 91182-2
**Giardino Armonico
Ensemble**

✔
Erato 4509 92132-2
**Ugo Orlandi (mandolin)/
I Solisti Veneti/
Claudio Scimone**

The mandolin concertos have become increasingly popular in the past twenty years and recordings have multiplied. In front by some distance at present is Il Giardino Armonico, a young Italian group that brings levels of vitality and expression to this music unimaginable even a decade ago. For a more stately approach, the great Italian ensemble led by Claudio Scimone, I Solisti Veneti, have a fine mid-price version currently on Erato, mixed with mandolin works by Paisiello and Caudioso, plus two other Vivaldi mandolin concertos.

● If you like this, try Albinoni's Oboe Concerto (235)

Mozart

134) SYMPHONY NO. 41 K551 ('JUPITER')

Wolfgang Amadeus Mozart
SYMPHONIEN NO. 41 »JUPITER« · NO. 40
Wiener Philharmoniker
Karl Böhm
STEREO

The last of the great symphonies Mozart wrote in the summer of 1788, this hasn't the immediate melodic impact of Symphony No. 40, but it has drama in the contrasts between the themes and harmonies, as well as a big dynamic range, which continually suggests an affinity with the stage, as if the music is enacting a dramatic production of sorts. In fact, one of the themes in the first movement is shared by an operatic aria Mozart had composed some time before. The symphony – and Mozart's symphonic career – ends in high spirits and in triumph.

★
Deutsche Grammophon
DG 413 547-2
**Vienna Philharmonic
Orchestra/
Karl Böhm**

✔
Naxos 8.550299
**Capella Istropolitana/
Barry Wordsworth**

Karl Böhm's 1977 version of the 'Jupiter' with the Vienna Philharmonic is a pleasure from start to finish. If cost is an issue, the Naxos version under Barry Wordsworth from 1988, though not the most inspired, is serviceable enough.

● If you like this, try Schubert's Symphony No. 5 (136)

Mendelssohn

135) A MIDSUMMER NIGHT'S DREAM

Shakespeare was a constant source of delight for Mendelssohn, as his involvement with *A Midsummer Night's Dream* demonstrates. The overture was written when he was just 17, although its atmospheric opening chords suggest a wonderfully mature musical mind at work. The rest (including a Wedding March for Oberon and Titania which is today unavoidable in any marriage) was written over a decade later for a production commissioned by Kaiser Friedrich Wilhelm IV.

At the heart of this music is sheer whimsy and untroubled joy. The two recordings here possess the correct lightness of touch along with a precision

★
Teldec 9031 74882-2
Pamela Coburn (soprano)/
Elisabeth von Magnus
(mezzo-soprano)/ Chamber
Orchestra of Europe/
Nikolaus Harnoncourt

Harmonia Mundi HMC 901502
Sandrine Piau (soprano)/
Delphine Collot (soprano)/
Choir of the Chapelle
Royale/Collegium Vocale/
Champs-Elysées Orchestra/
Philippe Herreweghe

of playing which allows unhindered enjoyment. In Harnoncourt's version the transitions between scenes and sections are seamless, the playing gossamer-smooth, the imagination unfettered. Herreweghe takes a slightly more studied approach. Harnoncourt wins out as a first recommendation. He carries *Die erste Walpurgisnacht* Op. 60 as a companion piece, while Herreweghe chooses the ever-popular Hebrides Overture Op. 26.

● If you like this, try Offenbach's *Les Contes d'Hoffmann* (146)

Schubert

136) SYMPHONY NO. 5

Schubert's way with a tune is nowhere more magically announced than in the opening of this symphony, where a graceful and sprightly melody emerges from the strings after a dainty chordal introduction from the woodwinds. Everything flows so organically, so naturally, that the dialogue segues into a slower, more pensive monologue (the *andante*) before anyone has noticed.

Both Böhm and Harnoncourt allow Schubert the grace and ease his music demands. Interestingly, Böhm somehow

Teldec 4509 97511-2
Concertgebouw Orchestra,
Amsterdam/Nikolaus
Harnoncourt

★

Deutsche Grammophon
DG 447 433-2
Vienna Philharmonic
Orchestra/
Karl Böhm

makes Schubert sound original and quite distinct, while Harnoncourt tends to reinforce his immediate Viennese heritage, allowing us glimpses of Mozart and Beethoven in the music. This may come through his added forcefulness, especially in the minuet, which borders on violence in its rhythmic declamations and harks back to the determination so often heard in Beethoven's symphonies. All things considered, the lighter touch of Böhm suits this particular symphony better.

● If you like this, try Mozart's *Sinfonia Concertante* (209)

Paganini

137) VIOLIN CONCERTO NO. 1

Paganini's incredible technical ability – and his gift for writing music that displayed it – had firm roots in the bravura style of the Italian and German baroque masters. What Paganini did was take things on to a completely new level, one that even today poses technical problems for all but the most outrageously gifted violinist. For Paganini wrote music that had to be interpreted as well as simply played.

Fortunately there are plenty of virtuosi around today who want to supply both parts of the deal, none more thrilling than Maxim Vengerov. His performance on Teldec could be used as a definition of the word bravura. A rather more sedate version (coupled with Violin Concerto No. 2) is available on Chandos, featuring Ilya Grubert with the Moscow Chamber Orchestra. Grubert has a sumptuous tone and superb technique, but the orchestra is more prim than Zubin Mehta's, the violin well forward in the mix. This throws the spotlight perhaps too sharply on Grubert, robbing the concerto of some of its colour and character.

★
Teldec 9031 73266-2
**Maxim Vengerov
(violin)/Israel Philharmonic
Orchestra/Zubin Mehta**

Chandos CHAN 9492
**Ilya Grubert (violin)/
Moscow Chamber
Orchestra/Constantine
Orbelian**

● If you like this, try Elgar's Violin Concerto (148)

Mozart

138) DON GIOVANNI

Don Juan is one of the great European fables, a fascinating tale of lust, betrayal and dissolution. Mozart's must stand as one of the supreme music-theatre incarnations, for he brings such a humanist understanding to his unprincipled hero that Don Giovanni becomes a fully rounded stage presence.

There are many fine recordings, and it would be churlish not to mention the marvellous 1959 version by Ferenc Fricsay for DGG. But pride of place must remain with an EMI recording made in 1961 but still ahead of the pack for its perfect balance of cast (headed by Wächter and Sutherland) and extraordinary direction by Carlo Maria Giulini, who coaxes miracles from the Philharmonia. The recording quality offers a fine balance. If a more modern version is what you are after, then Claudio Abbado's 1998 effort for DGG has the blessing of Bryn Terfel as Leporello and a noble Donna Elvira in Soile Isokoski, but the *frisson* between the various elements is not at Giulini's level.

★
EMI CDS 556232 2
**Eberhard Wächter
(baritone)/Dame Joan
Sutherland (soprano)/
Philharmonia Orchestra &
Chorus/Carlo Maria Giulini**

Deutsche Grammophon
DG 457 601-2
**Simon Keenlyside
(baritone)/Bryn Terfel
(baritone)/Carmela Remigio
(soprano)/Soile Isokoski
(soprano)/Ferrara Musica
Chorus/Chamber Orchestra
of Europe/Claudio Abbado**

● If you like this, try Beethoven's *Fidelio* (238)

Saint-Saëns

139) SAMSON ET DALILA

Appropriately, considering its biblical source, Saint-Saëns's great opera has the quiet intensity of a major religious work. It rarely goes in for sustained and noisy climaxes. The paradox of its success is that Saint-Saëns, the great aesthete and classicist, was able to inject sufficient sensuality and romance into his score to make the work and its characters come alive on-stage.

This is all apparent in the 1988 version recorded for Koch-Schwann by Sylvain Cambreling and featuring Marjana Lipovšek as Dalila and Carlo Cossutta as Samson. The heat between the two principals is tangible, the longing and passion completely convincing. A 1998 recording for Erato by Sir Colin Davis succeeds in coaxing voluptuous sounds from the orchestra and chorus, but José Cura appears uncomfortable and suspicious as Samson, while Olga Borodina is content to stress the dignity of her position rather than the passion that should be driving her.

> ★
> Koch-Schwann 317742
> **Carlo Cossutta (tenor)/
> Marjana Lipovšek (mezzo-soprano)/Sofia Chamber
> Choir/Bergenz Festival
> Chorus/Vienna Volksoper
> Chorus/Vienna
> Symphony Orchestra/
> Sylvain Cambreling**
>
> Erato 3984 24756-2
> **José Cura (tenor)/Olga
> Borodina (mezzo-soprano)/
> London Symphony
> Orchestra & Chorus/
> Sir Colin Davis**

● If you like this, try Tchaikovsky's *Eugene Onegin* (244)

Vivaldi

140) GLORIA IN D RV589

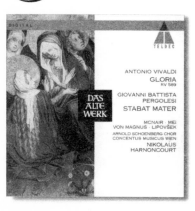

Vivaldi is world famous for his Four Seasons and the fact that he wrote some 500 concertos. It is less well known that he was a prolific opera composer and also wrote high-quality music for religious services. He was, after all, a priest. As with his instrumental works, Vivaldi had a very clear idea of what type of music suited his singers, and he composed accordingly. As a consequence his music is as sweet and natural-sounding as ever.

A good performance ensures that the exuberance of Vivaldi's creative spark is preserved. This requirement remains central to Nikolaus Harnoncourt's 1994 recording of the *Gloria*. With Simon Preston's 1978 version there is less bite and forward momentum, but the authentic instruments sparkle against the choir and we have as soloists Emma Kirkby and Judith Nelson. At mid-price this makes a persuasive case, but Harnoncourt offers more food for thought.

> ★
> Teldec 9031 76989-2
> **Sylvia McNair
> (soprano)/Elisabeth von
> Magnus (mezzo-soprano)/
> Marjana Lipovšek (mezzo-soprano)/Arnold Schoenberg
> Choir/Vienna Concentus
> Musicus/Nikolaus Harnoncourt**
>
> ✔
> L'Oiseau-Lyre 455 727-2
> **Emma Kirkby (soprano)/
> Judith Nelson (soprano)/
> Carolyn Watkinson
> (contralto)/Christ Church
> Cathedral Choir/Academy of
> Ancient Music/Simon Preston**

● If you like this, try Rossini's *Stabat Mater* (357)

Tchaikovsky

141) THE SLEEPING BEAUTY OP. 66

Tchaikovsky's second great ballet was started in 1888 and completed the following year. Avoiding the innocent errors of ballet diplomacy he had made with his first great ballet, *Swan Lake*, he wrote a score meticulously designed to please the dancers from the moment they heard it. The music is sumptuous and shows incredible flair: some of the themes have become world famous away from the ballet. Using a fairy story allowed Tchaikovsky to indulge his innocent pleasure in melody and lush orchestration, and plunge into the delightful fantasies of childhood, just as Ravel would some 40 years later in *Les Enfants et les Sortileges*.

★
Philips 434 922-2
**Kirov Opera Orchestra/
Valery Gergiev**

Telarc CD 80151
**Royal Philharmonic
Orchestra/
Sir Charles Mackerras**

Valery Gergiev and the Kirov Opera Orchestra give the most convincing reading of the full score currently on CD. They also benefit from brilliant recording quality supplied by Philips. For a selection of highlights (in the form of a popular concert suite fashioned by Alexander Siloti) there is an immensely stylish 1987 recording on Telarc by Sir Charles Mackerras, winningly combined with highlights from *Swan Lake*.

● If you like this, try Delibes's *Coppélia* (214)

Fauré

142) PAVANE

During his long career Fauré wrote only a modest amount of orchestral music, preferring other forms such as chamber and vocal music. What he did write for orchestras was almost always full of immense charm and elegance. The *Pavane* was no exception, bearing an instantly memorable, long-limbed melody over stately pizzicato accompaniment, as a true 18th-century pavane dance should.

★
Chandos CHAN 9416
**Renaissance Singers/
Ulster Orchestra/
Yan-Pascal Tortelier**

EMI CDC747938 2
**Orchestra du Capitole
de Toulouse/
Michel Plasson**

In this musical territory a conductor has to be careful not to push the music too hard or it becomes sentimental. The two chosen here avoid such obvious pitfalls with ease. Yan-Pascal Tortelier selects a tempo quite clearly suitable for the dance, allowing the long melody to retain its elegant lightness, unfurling itself with confident charm. Michel Plasson plumps for a similar speed, his Toulouse Orchestra seeming to glide through the music on a cushion of rustling air. Either version is recommendable, and both come with substantial Fauré orchestra music elsewhere in the programme, though Tortelier perhaps wins out by including the *Elégie* for cello and orchestra in his volume.

● If you like this, try Ravel's *Pavane pour une infante défunte* (183)

Canteloube

143) SONGS OF THE AUVERGNE

Frederica von Stade provides the ravishing heat of the Auvergne, Dawn Upshaw the breeze, in their two quite differing approaches to these charming songs. Canteloube brought a high degree of orchestral skill to his sumptuous arrangements of these simple folk melodies from the Auvergne region, making them seem like tone poems with the added attraction of a beautiful voice. Upshaw sings with soaring, clear tone and perfect diction, perfectly supported by Kent Nagano and his Lyon orchestra, while von Stade sings with a rich tone, good diction and,

Erato 0630 17577-2
**Dawn Upshaw (soprano)/
Lyon Opera Orchestra/
Kent Nagano**

✔
Sony SBK 63063
**Frederica von Stade
(soprano)/
Royal Philharmonic
Orchestra/
Antonio de Almeida**

most importantly, with an intensity that almost brings tears to the eyes. In this she is matched adroitly by the RPO and Antonio de Almeida. Choosing between the two may be influenced by the fact that von Stade is now at budget price and presents a complete programme, while Upshaw's 'Bailero', the most famous song here, appears on Volume 2 of her Auvergne recital, with around a third of the playing time taken up by unrelated orchestral songs by Emmanuel.

● If you like this, try Villa-Lobos's *Bachianas Brasileiras* (393)

Handel

144) SERSE

*S*erse was first performed in 1738 and was not a success, given its relatively novel style which demanded the concentration of the audience throughout. It has rarely been revived since, and its sole claim to fame outside the world of Handel scholars is the first-act aria 'Ombra mai fu'. The role of Xerxes was written for a female mezzo-soprano, although today it is more common for male singers to perform the aria.

There are two performances of the complete opera currently in the catalogue. The latest, on Conifer, dates from 1998 and is directed by Nicholas McGegan. It uses authentic instruments and a vocal cast echoing the original stagings. The second, by Jean-Claude

Conifer 75605 51312-2
**Hanover Band/
Hanover Band Chorus/
Nicholas McGegan**

★ ✔
Sony SM3K 36941
**Bridier Vocal Ensemble/
Grande Ecurie/
Jean-Claude Malgoire**

Decca 466 196-2
**Andreas Scholl (alto)/
Orchestra of the Age
of Enlightenment/
Roger Norrington**

Malgoire on Sony, is a little older (1979) and is also on authentic instruments. This version is at mid-price. There is not much to choose between the two; the Malgoire is the more consistent, although the recording is slightly thinner. If you want just the famous aria, then a distinctive version is available on Andreas Scholl's Decca recital, *Heroes*. This is a full-price CD.

● If you like this, try Purcell's *Dido and Aeneas* (180)

Grieg
145) FROM HOLBERG'S TIME

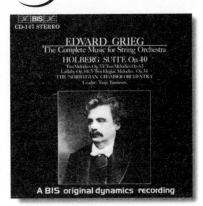

This selection of five orchestral pieces has for many years been known in Britain as the *Holberg* Suite. Originally composed at the piano but simultaneously scored for string orchestra, it was conceived by Grieg as a pastiche of many of the components of 18th-century French dance suites which were personal favourites of his. It allowed him to write music that has as its main characteristic an innocence and lightness not normally associated with late-19th-century music.

> Deutsche Grammophon
> DG 437 520-2
> **Gothenburg Symphony
> Orchestra/Neeme Järvi**
>
> ★
>
> BIS CD 147
> **Norwegian Chamber
> Orchestra/
> Terje Tønnesen**

The Gothenburg Symphony under Neeme Järvi possesses great finesse that makes its version of the Grieg suite highly enjoyable if a little glossy at times. When you compare it to the chamber orchestra recording by the Norwegian Chamber Orchestra on BIS, you can hear what you're missing out on. It's in the detail and in the timbres, ever shifting and a delight to trace through the music.

● If you like this, try Sibelius's Symphony No. 1 (270)

Offenbach
146) LES CONTES D'HOFFMANN

Offenbach died before completing his opera *The Tales of Hoffmann*, and other hands readied it for its première (in so doing leaving an entire act – Giulietta's – out). Only in recent times have attempts been made to reconstruct what Offenbach actually wanted to see (and hear) on-stage. None of this has dampened the public's enthusiasm for an effervescent composition thronging with larger-than-life characters, thrilling arias and compulsive dance music.

> ★
> Erato 0630 14330-2
> **Roberto Alagna (tenor)/
> Natalie Dessay (soprano)/
> Sumi Jo (soprano)/Leontina
> Vaduva (soprano)/Lyon
> Opera Orchestra & Chorus/
> Kent Nagano**
>
> Philips 422 374-2
> **Francisco Araiza (tenor)/
> Eva Lind (soprano)/
> Cheryl Studer (soprano)/
> Jessye Norman (soprano)/
> Leipzig Radio Orchestra/
> Staatskapelle Dresden/
> Jeffrey Tate**

Both recordings here make their own choices when it comes to performing editions and plot order. Both explain what they are doing with the material, making an absorbing detective story of the changes and developments. Of the two, the most idiomatic version is that under Kent Nagano, taken from a production mounted at Lyon Opera. The stars are Roberto Alagna, Natalie Dessay and José van Dam. The Philips recording with the Dresden Staatskapelle under Jeffrey Tate has its pleasures, but less of that French lightness and élan. The result? Lyon 1, Dresden 0.

● If you like this, try Lehár's *The Merry Widow* (200)

Rossini

147) GUGLIELMO TELL

The overture to *William Tell (Guglielmo Tell)* has got to be one of the most dramatic pieces of music ever. Its main 'fanfare' theme is also one of the most instantly recognisable. Yet the overture is only the start of a long opera (very long by the standards of the time). It was Rossini's last, though he was only 35 when he wrote it. The opera is his crowning achievement. Approach it with a fresh mind and you will derive great pleasure from this heroic but very human work.

Riccardo Chailly recorded an outstanding version of the full opera for Decca in 1979: his star singers included Pavarotti, Milnes and Freni. There is no need to look further. On the overture front there is a similar decision to be made. Chailly recorded a brilliant Rossini overtures disc in 1996, the *William Tell* overture being the first on the disc. Do not hesitate.

> ★
> Decca 417 154-2
> **Sherrill Milnes (baritone)/Mirella Freni (soprano)/Luciano Pavarotti (tenor)/Ambrosian Opera Chorus/National Philharmonic Orchestra/ Riccardo Chailly**
>
> Decca 448 218-2
> **La Scala Orchestra, Milan/ Riccardo Chailly**

● If you like this, try Suppé's *Poet and Peasant* (280)

Elgar

148) VIOLIN CONCERTO

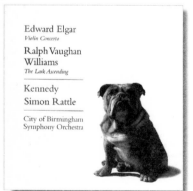

Elgar premièred his famous concerto in 1910 and, as phonographic quality improved, longed to make a definitive recording of it. This ambition was achieved in 1932 when he and a 16-year-old Yehudi Menuhin committed their triumphant partnership to wax. In many ways that version remains unsurpassable, but it would be wayward to suggest that the recording quality is remotely near today's pristine standards (it is currently available on EMI CDM 566979 2). Hence a hearty recommendation of Menuhin's second thoughts on the concerto, made in 1966 with Sir Adrian Boult conducting. The fact that it's Menuhin and mid-price would seem to constitute an unbeatable bargain, but then there is Nigel Kennedy to consider. His first recording, a mid-price release from the first, swept the board for awards in the mid-1980s, but his second version, with Sir Simon Rattle and the CBSO, is a more mature, elegiac artistic statement, full of the highest artistry and a singing, luscious tone.

> ✔
> EMI CDM 764725 2
> **Yehudi Menuhin (violin)/ New Philharmonia Orchestra/ Sir Adrian Boult**
>
> ★
> EMI CDC 556413 2
> **Nigel Kennedy (violin)/ City of Birmingham Symphony Orchestra/ Sir Simon Rattle**

● If you like this, try Barber's Violin Concerto (337)

Brahms

149) SYMPHONY NO. 3

Brahms struggled hard to create a symphonic approach with which he was content, and many of the scars of that battle can be heard in the titanic atmosphere of his First Symphony. The Third finds him at peace with himself and with the symphonic form. Here he creates a well-shaped work which dovetails in all the important places and whose elements are in good balance.

RCA 09026 63348-2
NDR Symphony Orchestra/
Günter Wand

RCA Nav 74321 17894-2
Staatskapelle Dresden/
Kurt Sanderling

This symphony is written for clarity and grace and requires the conductor to keep a rein on his orchestra so that this clarity is retained. Günter Wand, in a live recording from 1995, manages this with ease. His account has just been reissued at full-price, both on a single CD (with the Second Symphony) and in a boxed set of all four. Similarly, Kurt Sanderling's famous 1971 performance with the Staatskapelle Dresden is available separately or boxed in the same combination, but at budget price on RCA's Classical Navigator line.

● If you like this, try Mahler's Symphony No. 1 (150)

Mahler

150) SYMPHONY NO. 1

There is an extraordinary atmosphere about Mahler's first successful foray into symphony composition. From the first bars, with all time suspended and a long, high, held pitch on the strings, the air is full of tension and expectation. It contains most of the elements which would make Mahler famous – his use of folk tunes and dances, his ecstasies and his plunges into anguish and despair. But what appeals most of all in this music is its huge, generous heart.

Deutsche Grammophon
DG 431 769-2
Berlin Philharmonic
Orchestra/
Claudio Abbado

EMI CDC 754647 2
City of Birmingham
Symphony Orchestra/
Sir Simon Rattle

All this is captured brilliantly by both Claudio Abbado and the Berlin Philharmonic for DGG and Sir Simon Rattle and the CBSO for EMI. Both are committed Mahlerians who are completely at home with the characteristic musical expression the great Viennese uses. Rattle has the sharper vision of the two, the more incisive intellectual commentary, but Abbado's grasp of the big picture is impressive. Rattle includes the 'Blumine' movement, an extra movement which Mahler eventually discarded as not being fully integrated into the symphony's structure.

● If you like this, try Richard Strauss's *Alpine Symphony* (276)

Vivaldi

151) CHAMBER CONCERTO RV93

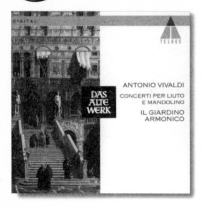

If you contrast this chamber concerto for lute, two violins and basso continuo with that for mandolin, strings and basso continuo (entry 133), the highly personalised nature of Vivaldi's beautiful concerto writing becomes clear. Here he is composing for a plucked string instrument, as with the mandolin, but its sound is mellow and soulful, its sustain just a little more pronounced, than the mandolin's. So the accompanying forces are scaled down to forestall any swamping of the soloist.

⭐
Teldec 4509 91182-2
**Giardino Armonico
Ensemble**

Hyperion CDA 66160
**Paul O'Dette (lute)/
Parley of Instruments/
Peter Holman (organ)/
Roy Goodman**

Once again Il Giardino Armonico have made a highly effective recording. They have stuck closely to the instrumental numbers indicated by Vivaldi and achieved a genuinely small-room sound. The Hyperion group go for a different sound, using an organ for keyboard accompaniment as against Il Giardino's brighter-sounding harpsichord. Paul O'Dette's lute is not so fully represented. Both groups are on original instruments, though their playing refutes any notion of this approach being difficult to listen to.

● If you like this, try Haydn's Cello Concerto No. 1 (320)

Tchaikovsky

152) SYMPHONY NO. 4

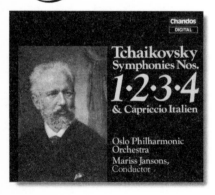

This symphony, completed in 1878, directly followed Tchaikovsky's only violin concerto and was the second major orchestral work he completed after his disastrous marriage. The music reflects the turmoil he had been living through and is, according to the composer, a musical exposition of the fact that it is impossible to avoid one's own fate. What he meant by this was only surmised later, when it was confirmed that he was a homosexual who for many years had tried to avoid acknowledging the fact to himself. The music's storms and rages all deal with his attempts to thwart his destiny.

⭐
Chandos CHAN 8361
**Oslo Philharmonic
Orchestra/Mariss Jansons**

Deutsche Grammophon
DG 429 675-2
**Berlin Philharmonic
Orchestra/
Herbert von Karajan**

As with the Fifth Symphony, the choice is between two outstanding Tchaikovsky cycles, both available as specially priced boxed sets or separately at mid-price. These are by Mariss Jansons and Herbert von Karajan. There is such artistry displayed in both versions (Tchaikovsky was a particularly good match for Karajan's musical temperament) that a choice is invidious, but as it was Karajan for the Fifth, we'll go with Jansons here.

● If you like this, try Bizet's Symphony in C (195)

Haydn

153) TRUMPET CONCERTO IN E FLAT

An important concerto, this, for it began the proper exploration of the trumpet's expressive possibilities, especially in the luscious second movement, the *andante*. It has all the usual virtues associated with Haydn – a wonderful balance between the soloist and orchestra, an unending stream of memorable melody and a welcome lightness of touch and mood. The last movement is the best known, and probably the most popular piece of trumpet music in the classical repertoire.

> Nimbus NI 7016
> **John Wallace (trumpet)/**
> **Philharmonia Orchestra/**
> **Christopher Warren-Green**
>
> ★
>
> Sony MK 39310
> **Wynton Marsalis**
> **(trumpet)/National**
> **Philharmonic Orchestra/**
> **Raymond Leppard**

Both John Wallace and Wynton Marsalis have the music's measure. Wallace possesses the lighter tone and the special poise, while Marsalis has a gravitas about his phrasing which makes the listener aware that something unusual is occurring. In this music where a full, singing tone is vital, Marsalis comes out slightly ahead, his huge sound and graceful playing grounding the music more successfully than Wallace. Be that as it may, neither man can be faulted on technical grounds. They also receive ideal support from their ensembles.

● If you like this, try Hummel's Trumpet Concerto (269)

Elgar

154) INTRODUCTION AND ALLEGRO FOR STRINGS

This work was written in 1905 when Elgar was firmly established as the leading English composer of his generation and the finest since Purcell. It reeks of self-confidence and maturity, purposefully stating its melodic case from the outset and then pursuing its own musical arguments for the rest of the piece.

The 1963 version for EMI by Sir John Barbirolli and the Sinfonia of London has long held prime position in recordings of this extrovert work, and

> ★ ✔
> EMI CDC 747537-2
> **Allegri String Quartet/**
> **Sinfonia of London/**
> **Sir John Barbirolli**
>
> ✔
>
> Naxos 8.550331
> **Capella Istropolitana/**
> **Adrian Leaper**

with good reason. Its discipline and responsiveness remain impressive by any standards, while the warmth Barbirolli brings to any conducting role benefits the music immensely here. This version is at mid-price and is wonderful value for money. If you're after an even more competitive entry-level performance, try Adrian Leaper's on Naxos.

● If you like this, try Elgar's *Chanson de Matin* (186)

Brahms

155) SYMPHONY NO. 4

After the completion of his Fourth Symphony, Brahms tinkered with the idea of a fifth and then abandoned it, destroying all his sketches. He told his friends he'd said all he wanted to say in the symphonic form – from then on it would be chamber and piano music. He kept his word. He was right to. The Fourth Symphony is an incredible achievement, showing the practised hand of a master of the form. We get an expansive sense of melody and harmony and an unhurried feeling of stillness at the work's core, even when the theme (such as the opening melody) carries that questing seriousness so typical of Brahms.

★
Erato 4509 95194-2
**Chicago Symphony
Orchestra/
Daniel Barenboim**

✔
RCA Nav 74321 24206-2
**Staatskapelle Dresden/
Kurt Sanderling**

The Erato recording from 1994 finds Daniel Barenboim and the Chicago Symphony in brilliant form and beautifully recorded. Barenboim makes the music sound so natural, so perfectly phrased, that it has the flowing qualities of Schubert. At budget price, the recording by Kurt Sanderling is keenly competitive and a disc of real stature.

● If you like this, try Mahler's Symphony No. 4 (176)

Rossini

156) IL BARBIERE DI SIVIGLIA

It's difficult to imagine a more ebullient operatic comedy than Rossini's *Barber of Seville*. The endless complications in this version of Beaumarchais's famous play *Figaro* feed Rossini with every imaginable excuse for providing memorable, effervescent music and carefree arias. The single most famous aria in the opera, by which the opera is endlessly identified and given its special comic character, is 'Largo al factotum della città', a ditty

★
EMI CDS 754863 2
**Tuscan Orchestra/
Gianluigi Gelmetti**

Decca 448 218-2
**Orchestra of
La Scala, Milan/
Riccardo Chailly**

Figaro sings, guitar slung around his neck, in the first act by way of introducing himself. Only the overture, with its wonderful series of memorable themes, can rival 'Largo al factotum' for pre-eminence. The 1993 EMI recording of the complete opera, with Thomas Hampson as Figaro and conducted by Gianluigi Gelmetti, is exemplary and a fine place to delve into the opera's delights. Riccardo Chailly's Rossini Overtures disc gives you the *Barber* overture along with many others if this is your stopping-off point.

● If you like this, try Offenbach's *Orphée aux Enfers* (258)

Tallis

157) SPEM IN ALIUM

Like many of his generation, Thomas Tallis led something of a double life. Highly successful as a composer for the newly Anglican Church in England under Henry VIII and Elizabeth, he harboured Catholic sympathies throughout his career, as his compositions occasionally attest. His 40-part motet *Spem in Alium* is one of his most ambitious and spectacular compositions, and certainly one of his most popular.

The two recordings recommended here both reach magnificent heights of choral dexterity. Winchester Cathedral Choir, directed by David Hill, aim at the complete experience of hearing Tallis as sung in a cathedral. The Tallis Scholars, under Peter Phillips, take a sparer and more closely focused look at the work, giving the listener the perspective of a small audience in a chapel. Hill's forces impress by their magnificence; Phillips's by their close accuracy. Buy according to your own choral preference, although in this case I go for the big sound.

★
Hyperion CDA 66400
Timothy Byram-Wigfield (organ)/Winchester Cathedral Choir/ Winchester Quiristers/ Winchester Vocal Arts/ David Hill

Gimell 454 906-2
Tallis Scholars/ Peter Phillips

● If you like this, try Tavener's *Song for Athene* (168)

Vaughan Williams

158) GREENSLEEVES FANTASIA

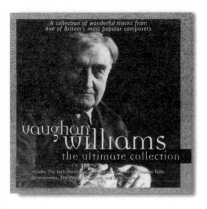

The magical fantasia Vaughan Williams wove around the old English folk song 'Greensleeves' could stand as a symbol for the whole rebirth of English music at the turn of the last century. Vaughan Williams does not mess around with the melody, allowing it its natural dignity and beauty, nor does he give it an alien musical setting, as an arch-modernist might be tempted to do. He gives it a seemingly simple and unaffected treatment, which in fact hides as much skill and artifice as it displays.

★ ✔
Teldec 3984 22125-2
BBC Symphony Orchestra/ Andrew Davis

✔
EMI CDC 747537 2
Sinfonia of London/ Sir John Barbirolli

Both conductors in our recommended recordings bring infinite good taste and expertise to their ensembles' performances, with Andrew Davis relying on dignified restraint to a larger degree than Barbirolli, whose passionate nature is more concerned to give vent to his strings' expressivity. The Davis is part of an all-Vaughan Williams miniatures programme, while the Barbirolli contains music by Elgar and Delius as well. Both are mid-price.

● If you like this, try Elgar's *Introduction and Allegro for Strings* (154)

Beethoven

159) TRIPLE CONCERTO

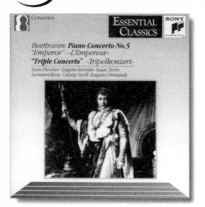

Beethoven probably wrote this work because of the unusual challenges presented by using what is virtually a piano trio as the solo instruments. This is unusual in classical music, especially given that combining the sustained notes of a bowed violin or cello with the natural decay of a struck note on the piano is notoriously difficult. Yet it works, and in the slow movement in particular, it more than works.

The Beaux Arts trio's recording dates from 1992, and firm support is granted by Kurt Masur and the Leipzig Gewandhaus Orchestra. Eugene Ormandy's guests in 1965 were Isaac Stern, Leonard Rose and Eugene Istomin. Stern still provides masterly performances in chamber settings and his playing here is a model for any other violinist interested in this form. Both have substantial fillers on their CDs, the Ormandy carrying an *Emperor Concerto* with Leon Fleischer as soloist, the Beaux Arts a polished *Choral Fantasia*. Considering it is a budget release, the Sony is hard to resist.

> Philips 438 005-2
> **Beaux Arts Trio/**
> **Leipzig Gewandhaus**
> **Orchestra/**
> **Kurt Masur**
>
> ★ ✔
>
> Sony SBK 46549
> **Isaac Stern (violin)/**
> **Leonard Rose (cello)/**
> **Eugene Istomin (piano)/**
> **Philadelphia Orchestra/**
> **Eugene Ormandy**

● If you like this, try Litolff's Piano Concerto No. 4 (178)

Stravinsky

160) THE RITE OF SPRING

Stravinsky's famous composition is not only a work that revolutionised the way ballet was written for, but one of the supreme orchestral work-outs for any audio system. For that reason alone it is sensible to buy a version that has been recorded during the digital era. Antal Dorati has made more than one recording of this complex stage work. His first stereo version, in 1959 for Mercury Living Presence, was for many years seen as something of a benchmark, but his 1982 Decca recording, directing the Detroit Symphony, is equally as visceral and in better recorded sound.

> ✔
> Decca 448 226-2
> **Detroit Symphony**
> **Orchestra/**
> **Antal Dorati**
>
> Sony SMK 60011
> **Columbia Symphony**
> **Orchestra/**
> **Igor Stravinsky**

The wildly exciting savagery of Dorati is largely toned down in the composer's own recording of the work dating from 1960. Stravinsky's playful detailing of the works' fantastic cross-rhythms makes for plenty of excitement of its own, but it is more of a performance for connoisseurs than first-time listeners.

● If you like this, try Saint-Saëns's *Danse Macabre* (177)

Tchaikovsky

161) CAPRICCIO ITALIEN

Tchaikovsky loved Italy for many reasons, not least because of its warm climate and friendly people. During one of his sojourns there he decided to cement this love by the writing of an orchestral piece which made use of a number of Italian themes, some of them literally from the streets of Rome. Following his usual practice, Tchaikovsky scored the resulting short work for a large orchestra and created a wonderfully lush texture upon which to cushion his melodies and themes.

Both Antal Dorati and Daniel Barenboim are experienced orchestral colourists and thrive on the opportunities presented them by Tchaikovsky in this score. Barenboim is a determined stickler for every detail of the instrumentation (the triangles sound marvellous) but Dorati has a bigger swagger (and a slightly less diffuse sound), giving him the edge here. Both are at mid-price.

★ ✔
Mercury 434 360-2
Minneapolis Symphony Orchestra/ Antal Dorati

✔
Deutsche Grammophon DG 445 523-2
Chicago Symphony Orchestra/ Daniel Barenboim

● If you like this, try Tchaikovsky's Symphony No. 4 (152)

Elgar

162) SERENADE FOR STRINGS

There is normally a hint of melancholy in Elgar, even in his most triumphal music, and it is not difficult to discern here, even though this is not music written in old age, but in the early years of success. But rather than concealing tragedy, this is music that seems to recall golden summers. Its glorious vein of melody is equally distributed through its three movements and Elgar's inspiration never falters. Vivacity and charm are the keywords here.

★ ✔
EMI CDM 566541 2
City of London Sinfonia/ Richard Hickox

Telarc CD 80192
Baltimore Symphony Orchestra/ David Zinman

And so they should be in performance. Both conductors have a special affinity with English music and have long been champions of Elgar, and both are happy to allow his music to delight through its own charm. Hickox goes for a broad and expansive sweep, while Zinman prefers rather more fastidious control. The Telarc sound is predictably fuller and more golden than EMI's. The romantics among us will prefer Hickox; the formalists Zinman.

● If you like this, try Elgar's *Salut d'Amour* (228)

Mozart
163) PIANO CONCERTO NO. 20 K466

In this D minor concerto, with its edge of anxiety and unease, it is the piano which speaks for optimism, the orchestra for doubts and second guesses. The *adagio* dispels this duality through the serenity of its glowing piano melody, one of the great Mozart melodies, regardless of genre. The finale continues the debate between major and minor outlooks on life before, together, pianist and orchestra, in a brilliant coda, decide that it is better to accentuate the positive.

> ★
> Sony SK 42241
> **Murray Perahia (piano)/**
> **English Chamber Orchestra**
>
> Philips 416 381-2
> **Mitsuko Uchida (piano)/**
> **English Chamber Orchestra/**
> **Jeffrey Tate**

With this concerto, as with the other Mozart piano concertos in the book, Murray Perahia occupies a central position. The relationship between soloist and orchestra is beautifully delineated, the timbre of the instruments given enormous presence by the recording engineers. An alternative point of view is offered by Uchida and Tate (with the orchestra a little too far away from the pianist at times), but Perahia must remain first choice. Both recordings are available on single CD and in complete concerto cycles.

● If you like this, try Mozart's Piano Concerto No. 27 (255)

Brahms
164) SYMPHONY NO. 1 OP. 68

An habitual self-doubter, Brahms struggled long and hard with the overpowering example of Beethoven's symphonies before he could map a way through a maze of musical precedent and create something he felt was his own. The image of Brahms as an unsmiling Teutonic 'great' is given a decided boost in this stern and dense musical argument. Even in the almost vivacious and dance-like *allegretto grazioso* of the

> Supraphon SU 1989-2
> **Czech Philharmonic**
> **Orchestra/**
> **Jiri Bélohlávek**
>
> ★
> RCA Nav 74321 21285-2
> **Staatskapelle Dresden/**
> **Kurt Sanderling**

third movement, the emotional temperature is hardly raised and high spirits never enter into it. But the fourth movement is a triumphant conclusion, duly celebrated, and done in a style which is unmistakably Brahms's.

Jiri Bélohlávek, with the Czech Philharmonic in 1987, gives a full-bodied, sympathetic and flexible mid-price reading of this titanic symphony, but considering the fire and conviction, plus the excellent engineering, brought to Kurt Sanderling's budget-price reissue on RCA Navigator, there is little reason to pay more. Sanderling can be bought as a single CD or in a boxed set.

● If you like this, try Elgar's Symphony No. 1 (170)

James Horner

165) TITANIC

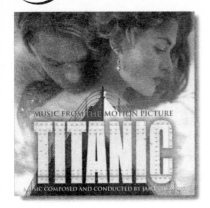

O ne may ask exactly what the soundtrack to a popular movie is doing in a classical hall of fame, but then there are acres of classical music written for other occasions which have been successfully appropriated for use in film, so why not commission orchestral music mainly in the classical tradition for a new movie undertaking? After all, the precedent is impeccable, from Korngold, Honegger, Auric, Virgil Thomson and John Williams up to more modish present-day composers such as Philip Glass and Michael Nyman. Horner's soundtrack is excellently observed and written in

★
Sony SK 63213
Original Soundtrack Recording/Sissel Kyrkjebe (singer)/James Horner

Sony SK 60691
Choir of King's College, Cambridge/London Symphony Orchestra/ Original Soundtrack Recording/ James Horner

the late Romantic style that seems to suit big-production motion pictures best. The complete music from *Titanic* is split over two separate Sony Classical CDs. The first contains the major orchestral music – the themes for the credits and the big scenes – while the second contains Horner's 'Titanic Suite' and the non-orchestral items which were such a big hit at the time, including the traditional Irish dance. Third class all the way, please!

● If you like this, try Villa-Lobos's *Bachianas Brasileiras* (393)

Handel

166) MUSIC FOR THE ROYAL FIREWORKS

H andel was commissioned to provide occasional music for the official celebrations that accompanied the conclusion of the Peace of Aix-la-Chapelle in 1749. These were held in Green Park in London and were highlighted by a huge fireworks display attended by the Royal Family and other dignitaries. This explains the extravagant and formal nature of the music Handel wrote for the occasion, as well as the stress the composer laid upon dignity and proper solemnity.

✔
Deutsche Harmonia Mundi
05472 77414-2
Collegium Aureum

★
Sony SK 63073
Tafelmusik/ Jeanne Lamon

Both versions selected for recommendation emphasise the bright, magnificent settings Handel gave his themes, and both use authentic instruments to very great effect. The Collegium Aureum disc is at mid-price and also contains the three *Water Music* suites, but its recording quality is a touch thin, while Tafelmusik's sound quality is superb and robust, its playing spirited and lively. The *Concerti a due Cori*, which make up the rest of the disc, are entirely in keeping with the mood of the *Fireworks* music, making this an easy recommendation.

● If you like this, try Zipoli's *Elevazione* (208)

Copland

167) FANFARE FOR THE COMMON MAN

Much abused by commentators and performers alike, this triumphant fanfare has stood the test of time and remains instantly recognisable to everyone. The music remains within the realm of brass and drums throughout, emphasising its occasional nature (it had been commissioned during wartime and received its première in 1943). The use of brass and drums has an obvious military connotation, but what Copland does brilliantly is avoid jingoistic triumphalism or any sort of marching beat. This is music aware of the serious business war is, not just of the misplaced patriotism that can trigger it. The famous 1968 recording by Copland himself is currently only available as part of a three-CD set of the composer conducting his own music: a lot to pay for three minutes of music. The modern Nimbus recording by William Boughton is a highly respectable (and well-recorded) alternative choice on one CD.

> ✔
> Sony SMK 60133
> **London Symphony Orchestra/**
> **Aaron Copland**
>
> ★
> Nimbus NI 5246
> **English Symphony Orchestra/**
> **William Boughton**

● If you like this, try Bernstein's *Candide* Overture (248)

Tavener

168) SONG FOR ATHENE

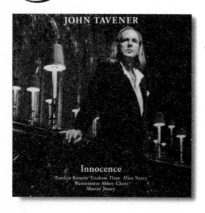

John Tavener's sustained popular success since the impact of 1988's *The Protecting Veil* is as astonishing in its own way as that of Górecki. Most of his compositions have been specifically for liturgical use. His music is deeply meditative in nature and reflects the choral and vocal traditions of Orthodox religious practice. The choral lament *Song for Athene* was composed in 1993 to commemorate the tragic death of a young actress who was a member of the Orthodox faith, Athene Hariades.

> Virgin VC 545340 2
> **Winchester Cathedral Choir/**
> **Stephen Farr (organ)/**
> **David Hill**
>
> ★
> Sony SK 66613
> **Westminster Abbey Choir/**
> **Martin Neary**

The two versions recommended here are both by English choirs. The Winchester Cathedral Choir, directed by David Hill, include in their recording a programme of short religious works from composers such as Barber and Poulenc. They bring great emotional force and clarity to the performance. The second recording, from Westminster Abbey, led by Martin Neary, brings more mystery to the piece. It is part of an all-Tavener recital of great power and is perhaps an ideal way to start investigating this uniquely affecting contemporary composer.

● If you like this, try Górecki's Symphony No. 3 (113)

Beethoven

169) PIANO SONATA NO. 8 IN C MINOR, OP. 13 (PATHÉTIQUE)

The soubriquet Beethoven added to this work to explain its content was not meant to imply that anything about it was pathetic. What he was indicating by subtitling it a '*Grande Sonata Pathétique*' was that it was written in the noble (and at times overwrought) style brought into fashion in late-18th-century Europe by French baroque composers. This demanded a dramatic overture, followed by an intense orchestral passage in the grand style. This is precisely what happens here, only Beethoven pulls it off on the piano alone.

★ ✔
Deutsche Grammophon
DG 400 036-2
Emil Gilels (piano)

✔
Deutsche Grammophon
DG 447 404-2
Wilhelm Kempff (piano)

Emil Gilels plays this music with an admirable lack of distortion. His rendition is a miracle of humility and communication. This could also be said of Wilhelm Kempff's playing. The difference between the two is a difference of basic temperament: Kempff is not as explosive as Gilels, relying on an elegance of expression to get to the core of the music. Both methods work, but Gilels is perhaps the more memorable in this sonata.

● If you like this, try Beethoven's Piano Sonata No. 23 ('Appassionata') (309)

Elgar

170) SYMPHONY NO. 1

This, the first great British symphony, was premièred in 1908 to huge acclaim but was begun – at least in concept – as early as 1899, when Elgar tried (and failed) to write a symphony on the theme of Gordon of Khartoum. Whatever the revisionist theory of Gordon and his ventures is, his perceived nobility of spirit is certainly prominent in this, a monumentally noble and optimistic symphonic work.

✔
EMI CDM 764013 2
**London Philharmonic Orchestra/
Sir Adrian Boult**

★
Teldec 9031 73278-2
**BBC Symphony Orchestra/
Andrew Davis**

Elgar's characteristic musical emotion could be described as a 'smoulder', or slow burn. The intensity is clearly at white heat, but it is not blatant: you have to be alert to it to catch it fully. The two conductors here, both lifetime Elgarians, are alert to it in their different ways. Sir Adrian Boult's recording for EMI with the LPO (now at mid-price) makes much of his experience. But Andrew Davis's 1991 recording with the BBC Symphony combines beautiful sound with soulful conducting to take pride of place.

● If you like this, try Brahms's Symphony No. 2 (203)

Beethoven

171) PIANO CONCERTO NO. 3

With this concerto Beethoven paid his last homage to the form and content of the great piano concertos written by his predecessor, Mozart. It opens with the conventional orchestral statement of the principal ideas to be developed, then introduces the piano for an unaccompanied passage before the two come together to begin their spirited dialogue on the material at hand. The slow movement is a beautiful *largo*. It is this movement which has earned the Third Concerto such sustained popularity over the years, its sense of hard-won peace being particularly pleasing to the modern ear. The finale begins with a jaunty minor theme that recalls cautionary tales from the music hall but is resolved in a blazing delight of octave arpeggios and orchestral chords. Maurizio Pollini's version is a masterful one, but the convenience of combining the concerto with Beethoven's Fourth Piano Concerto, as do Uchida and Sanderling on their 1998 recording for Philips, is a good reason for this being first choice.

Deutsche Grammophon
DG 445 850-2
**Maurizio Pollini (piano)/
Berlin Philharmonic
Orchestra/
Claudio Abbado**

★

Philips 446 082-2
**Mitsuko Uchida (piano)/
Concertgebouw Orchestra,
Amsterdam/
Kurt Sanderling**

● If you like this, try Saint-Saëns's Piano Concerto No. 2 (231)

Schubert

172) IMPROMPTUS

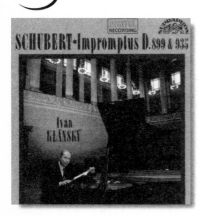

Schubert wrote two sets of *Impromptus*, both in the last quarter of 1827. By this time he was already aware of his desperate state of health (he was dying of syphilis) and determined to complete as many musical projects as possible. These *Impromptus* allowed him to take a much freer and lyrical approach to solo piano composition than had the sonatas he had mostly concentrated on prior to this.

The Czech pianist Ivan Klansky's combination of intellect and romance make for breathtaking listening which never distorts the message of the music for the purpose of mere grandstanding. A similar judgement could be passed on the superb Wilhelm Kempff recordings of the late 1960s for Deutsche Grammophon. Never an overt or flashy pianist, Kempff is concerned only with presenting the music's meaning in its truest state. Artistry of a high order is the rule throughout both recitals.

★
Supraphon 11 0366-2
Ivan Klansky (piano)

✔

Deutsche Grammophon
DG 459 412-2
Wilhelm Kempff (piano)

● If you like this, try Debussy's *Preludes* Book 1 (352)

Borodin

173) STRING QUARTET NO. 2

Alexander Borodin made chemistry his profession, rather than music, preferring to keep his composing for 'happy times' such as holidays and other rest periods, when he could enjoy his family and his freedom. Inevitably, this led to him not getting a great deal written before his untimely death. Still, what he did write (some of which was 'finished' by others) has become universally loved.

His second quartet is sparsely represented on CD at present. The pick of the bunch comes from the Chilingarian Quartet on Classic FM's own label. Their version stresses the sweet, rhapsodic core to the music. If you are after a more sumptuous approach, then there is a modern arrangement for string orchestra performed on Chandos by I Musici de Montréal under Yuli Turovsky's guidance. This has the requisite sway and swagger to trip the light fantastic and whisk the listener away to blue-skied imagined lands.

● If you like this, try Schubert's String Quartet No. 14 (245)

J. S. Bach

174) CELLO SUITES

The most extraordinary thing about Bach's cello suites is that the listener is always aware of the silence surrounding the notes. Bach was acutely aware of the fact that the sound of the cello ceases immediately the bow stops, and continually used it to the music's advantage, allowing at each pause a moment of reflection on what has just passed.

The man responsible for this music enjoying a resurgence of popularity was Pablo Casals, who in the 1940s made the first-ever complete recording of it. This is still available on EMI and is a basic text for any cellist, but the pre-tape sound quality will deter many non-expert listeners. Since then no important cellist has failed to issue their own set. We have chosen two: firstly, a finely sculpted 1997 version by Yo-Yo Ma which catches both the intense seriousness of the music and its more playful side; secondly, a recording by the Dutch cellist Pieter Wispelwey (using a baroque cello) who brings much eloquence to his performances. Buy either with confidence.

● If you like this, try Bach's *Goldberg Variations* (253)

Franck

175) PANIS ANGELICUS

Franck's popular choral piece started life in 1872 as a simple but affecting setting of four lines from the Latin Eucharist dealing with 'the bread of angels'. This first version was for a single male tenor voice, accompanied by organ, harp, cello and double-bass. Its success when published the following year led Franck to try to incorporate it into one of his larger religious compositions.

The two versions recommended here are quite differently scored. The Westminster Cathedral Choir and James O'Donnell use an arrangement by Andrew Gant that matches choir with organ only. This brings out the intensely spiritual nature of the music to its fullest degree. The other version, by tenor Joséf Mukk, the Hungarian State Opera Choir and Lászlo Kovács, takes the best of both worlds, starting with tenor accompanied by oboe and strings, latterly introducing a full choir and organ. The Hyperion collection is all choral; the Naxos collation pushes into semi-operatic territory with Bizet and Donizetti.

★
Hyperion CDA 66669
**Westminster
Cathedral Choir/
Iain Simcock (organ)/
James O'Donnell**

✔
Naxos 8.553751
**Joséf Mukk (tenor)/
Hungarian State Opera
Chamber Choir/
Budapest Camerata/
Lászlo Kovács**

● If you like this, try Schubert's *Ave Maria* (260)

Mahler

176) SYMPHONY NO. 4

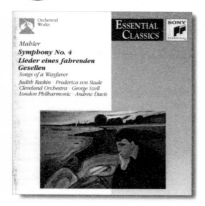

Mahler's Fourth Symphony inhabits an imagined ideal past, which the composer is happy to idealise. The first movement is as cloudless as an Alpine summer day, while the second holds mischief and innocent devilry. It is only with the third movement that a touch of awe seems to emanate from the music, but it is an awe that is not threatening to the listener.

Few conductors go too far wrong with the Fourth, unless they are trying to imbue it with qualities it simply doesn't possess. Sir Simon Rattle's 1997 recording offers a more complex mind and heart behind the music than does George Szell in his 1965 outing with the Cleveland Orchestra, but it is possible to argue that Szell gets more out of the music because he emphasises the idyllic. Considering it is at budget price, and the sound is more than acceptable for the period, there seems little reason not to recommend it as an excellent place to start.

EMI CDC 556563 2
**Amanda Roocroft
(soprano)/
City of Birmingham
Symphony Orchestra/
Sir Simon Rattle**

★ ✔
Sony SBK 46535
**Judith Raskin (soprano)/
Cleveland Orchestra/
George Szell**

● If you like this, try Bruckner's Symphony No. 7 (282)

Saint-Saëns

177) DANSE MACABRE

This famous short orchestral piece is one of the many successful classical music attempts to depict the Devil and his tricks. The Devil is often associated with the violin, an instrument with a long history in folk music and well suited to inspiring infernal dances. With this beautifully conceived dance Saint-Saëns starts with a jarring clarion call on the violin at the stroke of midnight, reflecting the words of the poem by Henri Caxalis that he is bringing to musical life.

Chandos CHAN 6503
**Royal Scottish National Orchestra/
Alexander Gibson**

✔
Sony SBK 47655
**Philadelphia Orchestra/
Eugene Ormandy**

The Chandos recording by Alexander Gibson and the Scottish National Orchestra is a mid-price issue recorded in 1973 in excellent sound which brings the images vividly to life. Also on the disc is the equally infernal *Sorcerer's Apprentice* by Paul Dukas and the Rossini/Respighi *La Boutique fantasque*. The Eugene Ormandy version for Sony Classical dates from 1959 and is part of a budget-priced all-Saint-Saëns disc including the Third Symphony and the *Carnival of the Animals*.

● If you like this, try Stravinksy's *Firebird* (239)

Litolff

178) PIANO CONCERTO NO. 4

Litolff's music is not widely represented on record. A journeyman piano teacher, performing musician and composer, he built up a respectable repertoire of conventionally conceived piano music that he could perform to great effect on his travels. He wrote five piano concertos, although only four are known to have come down to us today. It is the *scherzo* from his fourth which has largely kept his name alive outside of musicological circles.

Two of his concertos (Nos 2 and 4) are available on a Hyperion disc, and

Hyperion CDA 66889
**Peter Donohoe (piano)/
Bournemouth Symphony Orchestra/
Andrew Litton**

✔
Decca 466 376-2
**Clifford Curzon (piano)/
London Philharmonic Orchestra/
Sir Adrian Boult**

the dashing performances are by Peter Donohoe with the Bournemouth Symphony and Andrew Litton. This was recorded in fine modern sound in 1996 and is thoroughly recommendable. The scherzo from the 4th Concerto is available performed by Sir Clifford Curzon for Decca back in the 1950s (it is coupled with the Brahms's 1st Piano Concerto and the Franck *Symphonic Variations*). The sound is old but acceptable.

● If you like this, try Saint-Saëns's *Introduction and Rondo* (234)

Debussy
179) PRÉLUDE À L'APRÈS-MIDI D'UN FAUNE

This, one of the most sensual pieces of music ever conceived, is also one of the hardest to bring off in performance. The conductor has an enormous influence on the result, for any attempt at grandstanding or overemphasis and the whole piece crashes to the ground.

The two performances chosen here thrive through understatement. Tilson-Thomas and the LSO conjure up suitably lush tones and sensuality, the flute soloist arching his melody lazily

✔
Sony SMK 48231
London Symphony Orchestra/ Michael Tilson-Thomas

★
Sony SK 62599
Los Angeles Philharmonic Orchestra/ Esa-Pekka Salonen

without attempting to grandstand. Under such old masters as Beecham the moment where the second theme arrives is electric, even through second-rate acoustics. With the LSO and Tilson-Thomas it doesn't quite take off. For that experience we have to turn to our premier choice, with the Los Angeles Philharmonic conducted by Esa-Pekka Salonen. This conductor finds the magic in the piece, bringing us a quiet drama which tells the whole story. Blink and you've missed it. Concentrate and you'll have it for life.

● If you like this, try Debussy's *La Mer* (266)

Purcell
180) DIDO AND ÆNEAS

Purcell's only stage work in the form of an opera was *Dido and Æneas*. The *Dido* we know today is a torso of the complete work, missing as it is the Prologue and other less substantial pieces. That does not prevent audiences from appreciating both the reality of the drama being enacted and the beauty of the music Purcell created.

Dido has been recorded regularly since the 1940s. Today it is the exclusive preserve of the authentic instruments brigade, but in an opera where the voice is paramount, the accompaniment spare but telling, this is

Chandos CHAN 0521
Emma Kirkby (soprano)/ David Thomas (bass)/ Taverner Choir/Taverner Players/Andrew Parrott

★
Erato 4509 98477-2
Véronique Gens (soprano)/ Nathan Berg (baritone)/ Les Arts Florissants/ William Christie

not so much of a problem. The two productions here enjoy angelic Didos (Emma Kirkby for Andrew Parrott; Véronique Gens for Christie). They also boast heroic Æneases in David Thomas and Nathan Berg respectively. Sound quality is excellent on both, although the Chandos disc dates from 1981; however, the Chandos has just four CD index points and no libretto. In the absence of other criteria, this pushes the vote Erato's way.

● If you like this, try Rameau's *Les Indes Galantes* (199)

Borodin

181) IN THE STEPPES OF CENTRAL ASIA

The subject matter of this work – the journey of a caravan carrying rare goods through the exotic lands of central Asia – gave Borodin the excuse both to use his orientalist melodies to good advantage and to fire his imagination with the brilliant images conjured. It is one of a small number of works which this professional chemist and family man, who only composed in his spare time, managed to find the time to complete and orchestrate himself. It is crammed with Borodin's uniquely graceful and 'exotic' melodies, which also feature so prominently in his opera *Prince Igor*.

Deutsche Grammophon
DG 429 984-2
**Gothenburg
Symphony Orchestra/
Neeme Järvi**

★ ✔

Naxos 8.550051
**Slovak Philharmonic
Orchestra/
Daniel Nazareth**

Many recordings exist, from full down to budget price. At full price the exoticism so close to Borodin's heart is handled with panache by Neeme Järvi in a collection of Russian favourites from Borodin, Rimsky-Korsakov and Tchaikovsky. But there is a good budget-price version from Naxos, with Daniel Nazareth conducting the Slovak Philharmonic.

● If you like this, try Glazunov's *The Seasons* (310)

Schumann

182) PIANO CONCERTO IN A MINOR OP. 54

The unwary listener might at first listening think they'd stumbled upon a previously unheard piano concerto by Brahms, such is the similarity in approach between these two composers. The fact that Schumann befriended the young Brahms does not entirely explain this similarity; there is also a closeness of spirit and outlook between the two. But another common factor is that both men drew their personal inspiration from love of the same woman, Clara Schumann. The slow movement of this concerto is testament to the happiness

★
Sony SK 64577
**Murray Perahia (piano)/
Berlin Philharmonic
Orchestra/
Claudio Abbado**

✔

Naxos 8.550118
**Jeno Jandó (piano)/
Budapest Symphony
Orchestra/
Andras Ligeti**

the newly married composer was then sharing with her, before the dark clouds of his mental dissolution gathered.

Murray Perahia, accompanied by Abbado and the Berlin Philharmonic, is alive to every nuance: his piano sound is one of the most beautiful on record, and is in perfect balance with the orchestra. Jeno Jandó has a more immediate and brittle sound on Naxos, but he plays with great expressive range. A good budget alternative.

● If you like this, try Clara Schumann's Piano Concerto in A minor (346)

Ravel

183) PAVANE POUR UNE INFANTE DÉFUNTE

At the beginning of the 20th century many young French composers looked to older French forms of music for inspiration. During this time both Debussy and Ravel wrote pieces using classical French dance forms: this pavane is a direct result of that backward glance. The piece began life in 1899 as a solo for piano. Ten years later Ravel decided to orchestrate the work in order to give it a life in the concert hall.

✔
Decca 440 836-2
Pascal Rogé (piano)

★
Erato 0630 14331-2
**Lyon Opéra Orchestra/
Kent Nagano**

Good interpretations of this music avoid a funereal tempo. They also shun grandiloquent flourishes and temptations towards mawkish sentimentality. Pascal Rogé, on a mid-price Decca Ravel recital, manages to avoid most of the pitfalls. The orchestrated version has its snares: the young infantas can often suddenly sound heavy as the orchestra grinds almost to a halt. Kent Nagano and his Lyon Opéra orchestra begin a little slowly, but retain their poise and gently increase the tempo to the point where the piece lifts off.

● If you like this, try Ravel's *Daphnis et Chloé* (226)

Beethoven

184) BAGATELLE IN A MINOR WoO 59 'FÜR ELISE'

Luchino Visconti's Film *Death in Venice* demonstrated that Beethoven's 'trifle' (it is less than five minutes long) had been universally popular for the best part of a century or more. Even today, nearly 20 years later, 'Für Elise' continues to cast its spell, its minor-key arabesques capturing a mood of capricious, wistful indolence to perfection.

✔
Deutsche Grammophon
DG 459 135-2
Anatol Ugorski (piano)

★ ✔
Naxos 8.550168
Balázs Szokolay (piano)

There are thousands of recordings, many of them serviceable enough, but there are a lot which try to make too much of it. The performance by Anatol Ugorski on a special-price DGG collection of piano favourites named after Beethoven's piece manages to keep it intimate and not too overblown, although the rest of the programme bears little relation to it. A Naxos compilation of *Romantic Piano Favourites* is perhaps a little less self-effacing and therefore more of an experience. The rest of the programme shows a mite more solidarity with the little piece's sentiments, too.

● If you like this, try Mozart's Sonata for keyboard No. 11 (374)

Johann Strauss I
185) RADETZKY MARCH

Although there are a number of famous marches that have remained popular for a century or more, few could doubt that Father Strauss's march, named after the most distinguished Austrian general of his day, remains the most popular. The wonderful thing about the Strausses' marches and polkas is that they never take themselves too seriously: their sense of fun is always within reach.

Erich Kunzel and the Cincinnati Pops have just the right touch, allowing the music plenty of life and colour but never making it blatant or heavy-footed. Their version has plenty of impact but is as light as a soufflé. The recorded sound is first-rate. The *Radetzky March* also turns up, strangely, on Naxos's ten-CD set of Johann Strauss II's music with Ondrej Lenárd as conductor. The marchers are a little more jerky in their movements than are Kunzel's, the band not so poised, but at budget price it is still a good buy.

● If you like this, try Walton's *Crown Imperial* (313)

> ★
> Telarc CD 80098
> **Cincinnati Pops Orchestra/**
> **Erich Kunzel**
>
> ✔
> Naxos 8.554526
> **Bratislava Radio**
> **Symphony Orchestra/**
> **Ondrej Lenárd**

Elgar
186) CHANSON DE MATIN

Chanson de matin is the second of two short works Elgar wrote for violin and piano (the other is *Chanson de nuit*). The original scoring gives these melodious and dignified pieces a 'salon' feeling and rather limits their appeal. The orchestral versions, completed by the composer by the start of the new century, bring out the larger ambitions and seamless design of the music.

Nigel Kennedy has made a recording of the original violin/piano scoring and has probably given the music as much weight as it can possibly carry. Even then, it sounds more like a trifle than a serious statement, through no fault of Kennedy's. The orchestral version has been given a stylish and typically well-balanced reading by Sir Adrian Boult. His 1968 recording of both *Chansons* (with the LPO) is currently available as a juicy morsel filling out the CD release of his Elgar Symphony No. 1. Both are performances to look out for.

● If you like this, try Delius's *On Hearing the First Cuckoo in Spring* (259)

> ✔
> Chandos CHAN 8380
> **Nigel Kennedy (violin)/**
> **Peter Pettinger (piano)**
>
> ★ ✔
> EMI CDM 764013 2
> **London Philharmonic**
> **Orchestra/**
> **Sir Adrian Boult**

Bellini

187 NORMA

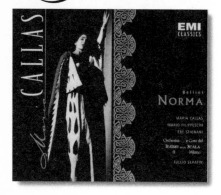

There is no way Bellini could have known what Maria Callas had in store for his operas when he wrote them, but listening to *Norma*, no matter who is taking the title role, forces one to think of the Callas voice and presence. The opera deals with the usual conflicts: love or honour, love or country. In this case it's Gaul and the enemies are the Romans and the Druids.

In her 1954 mono recording from La Scala, Callas is in fine voice and completely dominates the stage. The recording is passable, although the orchestra tends to get a bit lost. The 1979 recording by James Levine with Renata Scotto in the title role gives the listener good stereo sound and much more detail, but Scotto has already developed a high-note wobble that is not pleasant. The set is at mid-price and Callas is still at full, but those after the definitive self-immolation will turn to Callas every time.

★
EMI CDS 556271 2
**Maria Callas (soprano)/
Orchestra & Chorus of
La Scala, Milan/
H. Serafin**

✔
Sony SM2K 35902
**Renata Scotto (soprano)/
Tatiana Troyanos (mezzo-
soprano)/Ambrosian
Opera Chorus/National
Philharmonic Orchestra/
James Levine**

● If you like this, try Donizetti's *Lucia di Lammermoor* (198)

Vivaldi

188 NULLA IN MUNDO PAX SINCERA

Nulla in mundo pax sincera is a motet for soprano and string accompaniment in gentle 3/4 time. Its theme is stated in its first line: 'there is no peace in the world without bitterness'. The only hope of escape from this cycle, Vivaldi teaches us, is through 'sweet Jesus'. His setting of these words combines grace and almost unearthly beauty of vocal melodic line with occasional dips into bittersweet admonition from the vocalist.

Both recordings feature sopranos who possess supreme beauty of tone and purity of line. For Robert King on Hyperion the soloist is Deborah York, a singer blessed with grace and dignity. The L'Oiseau-Lyre performance from 1978 under Hogwood offers us Emma Kirkby's young and gloriously pure voice. The accompaniment is a little thin and this may put a few off: if so, the Hyperion is an excellent choice. Otherwise, the Hogwood is mid-price and a slimline double CD of Vivaldi, should you want a generous slice of his vocal music.

★
Hyperion CDA 66779
**Deborah York (soprano)/
King's Consort/
Robert King**

✔
L'Oiseau-Lyre 455 727-2
**Emma Kirkby (soprano)/
Academy of Ancient Music/
Christopher Hogwood**

● If you like this, try Mozart's *Exsultate, jubilate* (207)

Wagner

189) LOHENGRIN

ohengrin was premièred by Franz Liszt in 1850. The hero is a knight of the Holy Grail who comes to the aid of a pure princess but is forced into compromising his position through the deceit of the princess's enemies. The music that accompanies this tragedy of good intentions and evil betrayals is often gloomy, but essentially lyric, in keeping with Wagner's contention that it was a Romantic opera. The great exception, of course, is the overture to the third act and its bustling, anticipatory music for the upcoming wedding of Lohengrin and Elsa, which blossoms into the world-famous theme known in English-speaking countries as 'Here comes the bride'.

We are blessed with a first-rate modern version of *Lohengrin* by Daniel Barenboim, made in 1998 and with a superb cast. It is one of a only a handful of performances which contains the complete, uncut score. If highlights suit you better, there is a very good mid-price single disc excerpted from Peter Schneider's 1990 Bayreuth recording.

Teldec 3984 21484-2
Peter Seiffert (tenor)/
Emily Magee (soprano)/
Berlin Deutsche Opera
Chorus/Berlin Staatskapelle/
Daniel Barenboim

Philips 446 619-2
Paul Frey (tenor)/
Cheryl Studer (soprano)/
Bayreuth Festival
Orchestra & Chorus/
Peter Schneider

● If you like this, try Wagner's *The Flying Dutchman* (367)

Puccini

190) GIANNI SCHICCHI

his one-act opera is part of Puccini's *Il Trittico* production premièred in New York in 1918. The last of the three on-stage, it is a witty piece of comic opera which proves conclusively that Puccini had what it took to write such things. None of the three has ever been immensely popular, but the one great aria from *Schicchi*, Lauretta's 'O mio babbino caro', has become widely loved.

Complete performances of *Schicchi* tend to come and go. Of the current crop, the Bartoletti on Decca comes from a complete *Trittico* starring Mirella Freni, recorded in 1994. This benefits from spacious modern recorded sound and a suitably grouchy Gianni in Leo Nucci. But Freni, though a great soprano, really is decades too old for her role. A surprisingly well-balanced sound is present on the 1959 EMI recording (another complete *Trittico*) featuring Victoria de los Angeles and Tito Gobbi. De los Angeles's voice sounds convincingly young and coy, Gobbi very much the patriarch. The orchestra is properly conversational in phrasing. 'O mio' is gorgeous and the whole thing comes convincingly alive.

Decca 444 395-2
Leo Nucci (baritone)/Mirella
Freni (soprano)/Maggio
Musicale/Fiorentino
Orchestra/Bruno Bartoletti

EMI CMS 764165 2
Tito Gobbi (baritone)/
Victoria de los Angeles
(soprano)/Rome Opera
Orchestra/Gabriele Santini

● If you like this, try Puccini's *La Rondine* (271)

Tárrega

191) RECUERDOS DE LA ALHAMBRA

Music of Spain
La guitarra
romàntica
Tárrega
Pujol
Llobet

Julian BREAM EDITION
VOLUME 26

F rancisco Tárrega made a huge contribution to the classical guitar repertoire, helping introduce the Spanish folk and ethnic elements that would give it a completely new lease of life. He drew his inspiration from Spanish life and culture, as this piece perfectly illustrates. It is his musical response to the impact made upon him by the fantastic Alhambra Palace built by the Moors in southern Spain.

> Deutsche Grammophon
> DG 410 655-2
> **Narciso Yepes (guitar)**
>
> ★ ✔
>
> RCA 09026 61609-2
> **Julian Bream (guitar)**

The two guitarists selected for their interpretations have long been regarded as leaders in the field of classical guitar, especially the Spanish repertoire. Narciso Yepes takes the piece quite fast, guiding us through the palace with little time to rest, retaining his poise throughout. It is only when we turn to Julian Bream's interpretation (at mid-price) that we realise what we missed on the first tour. Bream's pace is much slower, he takes bigger risks, but he pulls off such a rich and detailed portrait that the first impulse the listener has at its conclusion is to play the piece again. What better recommendation is there?

● If you like this, try Rodrigo's *Fantasia para un gentilhombre* (333)

Wagner

192) DIE MEISTERSINGER VON NÜRNBERG

DIE MEISTERSINGER VON NÜRNBERG
RAFAEL KUBELIK CALIG
WAGNER
THOMAS STEWART
SANDOR KONYA
GUNDULA JANOWITZ
THOMAS HEMSLEY
BRIGITTE FASSBAENDER
GERHARD UNGER
FRANZ CRASS
Chor und Symphonieorchester
des Bayerischen Rundfunks

A comic opera from Wagner? Well, almost. He himself had doubts about its true character, finally designating it an opera rather than a comic opera, although the latter had been his first intention. But it has its light-hearted side and deals with real people, rather than myths and superhumans. It also has a happy ending: reason enough to celebrate in a Wagner opera. It is set in the Middle Ages and is based on a tale by Germany's greatest storyteller of that era, Wolfram von Eschenbach, which deals with a singing competition. Surviving riots, rejection and subterfuge, the young hero, Walther, eventually wins the competition and the hand of his true love, Eva.

> ★
> Calig CAL 50971/4/
> **Thomas Stewart (baritone)/**
> **Sándor Kónya (tenor)/**
> **Bavarian Radio Chorus &**
> **Symphony Orchestra/**
> **Rafael Kubelik**
>
> ✔
>
> Sony SMK 64108
> **New York**
> **Philharmonic Orchestra/**
> **Pierre Boulez**

The opera has been prolifically recorded. The version with the most atmosphere and lightest touch currently available is that by Rafael Kubelik, recorded 'live' in excellent sound in 1967 and released on the German label Calig. A highly engaging version of the overture by Pierre Boulez is available at mid-price on Sony Classical.

● If you like this, try Wagner's *Siegfried* (215)

Verdi

193) LA FORZA DEL DESTINO

Another great middle-period Verdi opera, this time with a highly charged overture guaranteed to pin the audience to the back of their seats and give Rossini's *William Tell* overture a run for its money. Premièred in St Petersburg in 1862, it also includes more than its fair share of outstanding arias, for both hero and heroine, soprano and tenor. This breathless tale of impossible love, fights, supposed death, wars and slow-burn revenge, where every table that can be turned is duly turned before the end and only madness and death can halt the mad spiral of events, is painted in bold colours by Verdi and grips its audience from first note to last. At least, it should do, and this is the case with the two performances here. Despite its Russian première, this is an Italian opera, and the mostly Italian cast of Gardelli, now available at mid-price (with libretto), is hard to beat indeed.

> Philips 446 951-2
> **Galina Gorchakova (soprano)/**
> **Gegam Grigorian (tenor)/**
> **Kirov Opera Orchestra & Chorus/**
> **Valery Gergiev**
>
> ★
>
> EMI CMS 764646 2
> **Martina Arroyo (soprano)/**
> **Carlo Bergonzi (tenor)/**
> **Ambrosian Opera Chorus/**
> **Royal Philharmonic Orchestra/**
> **Lamberto Gardelli**

● If you like this, try Verdi's *Otello* (292)

Caccini

194) AVE MARIA

Caccini's *Ave Maria*, like most of his church music, has not been recorded often and has only come back into the repertoire through its discovery by a handful of modern-day singers. A melancholy hymn of praise to the Mother of Christ, it exhibits his customary grace and penchant for long and gradually unfolding melodies. It was brought back into the light by Inessa Galante at the beginning of thè 1990s and made popular worldwide by her renditions, live and on CD. The arrangement she favours uses strings to bolster the original harpsichord *continuo*: although it introduces a modern note into the proceedings, it is not inappropriate to a pleasing melody. Other vocal versions currently available have technical and musical problems that mar their effectiveness, while the instrumental version recorded by Julian Lloyd Webber lacks the words which make the song that much more effective.

> ★
> Campion RRCD 1335
> **Inessa Galante (soprano)/**
> **Latvian National Symphony Orchestra/**
> **Alexander Vilumanis**

● If you like this, try Rutter's *Requiem* (216)

Bizet

195) SYMPHONY IN C

izet wrote this when he was still a student at the Paris Conservatoire. The work is a model of decorous invention, showing little of the high exoticism that was to come in his later stage works. A tidy and successful if rather derivative work, it evidently found little favour with Bizet, who put it in a drawer and forgot about it. It received its première in the 1930s, 60 years after his death.

Both recordings make much of the delights the symphony harbours. López-Cobos and the Cincinnati Symphony, in an all-Bizet programme (*Carmen Suite, L'Arlésienne Suite*), play with brio and flavour. The recording quality is superb. Saraste's version, included in a two-CD programme of French music encompassing Bizet's symphony, Berlioz and Chausson, has a less beautiful sound with the Scottish Chamber Orchestra, but no less urgency. This is a budget release and therefore good value, but the López-Cobos is the one to aim for, if you don't mind paying full price.

Telarc CD 80224
**Cincinnati Symphony Orchestra/
Jesús López-Cobos**

✔
Virgin VBD 561513 2
**Scottish Chamber Orchestra/
Jukka-Pekka Saraste**

● If you like this, try Franck's *Symphonic Variations* (395)

Shostakovich

196) JAZZ SUITE NO. 1

In this music, written in 1934, Shostakovich made no attempt to compose actual jazz. The three movements, waltz, polka and foxtrot, rarely aim higher than European salon and cabaret music, with only the foxtrot bearing signs of such jazz staples as syncopation and the occasional blue note. Only in the instrumentation – which includes saxophones, guitars and drums – are modern American popular music practices acknowledged.

Riccardo Chailly and members of the Concertgebouw clearly enjoyed themselves immensely on their Decca recital, which encompasses the other jazz-inspired Shostakovich music, including the First Piano Concerto. The recital by Dmitri Kitaenko, which includes both jazz suites, is highly idiomatic and also includes ballet suites 1 and 3 taken from *The Age of Gold, The Bolt* and *Bright Stream*. These are charming orchestral dance miniatures and sit comfortably with the so-called jazz suites, making this a very attractive disc of 'light music'.

★
Decca 433 702-2
**Concertgebouw Orchestra, Amsterdam/
Riccardo Chailly**

RCA 09026 68304-2
**Frankfurt Radio Symphony Orchestra/
Dmitri Kitaenko**

● If you like this, try Dvořák's *Slavonic Dances* (247)

Haydn

197) DIE SCHÖPFUNG (THE CREATION)

The orchestral overture vividly depicts the first second of creation, when 'the earth was without form and void. And darkness was upon the face of the deep.' The rest of the oratorio alternates soloists with choir as well as biblical text with additional text supplied by Haydn's collaborator, Gottfried van Swieten, to sustain the drama and wonder of the opening chapters of Genesis. Haydn is never at a loss for music to match the actions, either of God or of his final creation, Adam and Eve.

Haydn was a humble creator, even if he was a genius, and his *Creation* requires decorum, not hubris. The two versions recommended here both contain that sense of man's relationship to his Creator, with a wonderfully managed authentic performance by Tafelmusik and soloists under Bruno Weil being a stand-out. Also scrupulous in his observance of Haydn's intentions is Nikolaus Harnoncourt in a considered recording of the English text on Teldec, although his is the more traditionally minded performance.

> ★
> Sony SX2K 57965
> **Ann Monoyios (soprano)/**
> **Jörg Hering (tenor)/**
> **Harry van der Kamp (bass)/**
> **Tölz Boys Choir/Tafelmusik/**
> **Bruno Weil**
>
> Teldec 0630 10026-2
> **Edita Gruberová (soprano)/**
> **Josef Protschka (tenor)/**
> **Robert Holl (bass)/Vienna**
> **Symphony Orchestra/Arnold**
> **Schoenberg Choir/**
> **Nikolaus Harnoncourt**

● If you like this, try Berlioz's *L'Enfance du Christ* (232)

Donizetti

198) LUCIA DI LAMMERMOOR

Donizetti's most famous opera, the quintessential example of Italian *bel canto* composing, is based on the old novel by Sir Walter Scott, *The Bride of Lammermoor*. With this blood-and-gore subject Donizetti found his inspiration running at white heat. There is plenty of great dramatic music, an outstanding mad scene and a libretto that for once is commensurate with the music that adorns it.

Two superb recordings are represented here. Joan Sutherland in part created her international reputation through her singing of Donizetti in general and Lucia in particular. This recording was her second, made in 1971, and features her in prime form. Richard Bonynge brings an uncut score brilliantly to life. Should a highlights disc be your preference, then there is one from a much more recent Bonynge performance, from 1992, featuring the brilliant Edita Gruberová in the title role. This is on Teldec and is mid-price. The complete version it is extracted from is also still available.

> Decca 410 193-2
> **Joan Sutherland (soprano)/**
> **Royal Opera House**
> **Orchestra & Chorus/**
> **Richard Bonynge**
>
> ★ ✔
> Teldec 0630 13803-9
> **Edita Gruberová (soprano)/**
> **Ambrosian Singers/London**
> **Symphony Orchestra/**
> **Richard Bonynge**

● If you like this, try Donizetti's *L'Elisir d'Amore* (387)

Rameau
199) LES INDES GALANTES

Rameau was a dominant figure in French classical music during the first decades of the 18th century, further developing a specifically French genre of opera, ballet and instrumental music which had risen to such prominence in the late 17th century. The plot of this work may be incidental, but it indulges that century's taste for the exotic, bringing the 'Indes' of Peru, Persia and Turkey together with those of North America. Music and the spectacle are the thing, not veracity.

★
Harmonia Mundi
HMC90 1367-2
Les Arts Florissants/
William Christie

Philips 438 946-2
Eighteenth Century
Orchestra/
Frans Brüggen

Hence it's important that any performance does not approach the work as a dusty corpse: it needs blood pumping through its veins. The complete opera as recorded by William Christie for Harmonia Mundi in 1991 is vividly brought to life (authentic instruments, but still very pretty) and certainly proves itself musically exotic. There is some exquisite singing. The purely instrumental suites (arranged by Rameau himself) are available on a single CD performed by Frans Brüggen's Eighteenth Century Orchestra (authentic again, I'm afraid, but very good).

● If you like this, try Handel's *Serse* (144)

Lehár
200) DIE LUSTIGE WITWE

Lehár hit the jackpot with a number of his works, but never more so than with *The Merry Widow*. His combination of risqué plot and gloriously cheerful melody has not been surpassed in operetta this century, and in the aria 'Vilia' he composed one of the most popular tunes of the past 100 years.

The *Widow* has long been given in either German or English translation in this country: correspondingly, we recommend one recording in each language. The original German version receives a characterful interpretation from a cast starring Cheryl Studer and directed by John Eliot Gardiner on

★
Deutsche Grammophon
DG 439 911-2
Cheryl Studer (soprano)/
Vienna Tschuschenkapelle/
Vienna Philharmonic
Orchestra/
John Eliot Gardiner

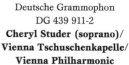

Belart 461 315-2
Joan Sutherland (soprano)/
Ambrosian Singers/National
Philharmonic Orchestra/
Richard Bonynge

DGG. Her German accent doesn't have a Balkan twang (as her character should have) but she has plenty of chutzpah. A highlights disc of an English-language production by Richard Bonynge from 1978 and featuring Joan Sutherland is available – incredibly – at budget price on Belart, making it hard to ignore.

● If you like this, try J. Strauss's *Casanova* (311)

Monteverdi

201) VESPERS 1610

This wonderfully elaborate, part-operatic Vespers service was written in honour of the Gonzaga family. What is so striking about this music is that it does not attempt merely to go through the ecclesiastical motions: it demands an intense engagement from the listener, as its texts are given powerful, complex melodies and counter-melodies through which their meaning is distilled.

With such intensely personal music the scale of the performance needs to be right: amplifying the musical forces completely distorts the message. The 1989 recording by Jordi Savall on Astree makes you strongly aware of the personalities behind the voices; the period instrumentation is a properly supportive cushion. If a complete performance of the *Vespers* (two CDs in most cases) is beyond you, then a highly attractive alternative is on *Musica Sacra*, by Rinaldo Alessandrini and the Concerto Italiano on Opus 111. This features many of the highlights from the *Vespers*. It is an authentic practice performance.

Astree ES9936
Monserrat Figueras (soprano)/Maria Cristina Kiehr (soprano)/Paolo Costa (alto)/Guy de Mey (tenor)/ Gianpaolo Fagotto (tenor)/ Gerd Türk (tenor)/Pietro Spagnoli (baritone)/Roberto Abbondanza (baritone)/ Daniele Carnovich (bass)/ Padua Centro Musica Antica Choir/Jordi Savall

Opus 111 OPS30-150
Concerto Italiano/ Rinaldo Alessandrini

● If you like this, try Rachmaninov's *Vespers* (324)

Sibelius

202) THE SWAN OF TUONELA

'The Swan of Tuonela' is a self-contained section of a larger work, the tone poems called the *Lemminkäinen Legends*, Op. 22. It is a concert suite of four pieces drawn from material originally composed for a stage work, in this case an abandoned opera. The *Legends* deal with the exploits of a hero by the name of Lemminkäinen, who is a character in the Finnish national epic, the *Kalevala*. 'The Swan of Tuonela' deals with an episode where Lemminkäinen has to shoot a swan with a single arrow to win the hand of a young maiden he lusts after.

★
BIS CD 610
Gothenburg Symphony Orchestra/ Neeme Järvi

Sony SK 48067
Los Angeles Philharmonic Orchestra/ Esa-Pekka Salonen

Both versions listed here use the complete set of four symphonic poems which make up the *Lemminkäinen Legends*: Neeme Järvi places 'The Swan' second in his recording, following Sibelius's opus numbering, while Esa-Pekka Salonen puts it third, following the original sequence of the first performance. Both conductors handle the piece beautifully, but the superior BIS recording puts Järvi in front.

● If you like this, try Delius's *La Calinda* (256)

Brahms

203) SYMPHONY NO. 2

Brahms's Second Symphony was composed in 1877, just one year after his long battle to complete his first symphony was won. In comparison, the Second is more relaxed, with many more shafts of sunlight and sustained string passages to help it on its serene way. As usual with this composer, the music is carefully worked into a satisfying formal design and orchestrated to give maximum impact to the melodies and themes that are its outstanding feature.

★
RCA 09026 63348-2
NDR Symphony Orchestra/
Günter Wand

✔
Philips 426 632-2
Concertgebouw Orchestra,
Amsterdam/
Bernard Haitink

Günter Wand manages to sustain a forward momentum in a work that has fewer dynamic contrasts than usual in Brahms. He does this through a perfect understanding of the shading required for contrast and by getting his tempi right. Herbert von Karajan also managed this with the Berlin Philharmonic in his famous 1963 version for DGG, but this is currently unavailable. For a comparable mid-price alternative, try the 1970s Haitink with the Concertgebouw on Philips. It is less imaginatively highlighted, but Haitink's instincts for the work are right.

● If you like this, try Brahms's *Rhapsody* Op. 53 (334)

Shostakovich

204) JAZZ SUITE NO. 2

This second so-called jazz suite is a little more substantial than the first. For a start, it is composed of eight miniatures rather than just three. It also features an entire orchestra rather than a salon-size chamber group. But it must be admitted that it is hard to find any sort of jazz content here. Taken for what it is, though, the music is highly enjoyable 'light music'.

Decca 433 702-2
Concertgebouw Orchestra,
Amsterdam/
Riccardo Chailly

★
RCA 09026 68304-2
Frankfurt Radio
Symphony Orchestra/
Dmitri Kitaenko

The same two discs recommended for the *Jazz Suite No. 1* (entry 196) are equally appropriate here. Both supply excellently drilled ensembles playing the music with heart and imagination as well as exemplary discipline. Chailly's forces are remarkably smooth and urbane, while Kitaenko's go for a little more 'edge' in their approach, in the process generating just a bit more excitement. The Kitaenko programme is rather more homogeneous in its make-up, so it gets the nod this time.

● If you like this, try Shostakovich's Symphony No. 5 (213)

Beethoven

205) EGMONT OVERTURE

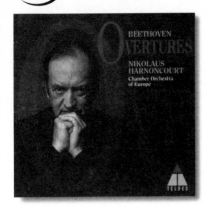

In 1809 Beethoven was commissioned to write music for a new production of Goethe's play *Egmont*, a work that dealt with issues close to Beethoven's heart: freedom for the individual and the liberty of nations. This is an overture to a theatrical work, so it is entirely right that the music should be utterly theatrical, announcing itself with commendable vigour and stirring the spirits of the actors in the wings.

Both recordings bring brio and attack to the music, relishing the opportunity to go for the big, dramatic gesture. Kurt Masur and his Leipzig orchestra, on their 1972 recording, use the full force of a modern symphony orchestra, bringing the work very much into the realm of the concert hall. Harnoncourt and the Chamber Orchestra of Europe in 1996 use smaller forces and get that theatre feeling as well as a more cutting edge of dramatic tension. Of the two, they are the band that will bring you to the edge of your seat in anticipation.

Philips 438 706-2
Leipzig Gewandhaus Orchestra/ Kurt Masur

★

Teldec 0630 13140-2
Chamber Orchestra of Europe/ Nikolaus Harnoncourt

● If you like this, try Berlioz's *Harold in Italy* (317)

Beethoven

206) PIANO CONCERTO NO. 1

The Beethoven of this first concerto is still a young man using the musical language of his great contemporaries. Although full of his own special musical ideas and typically strong, broad melodies, this work is a direct extension of Mozart's final piano concertos in style and mood. Only the rather more expanded piano role, and the broader sense of humour, hints at what Beethoven will later deliver to the world.

Performers are well advised not to try to make the work more imposing than it actually is. The Brendel/Rattle combination keep things commendably light, the London Philharmonic creating a good-humoured atmosphere. Brendel plays with his customary authority, but the piano is a little too prominent in the mix. This is not a problem with Pollini and Abbado, along with the Berlin Philharmonic, on DGG. Apart from Pollini's own electric playing, the piano is aided by a crystalline sound that avoids the pitfalls of Brendel's recording.

Philips 462 781-2
Alfred Brendel (piano)/ London Philharmonic Orchestra/ Sir Simon Rattle

★

Deutsche Grammophon DG 445 852-2
Maurizio Pollini (piano)/ Berlin Philharmonic Orchestra/ Claudio Abbado

● If you like this, try Brahms's Piano Concerto No. 1 (223)

Mozart

207) EXSULTATE, JUBILATE K165

A motet for church use which usually lasts around fifteen minutes in performance, this is composed in Mozart's operatic style, giving the soprano soloist graceful lines to sing and apposite accompaniment from a small orchestra dominated by strings and woodwind. The last section, containing just the word 'allelujah', is the work's most famous part. Its elegant melody quite perfectly communicates the sublime joy quietly reflected through the whole work.

Teldec 4509 95985-2
Barbara Bonney (soprano)/
Vienna Concentus Musicus/
Nikolaus Harnoncourt

★ ✔

Belart 450 048-2
Elly Ameling (soprano)/
English Chamber Orchestra/
Raymond Leppard

Both versions here come on compilation CDs. The Harnoncourt selection from 1990 is an all-Mozart one, concentrating on his shorter devotional works, and its acoustic reflects an interest in authentic sound. Barbara Bonney is the soloist. The Elly Ameling performance with Raymond Leppard goes back to 1970 but is in excellent sound, and Ameling is outstanding in producing perfectly formed phrasing. The rest of the CD features famous devotional music from Mozart, Schubert, Bach, Gounod and Franck, and is an outstanding bargain.

● If you like this, try Schubert's 'Ave Maria' (260)

Zipoli

208) ELEVAZIONE

The Italian Jesuit composer Domenico Zipoli was an almost exact contemporary of Bach, Telemann and Vivaldi. His work is in relative obscurity because he spent most of his adult life in Mexico and Argentina as part of a Jesuit mission.

★ ✔

Classic FM CFMCD4
Consort of London/
Robert Haydon Clark

Not a great deal of his output remains. *Elevazione* is one of the few surviving pieces for chamber orchestra and soloists to be found on CD. The performance here is by Robert H. Clark and the Consort of London, and it is a generally sympathetic one, bringing out the yearning quality that is the core of the piece's appeal.

This performance is available on a Classic FM compilation of baroque music which contains well-known and much-loved excerpts and short works (many of them vocal) by composers such as Vivaldi, Handel, Bach, Pachelbel, Couperin and Purcell. The performances are by as wide-ranging a selection of groups as there are composers on the disc.

● If you like this, try Marcello's Oboe Concerto in D minor (371)

Mozart

209) SINFONIA CONCERTANTE K364

Mozart wrote two *Sinfonia Concertantes*: this for violin, viola and orchestra, K364, and one for oboe, clarinet, horn, bassoon and orchestra, K297b. This work from his middle years is full of sunlight: brilliant shafts of melody, wonderful musical conversations between the violin and viola, and affable interjections from the chamber orchestra in support.

Performances work best when undertaken by artists who are completely at home with the idea of sharing the spotlight. The Orpheus Chamber Orchestra exists on the understanding that music-making is a collective pursuit, so their DGG outing from 1991 is a wonderfully balanced affair. It is no surprise to find that Yehudi Menuhin's 1963 recording for EMI is a similar success, his sweetness of tone matched only by his closeness to violist Rudolf Barshai's phrasing. The single Orpheus CD is probably the one to go for, as Menuhin's is tagged onto a mid-price two-CD set of all the Mozart violin concertos.

> ★
> Deutsche Grammophon
> DG 429 784-2
> **Todd Philips (violin)/**
> **Maureen Gallagher (viola)/**
> **Orpheus Chamber Orchestra**
>
> ✔
>
> EMI CES 568530 2
> **Yehudi Menuhin (violin)/**
> **Rudolf Barshai (viola)/**
> **Bath Festival Orchestra**

● If you like this, try Haydn's Cello Concerto No. 1 in C (320)

Barber

210) AGNUS DEI

This celebrated piece of music, now used on many film soundtracks, began life as the slow movement of Barber's one string quartet. It disappeared into the oblivion of cult status with chamber music fans. Only with its arrangement for string orchestra did it come to prominence, at which point Barber also arranged it for choir.

Two perfectly serviceable performances are available sung by English choirs. The Erato performance is by the New College, Oxford Choir directed by Edward Higginbottom and is mixed in with pieces by Fauré, Mozart, Bach, Tavener, Allegri and the rest, while the Hyperion recording with the Corydon Singers under Matthew Best is an all-American programme. The Hyperion disc probably represents the better value, as the programme is a lot more coherent (Bernstein's striking *Chichester Psalms* and three pieces from Copland make up the content), and while the singing can be a little scary at points, its very human imperfection is reassuring.

> Erato 0630 14634-2
> **Choir of New**
> **College, Oxford/**
> **Edward Higginbottom**
>
> ★
>
> Hyperion CDA 66219
> **Corydon Singers/**
> **Matthew Best**

● If you like this, try Allegri's *Miserere* (25)

Paul McCartney

211) STANDING STONE

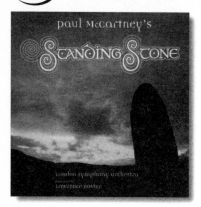

There's only one recording of this, so it's not difficult to recommend it unreservedly. McCartney's method of composing may raise eyebrows (he brings in other people to score his work for larger forces, having no desire to learn the intricacies of orchestral scoring), but there is no denying his innate melodicism. This, and his natural gift for harmony, easily transfer from the rock genre into the classical idiom. It might have been better if he had undertaken his own orchestration, because his ear is a good one, and he would undoubtedly bring a fresh approach to the set of orchestral colours overused by professional arrangers. It may seem to some a rather inappropriate comparison, but 'Dear Friend', written and recorded by him in 1970/1, and pushed along with the rhythmic vernacular of a drum kit, remains his single most moving and coherent large ensemble work. And he sings on it.

★
EMI CDC 556484 2
**London Symphony
Orchestra & Choir/
Lawrence Foster**

● If you like this, try Pergolesi's *Stabat Mater* (265)

Dvořák

212) SYMPHONY NO. 8

Dvořák's music is full of colour and light, rarely holding itself back expressively but rarely delving into the cosmic angst experienced by a parallel generation of symphonic composers. His 8th Symphony is full of warmth, graceful and balanced music, and generally happy, occasionally excited moods.

Interpreters of this music do well to stick to the spirit of joy and contentment that permeates it. Two conductors who manage this with panache are Vernon Handley on Chandos and Rafael Kubelik on DGG. Handley's is the younger recording, dating from 1984, and it benefits from the usual crystalline Chandos sonic and balance. Kubelik's outing with the Berlin Philharmonic dates from 1972, and for a long time was regarded as an automatic recommendation for this music. Kubelik certainly captures the poetry of the music and the sound is excellent, but Handley is worthy of the high ground here, especially being in digital sound. Both releases are at mid-price.

★ ✔
Chandos CHAN 7123
**Ulster Orchestra/
Vernon Handley**

✔
Deutsche Grammophon
DG 439 663-2
**Berlin Philharmonic
Orchestra/
Rafael Kubelik**

● If you like this, try Beethoven's Symphony No. 4 (358)

Shostakovich

213) SYMPHONY NO. 5

Few symphonies since the death of Mahler have made any real impact on the popular consciousness: this monumental work is only an exception proving the rule. It is one of the most emotionally focused and torrid symphonies, and one also with the special gift of calling up specific and disturbing images as the movements unfold.

The symphony has amassed hundreds of vinyl and CD releases over the years. Most of these are adequate without being thrilling, but the two selected here penetrate to the heart of the matter. Neeme Järvi and the Scottish National Orchestra deliver the kind of reading that gives you butterflies in the stomach. Their attack is gripping, their discipline impeccable. Haitink and the Concertgebouw take a more measured, elegiac approach, allowing the momentum of the music's argument to build more slowly, making the climaxes shattering in their unexpectedness. Both readings are valid, but for their stunning depiction of cold fire at its most intense, the decision must go to Jarvi and his players.

★
Chandos CHAN 8650
Royal Scottish National Orchestra/
Neeme Järvi

✔
Decca 425 066-2
Concertgebouw Orchestra, Amsterdam/
Bernard Haitink

● If you like this, try Prokofiev's *Lieutenant Kijé* Suite (227)

Delibes

214) COPPÉLIA

Delibes's music is aided by what at the time was seen as a fault of the ballet – that it was too episodic, with too little continuity from scene to scene. In these days of soundbites and samples, this episodic quality means that a Delibes can be conveniently broken down into smaller chunks and enjoyed as a series of sparkling highlights.

The advantage of CD, of course, is that a recording of the complete ballet such as Kent Nagano's (our first choice here) can deliver the entire work to those with time, or can be programmed to select just the juicy bits. Whichever approach is taken, the performance will not be an anticlimax, any more than the fine recorded sound will be. If two CDs and one ballet are not enough for you, then the mid-price three-CD Mercury collation of *Coppélia* with Delibes's other favourite, *Sylvia*, is a worthy alternative, Antal Dorati conducting *Coppélia*, Anatole Fistoulari dealing with *Sylvia*.

★
Erato 4509 91730-2
Lyon Opéra Orchestra/
Kent Nagano

✔
Mercury 434 313-2
Minneapolis Symphony Orchestra/
Antal Dorati

● If you like this, try Ravel's *Daphnis et Chloé* (226)

Wagner

215) SIEGFRIED

The third part of Wagner's *Ring des Nibelungen* starts with a prelude soaked in foreboding, as if primeval beings have been set loose in the land. Which is not that far from the truth: young Siegfried, the orphaned hero, will have to do battle with all manner of perils in his quest for the ring. He will also have to deal with deceit, evil intentions and his own passionate nature, especially when he comes across Brünnhilde. Parts of the opera to listen out for especially are the Prelude to Act 2, Siegfried's battle with the dragon, the opening prelude and forging scene, and the climactic union at the end between Siegfried and Brünnhilde, where Wagner once again equates carnal love with happy death. As before, the recommended recording comes from Barenboim's complete Bayreuth cycle from the 1990s, with Siegfried Jerusalem in the title role and Anne Evans as Brünnhilde. The two-CD highlights set from Solti's old but superb *Ring* makes a fine selections starter.

> ★
> Teldec 4509 94193-2
> **Siegfried Jerusalem (tenor)/**
> **John Tomlinson (bass)/**
> **Bayreuth Festival Orchestra/**
> **Daniel Barenboim**
>
> Decca 466 261-2
> **Vienna Philharmonic**
> **Orchestra/**
> **Sir Georg Solti**

● If you like this, try Wagner's *Rienzi* (398)

Rutter

216) REQUIEM

Rutter, an expert choral conductor and a highly knowledgeable historian of sacred vocal music, has taken the Fauré approach to his *Requiem*. Not only has he selected only part of the complete Catholic Church requiem Mass to set, he has concentrated on the gentle and reassuring aspects of the liturgy. A quick check of the beatific 'Pie Jesu' will convince the uninitiated of this.

Rutter's work has been recorded on a number of occasions, most notably by Polyphony and the Bournemouth Sinfonietta under Stephen Layton, and by Rutter himself. The distinctions between the two are not that marked, and mostly come down to the differing qualities of the recorded sound. The soloists for both ensembles are affecting and professional (though there are some wobbles on the Rutter version). While the Hyperion recording of Layton's group is more diffuse and 'religious', Rutter's is more sharply focused and exposed. On that basis, then, make your choice, for neither is a disappointment.

> ★
> Hyperion CDA 66947
> **Polyphony/Bournemouth**
> **Sinfonietta/Stephen Layton**
>
> Collegium CSCD 504
> **Cambridge Singers/**
> **City of London Sinfonia/**
> **John Rutter**

● If you like this, try Stainer's *The Crucifixion* (377)

Mendelssohn

217) ELIJAH

Harmonia Mundi
HMC90 1463/4
**Petteri Salomaa (bass)/
Soile Ifokoski/Monica Groop
(mezzo-soprano)/John Mark-
Ainsley (tenor)/La Chapelle
Royal/Collegium Vocale/
Orchestra de Champs-Elysées/
Philippe Herreweghe**

★

Chandos CHAN 8874/5
**Rosalind Plowright (soprano)/
Jeremy Budd (treble)/Linda
Finnie (mezzo-soprano)/
Arthur Davies (tenor)/
Willard White(bass)/London
Symphony Orchestra &
Choir/Richard Hickox**

Mendelssohn completed only two oratorios, but both have long been staples of musical life across Europe and America. Indeed, for much of the 19th century Mendelssohn's great 1846 triumph was regarded as the equal in status and popularity of Handel's *Messiah* and Bach's great oratorios. The music that cloaks the biblical story of the prophet Elijah is highly dramatic and tells the story with implacable momentum.

Mendelssohn prepared both English-language and German-language versions for performing purposes. Of the German-language version there is a live 1993 recording by Philippe Herreweghe featuring Petteri Salomaa as the prophet. This has tremendous gravitas and builds impressive pace. It is also very accurately sung by soloists and choir. The English-language version is directed by Richard Hickox and has Willard White in the role of Elijah. His is a commanding performance. This, added to the ease of listening in English and the general high standard of interpretation, gives it a decided edge for English-speaking music-lovers.

● If you like this, try Gounod's *Judex* (246)

Gounod

218) ST CECILIA MASS

★
EMI CDC 747094 2
**Barbara Hendricks (soprano)/
Laurence Dale (tenor)/
Jean-Philippe Lafont
(baritone)/French Radio
National Choir/French
Radio New Philharmonic
Orchestra/Georges Prêtre**

Philips 432 731-2
**Jessye Norman (soprano)/
Ile de France Regional
Choir/FNR Maîtrise/Lyon
Opéra Orchestra/
Lawrence Foster**

In his own time Gounod was seen primarily as a composer for the church. These days he is better remembered as the composer of *Faust*. Yet from time to time someone exhumes one of his lesser-known religious works and discovers that at least part, if not all, of it is eminently palatable. This Mass is dedicated to the patron saint of music, St Cecilia, and takes as its cue not the turbulent religious music of Berlioz but the simpler grandeur of Mozart and Beethoven. This is apparent from the opening 'Kyrie', which offers pleasing, open-faced harmonies and heavenly melody lines rather than storm and conflict.

There is not an abundance of recordings. The best is on EMI and is conducted by Georges Prêtre. Prêtre handles these considerable forces ably and Barbara Hendricks is outstandingly sweet in her solo parts. If you just want the 'Sanctus' by itself, then it is available on a *Jessye Norman Christmas Concert* recital disc recorded in Notre Dame.

● If you like this, try Berlioz's *Grande Messe des Morts* (289)

Butterworth

219) THE BANKS OF GREEN WILLOW

One of many artistically gifted young men whose promise was destroyed by the Great War, Butterworth left little behind after what was a relatively brief composing career. *The Banks of Green Willow* has enjoyed continual popularity since its première in 1914, its combination of transparent scoring for the strings and folksy melody proving irresistible to the British public.

Nimbus NI 5068
**English String Orchestra/
William Boughton**

★ ✔

Chandos CHAN 6566
**Bournemouth Sinfonietta/
Norman del Mar**

Both recommendations here are by long-established experts in the English music of this period. The English String Orchestra, conducted by William Boughton, conjure the shimmering light and heat of a sunny spring day in rural England. Three other Butterworth pieces, as well as works for string orchestra by Parry and Bridge, make up the rest of the programme. The other recording is by Norman del Mar. It stretches its stylistic palette a little wider, embracing pieces by Granville Bantock and Frank Bridge. *The Banks of Green Willow* is exquisitely played, the clarity of the Chandos recording and its middle price point perhaps giving it the edge over its Nimbus rival.

● If you like this, try Vaughan Williams's *Serenade to Music* (362)

Verdi

220) IL TROVATORE

This famous opera was completed between two virtuoso triumphs of the operatic art, *Rigoletto* and *La Traviata*. Unlike these, *Trovatore* is a farrago of swashbuckling melodramatic nonsense which gives the right excuses at the right moments for the four principal singers to deliver some of the most fetching set-piece arias in 19th-century Italian opera, which, together with the 'Anvil Chorus' and the duets, all claim a healthy place in every Verdi recital CD or concert.

A good 1994 recording of the complete opera comes from Sony, directed by James Levine. Singers include Domingo, Aprile Millo, Dolora Zajick and Vladimir Chernov. An

★
Sony S2K 48070
**Placido Domingo (tenor)/
Aprile Millo (soprano)/
New York Metropolitan
Opera Orchestra & Chorus/
James Levine**

Deutsche Grammophon
DG 415 285-2
**Rosalind Plowright (soprano)/
Anna di Stasio
(mezzo-soprano)/
Santa Cecilia Academy
Orchestra & Chorus, Rome/
Carlo Maria Giulini**

earlier version (from 1985) featuring Domingo and conducted by Carlo Maria Giulini for DGG also makes the right noises and is available in highlights, which may be the best way to start with this one, considering its wayward plot.

● If you like this, try Wagner's *The Flying Dutchman* (367)

Chopin

221) NOCTURNE IN E FLAT OP. 9 NO. 2

This beautiful melody has 'instant recognition' quality, and has also come to represent Chopin better than any other single piece. Thirty years ago this would not have been the case, as the public perception of the composer then was more to do with his virtuosity than his deeply Romantic nature. Vladimir Ashkenazy was one of the key players who helped move public opinion away from the pyrotechnics of the concertos, waltzes and polonaises and on to the études and nocturnes. His recordings are as much a milestone in Chopin discography as those of Rubinstein. He tried to give the music a tautness and momentum few others were prepared to allow it. Today his version sounds a little undercooked, though still impressive. A perhaps more balanced view is taken by Livia Rév in her 1988 recording for Hyperion of the complete nocturnes, like Ashkenazy's version available at special price. Rév's beautiful touch and intimacy make this an outstanding way to experience the tender side of Chopin.

> ✔
> Decca 430 751-2
> **Vladimir Ashkenazy (piano)**
>
> ★ ✔
> Hyperion CDD 22013
> **Livia Rév (piano)**

● If you like this, try Chopin's Etude in E major Op. 10 No. 3 (264)

Delius

222) THE WALK TO THE PARADISE GARDEN

Sir Thomas Beecham was the single biggest reason for the swell of interest in Delius's music late in the composer's life. His enthusiasm established a number of Delius compositions as favourites, and he also championed lesser-known works, including his operas. Beecham made an orchestral arrangement of an interlude from the Delius opera *A Village Romeo and Juliet* where the two lovers walk to an inn called Paradise Garden and take their fateful vow of death. The piece quickly became a concert favourite. It is unusually dramatic for Delius: at its end the music becomes almost unbearably poignant as the true significance of the lovers' decision sinks in.

> ✔
> EMI CMS 565119 2
> **London Symphony Orchestra/ Sir John Barbirolli**
>
> ★
> Unicorn UKCD 2073
> **Royal Philharmonic Orchestra/ Norman del Mar**

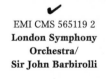

There are not that many successful recordings currently available (Beecham's isn't, for example). The Barbirolli from 1965 is a committed reading, with only the slightly compressed climax betraying the recording's age. Norman del Mar's 1980 effort is longer and uses an augmented Beecham arrangement, its lushness and good sound giving it top position.

● If you like this, try Butterworth's *The Banks of Green Willow* (219)

Brahms
223) PIANO CONCERTO NO. 1

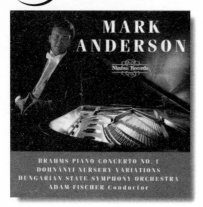

The stormy and dramatic opening bars of this massive concerto are some of the most testing for an orchestra to deliver. Many performances fall at this earliest of hurdles. One wonders sometimes whether Brahms would have been better off rescoring it to bring in reinforcements, but perhaps that very sense of strain was the effect he wanted. It gives the piano, on its entry, the chance to establish a very different character for itself.

The concerto has attracted hundreds of recordings. A very fine version from 1994 matches pianist Mark Anderson with Adám Fischer and the Hungarian State Symphony in a rendition which is as expressive, robust and responsive, yet as subtle and delicately graded, as one could wish for. The recorded sound from Nimbus is faultless, and as an extra bonus Dohnanyi's charming *Variations on a Nursery Song* are included. If more august names from the past attract you, then it is difficult to better the famous Emil Gilels/Eugen Jochum DGG recording from 1972.

★
Nimbus NI 5349
Mark Anderson (piano)/
Hungarian State
Symphony Orchestra/
Adám Fischer

✔
Deutsche Grammophon
DG 447 446-2
Emil Gilels(piano)/
Berlin Philharmonic
Orchestra/
Eugen Jochum

● If you like this, try Saint-Saëns's Piano Concerto No. 2 (231)

Tchaikovsky
224) SERENADE FOR STRINGS

For a man with a catastrophic private life and prone to depression, Tchaikovsky wrote more than his fair share of carefree music. The *Serenade for Strings* is a case in point. One listen to the gay and graceful waltz of the second movement will confirm that.

No performance can hope to succeed unless it, too, plays 'from the heart' and finds joy in doing so. Neither of our recommended ensembles has difficulty connecting with their emotions. Colin Davis and the BRSO use the full weight of their combined string sections to deliver full concert-hall impact, but lose no delicacy of phrasing or sound in doing so. Korsten and the COE provide more attack and urgency, their smaller numbers bringing a brighter sheen to the music but lacking the body of sound Davis's forces can muster. Both are immensely enjoyable: on the Korsten the fill-up music is the sun-filled *Souvenir de Florence*; with Davis, Dvořák's own beautiful *Serenade for Strings*. The Davis is at mid-price.

✔
Philips 442 402-2
Bavarian Radio
Symphony Orchestra/
Sir Colin Davis

★
Deutsche Grammophon
DG 437 541-2
Chamber Orchestra
of Europe/
Gerard Korsten

● If you like this, try Dvořák's *Serenade for Strings* (225)

Dvořák

225) SERENADE FOR STRINGS

Composed in the late spring of 1875, this is a suite of five movements bursting with optimism, sunlight and warmth. Dvořák being the author, it is also full of alluring, captivating melodies, as the opening bars of the first movement will attest. Even the *larghetto*, cast in a minor key, is flooded with a warm nostalgia rather than any sense of regret.

The Davis set on Philips combines the Tchaikovsky *Serenade* with the Dvořák; the two make a handsome pair and are unbeatable at the price. As with the Tchaikovsky, Davis has chosen highly appropriate tempos and has kept the proceedings light. This music has sometimes been 'over-interpreted' in the past by conductors trying to uncover deep psychological truths. A viable alternative in this repertoire is Christopher Hogwood's recording with the LPO of Dvořák's original 1885 version of the *Serenade*, coupled with his *Serenade for Winds* Op. 44. This is now available on a Decca mid-price release with Dorati's recording of the *American Suite*.

> ★ ✔
> Philips 442 402-2
> **Bavarian Radio Symphony Orchestra/Sir Colin Davis**
>
> ✔
> Decca 448 981-2
> **London Philharmonic Orchestra/ Christopher Hogwood**

● If you like this, try Dvořák's String Quartet in F (354)

Ravel

226) DAPHNIS ET CHLOÉ

Ravel created *Daphnis et Chloé* for Diaghilev's Ballets Russes. It had originally been conceived as a solo piano piece, but Ravel's genius for orchestral scoring transformed it into one of the most colourful of all the exotic scores that Diaghilev's troupe danced to. Later, Ravel crafted two inspired orchestral suites from the original so that the score could be heard in concert halls. These two suites have earned the music a permanent place in classical music's hit parade.

The complete ballet is not often heard, but in these days of CDs that last well over an hour there is no technical reason why we should deny ourselves the complete score. The two recordings here are by experts. Boulez's 1995 rerecording for DGG has breathtaking aural depth. This is a brilliant evocation of ancient Greek life and is a clear first recommendation. The Charles Munch recording for RCA is decades older, and not so spectacular sound-wise, but Munch knew and loved this score, as his vigorous reading points up.

> ★
> Deutsche Grammophon
> DG 447 057-2
> **Berlin Radio Chorus/ Berlin Philharmonic Orchestra/ Pierre Boulez**
>
> ✔
> RCA 09026 61846-2
> **New England Conservatoire Chorus/ Boston Symphony Orchestra/ Charles Munch**

● If you like this, try Ravel's *Le Tombeau de Couperin* (360)

Prokofiev

227) LIEUTENANT KIJÉ SUITE

Lieutenant Kijé's music started as a film score and was then adapted by the composer into a concert suite. The suite is quite short and encompasses the entire life of the fictional army lieutenant created by an administrative error and given flesh and bones by panicking civil servants terrified of having their incompetence exposed.

This popular suite has been recorded countless times. Two outstanding versions in the catalogue at something less than full price are those by Neeme Järvi for Chandos (dating from 1980) and by George Szell for Columbia/Sony, from 1970. Both conductors have the discipline to keep the beautiful array of sounds across the orchestra completely in perspective and proper balance, but also to let the life and colour in the music blossom naturally. Järvi's disc also has music from *The Stone Flower* and other, smaller works; Szell has the Mussorgsky/Ravel *Pictures at an Exhibition* and Kodály's marvellous *Háry János Suite*.

★ ✔
Chandos CHAN 8806
**Royal Scottish National Orchestra/
Neeme Järvi**

✔
Sony SBK 48162
**Cleveland Orchestra/
George Szell**

● If you like this, try Khachaturian's *Gayaneh* (325)

Elgar

228) SALUT D'AMOUR

Elgar's little trifle has remained popular to the present day in any number of arrangements. The piece started life as one for solo piano but quickly gained a piano, violin and cello setting as well as an orchestral one. Of these, the arrangement for violin, cello and piano is the closest to out-and-out salon music. This is the arrangement to be found on the Nigel Kennedy Elgar recital on Chandos, recorded in 1984 with Steven Isserlis on cello and Peter Pettinger on piano.

✔
Chandos CHAN 8380
**Nigel Kennedy (violin)/
Peter Pettinger (piano)**

★ ✔
Naxos 8.554161
**Bratislava Radio Symphony Orchestra/
Adrian Leaper**

The string orchestra version brings the music into line with the tradition of English pastoral music. Avoiding the possible mawkishness of the chamber arrangement, it carries its own quiet dignity, especially in the version offered by Adrian Leaper on Naxos accompanying his *Enigma Variations* recording. Leaper resists the temptation to slow the piece to a crawl, keeping its spirits high. The recorded sound is clear but a mite thin.

● If you like this, try Elgar's Symphony No. 2 (336)

Johann Strauss II
229) DIE FLEDERMAUS

A new generation of musicologists has discovered that Strauss's stage works have for decades been performed in versions that differ importantly from those conceived and approved by Strauss himself. The unlikely hero of this 'back to the roots' campaign is Nikolaus Harnoncourt. The conductor was concerned to strip away the false sentimentality and return to the operetta the satiric edge that originally got it into trouble with the Austrian censors. In doing this he has made his own changes, but there are many more gains than losses.

Many 'traditional' performances and recordings made cuts, rearrangements and interpolations of music from elsewhere. If you want a thorough reworking in the grand style, the one to opt for is the famous 'gala performance' presided over by Herbert von Karajan, made for Decca in 1960. Apart from a predictably sumptuous reading of the score, Karajan supplies a personal invitation to Prince Orlovsky's Ball which includes cameos from a huge range of opera stars.

● If you like this, try Rossini's *Il barbiere di Siviglia* (156)

★
Teldec 0630 10024-2
**Werner Hollweg (tenor)/
Edita Grubarová (soprano)/
Marjana Lipovšek
(mezzo-soprano)/
Josef Protschka (tenor)/
Royal Concertgebouw
Orchestra, Amsterdam/
Chorus of the Netherlands
Opera/Nikolaus Harnoncourt**

Decca 421 046-2
**Hilde Gueden (soprano)/
Erika Köth (soprano)/
Waldemar Kmentt (tenor)/
Giuseppe Zampieri (tenor)/
Vienna State Opera Chorus/
Vienna Philharmonic
Orchestra/
Herbert von Karajan**

Beethoven
230) PIANO TRIO OP. 97 (ARCHDUKE)

Piano trios can be ghastly experiences in lesser hands, especially when the composer has no real idea of how to go about matching the very different sonorities of the piano and the two stringed instruments. Needless to say this is not a problem for Beethoven, who manages such a wonderful 'match' between the instruments that you would swear it is a natural combination (which it isn't, really). The 'Archduke' has four movements, all flowing with beautiful musical logic organically one from another.

The Philips recording with Mullova, Schiff and Previn is superbly matched and ideally recorded. The players bring that relaxed air of fraternity to the proceedings which is an essential prerequisite of this trio. The coupling on this 1993 disc is Brahms's beautiful early trio Op. 8. This is at full price. Should you want a fine budget-price version, then a Sony recording from 1966 holds up remarkably well acoustically and the artistry from Stern, Rose and Istomin is second to none.

★
Philips 442 123-2
**André Previn (piano)/
Viktoria Mullova (violin)/
Heinrich Schiff (cello)**

✔
Sony SBK 53514
**Isaac Stern (violin)/
Leonard Rose (cello)/
Eugene Istomin (piano)**

● If you like this, try Borodin's String Quartet No. 2 (173)

Saint-Saëns
231) PIANO CONCERTO NO. 2

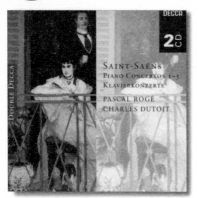

Saint-Saëns wrote five piano concertos in all, and though the second has always been everybody's favourite, all five are worth investigating. The attraction of the Second Concerto has always been the sparkling *scherzo*, a middle movement that casts off the cares of the world as it skips through to its conclusion. The piano part in this concerto is spectacular and, as always with Saint-Saëns, perfectly judged.

Pascal Rogé has long been a great champion of French piano music and a fine interpreter of its treasures, from Saint-Saëns onwards. His 1981 recording with Charles Dutoit of the complete Saint-Saëns concertos stands as a benchmark by which to measure others. It is now available as a mid-price two-CD set and is a stand-out recommendation. If you are after a single CD's worth of this music then Idil Biret's stylish playing of the Second and Fourth Concertos on Naxos (James Loughran conducting) is a sound choice.

★ ✔
Decca 443 865-2
Pascal Rogé (piano)/
Royal Philharmonic
Orchestra/
Charles Dutoit

✔
Naxos 8.550334
Idil Biret (piano)/
Philharmonia/
James Loughran

● If you like this, try Tchaikovsky's Piano Concerto No. 2 (331)

Berlioz
232) L'ENFANCE DU CHRIST

Berlioz's beautiful choral work *L'Enfance du Christ*, with its simple construction, unadorned melodies and spare orchestral accompaniment, tells of Jesus's escape from Herod's evil plans. The most famous selection from this work is the 'Shepherds' Farewell', which comes in the second of *L'Enfance*'s three 'parts'. This is so often performed separately that many people have no idea that it is in fact part of an oratorio. The recommendations made here are for the whole work.

Hyperion's production is conducted by the experienced Matthew Best, and his soloists include Jean Rigby, John Aler and Alastair Miles. The recording dates from 1994 and the production values are consistently excellent. The singers may not be French but their accents are perfectly acceptable, while the devotional atmosphere is perfectly maintained. The ASV recording directed by Philip Ledger is derived from a TV production of 1985, also featuring British singers. First choice goes to Best.

★
Hyperion CDA 66991/2
Jean Rigby (mezzo-soprano)/
John Aler (tenor)/St Paul's
Cathedral Choir/Corydon
Singers & Orchestra/
Matthew Best

ASV CDDCD 452
Anthony Rolfe Johnson
(tenor)/Richard van Allan
(bass)/Chorus/English
Chamber Orchestra/
Philip Ledger

● If you like this, try Beethoven's *Missa Solemnis* (281)

Schubert

233) ROSAMUNDE

O ddly for a man with such a genius for melody, Schubert experienced nothing but failure in the opera house during his brief career. The play *Rosamunde*, for which he wrote a quantity of engaging music, was no exception, achieving just two performances before disappearing so completely that nothing remains of the script. Luckily we still have most of its incidental music.

The overture known popularly as the 'Rosamunde' is in fact that composed for an obscure Schubert opera, *Alfonso und Estrella*, while the real 'Rosamunde' overture was later attached to an even more obscure play, *Die Zauberharfe*. The latter is the overture found on an excellent recording of the complete extant *Rosamunde* music by Bernard Haitink. This is with the Concertgebouw and dates from 1965. A makeweight of Haitink's 1978 version of the *Unfinished Symphony* brings the playing time up to over 80 minutes – a bargain if ever there was one.

● If you like this, try Schubert's Octet in F (298)

> ★ ✔
> Philips 446 574-2
> **Aafje Heynis (contralto)/**
> **Netherlands Radio Chorus/**
> **Concertgebouw Orchestra,**
> **Amsterdam/**
> **Bernard Haitink**

Saint-Saëns

234) INTRODUCTION AND RONDO

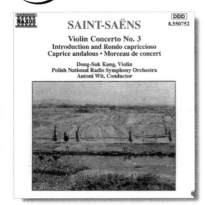

T his famous piece was written by Saint-Saëns for the greatest violin virtuoso of the day, Pablo Sarasate. In it he made no pretence of giving the poor old orchestra much else to do but support the violin fireworks. They supply the harmonic accompaniment, the odd loud crescendo to make a musical point, and the rhythmic thrust to keep the whole performance moving forward.

On the two recommended recordings here, both soloists are big enough personalities to dominate the listener's attention. Maxim Vengerov's recording makes up part of the programme for his first CD recital (along with Saint-Saëns's *Havanaise* and Paganini's First Violin Concerto) and it is as thrillingly energetic as one could hope for. Dong-Suk Kang also provides a whirlwind of technical expertise on his 1993 Naxos disc. This is an all-Saint-Saëns programme which includes the Third Violin Concerto. Antoni Wit conducts the Katowice Radio Symphony. All things considered (including the price) I'd plump for the Naxos disc.

● If you like this, try Lalo's *Symphonie Espagnole* (383)

> Teldec 9031 73266-2
> **Maxim Vengerov (violin)/**
> **Israel Philharmonic**
> **Orchestra/**
> **Zubin Mehta**
>
> ★ ✔
> Naxos 8.550752
> **Dong-Suk Kang (violin)/**
> **Katowice Radio**
> **Symphony Orchestra/**
> **Antoni Wit**

Albinoni
235) OBOE CONCERTO IN D MINOR OP. 9 NO. 2

Albinoni's oboe concertos are to be found in a number of his collected concertos published under various opus numbers: in his Opus 9, for example, eight are written for either a single oboe or for two oboes in duet as the lead instruments. The rest feature the more standard violin. The gem in this concerto is the affecting *adagio* with its beautiful, mellow oboe melody which is the heart of the piece and the reason it is so popular.

Scimone and I Solisti Veneti, in their budget-price two-CD recording of the entire Opus 9, achieve an impressively light tone, while the oboe soloist Pierre Perlot gets a rich and concentrated sound and phrases beautifully. Simon Standage and his group use their two budget Chandos CDs to record all of Albinoni's oboe concertos, and occasionally the unrelieved nature of the instrumentation palls. Better to go with the variety and spirit (as well as excellent recorded sound) of the Scimone set.

★ ✔
Erato 3984 25593-2
Pierre Perlot (oboe)/
I Solisti Veneti/
Claudio Scimone

✔
Chandos CHAN 0579
Anthony Robson (oboe)/
Collegium Musicum 90/
Simon Standage

● If you like this, try Mozart's Oboe Concerto (366)

Bruch
236) VIOLIN CONCERTO NO. 2 OP. 44

The unfailing popularity of Bruch's first violin concerto left him a frustrated and bitter man: he felt that his other works were as good if not better, and could not understand why no one else agreed with him. Listening to his second concerto, one can understand why he felt aggrieved. This is a big work, full of large emotions and dramatic musical statements, as well as pyrotechnics on the fingerboard. There is at least one meltingly beautiful melody – the second theme ushered in by the violin in the first movement. The concerto has a preponderance of slow tempi (something an audience can tire of), but in the finale the composer increases the speed to bring off a brilliant audience-pleasing finish. Lydia Mordkovitch's style and technical excellence perfectly suit this romantic concerto full of large gestures and big emotions. The recording is coupled with Bruch's Third Symphony, making an attractive programme of lesser-known Bruch.

★
Chandos CHAN 9738
Lydia Mordkovitch (violin)/
London Symphony
Orchestra/
Richard Hickox

● If you like this, try Barber's Violin Concerto (337)

Mussorgsky
237) NIGHT ON THE BARE MOUNTAIN

Abbado is something of an expert on this piece of music, having recorded it repeatedly and in an array of versions. In this latest DGG offering he gives us the original version, orchestrated by Mussorgsky and given the title *St John's Night on the Bare Mountain*. This is a fantastic picture of the saint's ordeal on Midsummer Night on top of Bare Mountain, resisting the attentions of the evil spirits traditionally at play that night. The music leaped to worldwide fame when it was included in the stirring Disney animated film *Fantasia*.

★
Deutsche Grammophon
DG 445 238-2
**Berlin Philharmonic
Orchestra/
Claudio Abbado**

✔

RCA 09026 61958-2
**Chicago Symphony
Orchestra/
Fritz Reiner**

Although it has dropped from that peak of popularity, it remains a glorious orchestral showcase and a guaranteed conjurer of weird and exotic visions. The Abbado version, using the original Mussorgsky orchestration, has an additional edge and rawness which many will find exciting. For the traditionalists, however, the famous recording of the Rimsky-Korsakov-orchestrated version from Fritz Reiner and the Chicago Symphony, now at mid-price, will do very well indeed.

● If you like this, try McCunn's *Land of the Mountain and the Flood* (263)

Beethoven
238) FIDELIO

Considering his extensive output as a composer, it is telling that Beethoven wrote just one opera. He was a stickler for a text and subject-matter worthy of his talent and – equally important for him – morally uplifting.

He was an obsessive reviser, and with *Fidelio* he was particularly determined to iron out 'difficulties'. Thus any production has many variants in music and text to choose from. The Barenboim Teldec version uses an overture associated with an earlier incarnation, and also cuts the spoken dialogue. This all makes for a taut, dynamic delivery. The other three alternative overtures are tagged on at

★
Teldec 3984 25249-2
**Valtaud Meier (soprano)/
Placido Domingo (tenor)/
Orchestra & Chorus of
German State Opera, Berlin/
Daniel Barenboim**

Deutsche Grammophon
DG 453 106-2
**Leonie Hysanek (soprano)/
Ernst Haefliger (tenor)/
Bavarian State Opera
Orchestra & Chorus/
Ferenc Fricsay**

the end of the second CD. Equally pleasurable is the more traditional Ferenc Fricsay recording from 1957. This preserves Beethoven's final version from 1814 and also uses a chamber-sized orchestra to great effect. The cast is outstanding and the sound, for its age, excellent.

● If you like this, try Gounod's *Faust* (251)

Stravinsky

239) THE FIREBIRD

The Firebird was Stravinsky's first big success with Diaghilev's Ballets Russes, in 1910. It is a ballet set to an old Russian fairy tale, which dictates its character to a great extent. The presence of the fantastic is strong, with Stravinsky weaving musical spells conveying his own complex rhythmic genius but carrying the flavour of scores by Tchaikovsky and Rimsky-Korsakov as well. The worldwide success Stravinsky achieved with this work led him to

★ ✔
Sony SMK 60011
Columbia Symphony Orchestra/
Igor Stravinsky

✔
Decca 448 226-2
Detroit Symphony Orchestra/
Antal Dorati

make a concert suite of the music. This suite, revised in 1945, has become the standard way of hearing the work in a concert-hall setting. Both recordings of the suite here offer excellent sound: Dorati gives the full ballet, while Stravinsky offers the 1945 revision of the suite, which sheds little music but has a lighter, leaner texture than the first suite from 1911. Given Stravinsky's unique position with regard to the music (he also recorded the complete ballet), his version is difficult to resist.

● If you like this, try Rachmaninov's *Symphonic Dances* (378)

Mahler

240) SYMPHONY NO. 8

Obsessed with finding man's proper place in the scheme of things, Mahler here allowed himself a direct appeal to the Creator of all things. This led to a massive symphony, both in scale and in numbers, made up of two movements which are then subdivided into many smaller musical sections calling for a large range of combinations, from solo vocalist with orchestra to duets to full choral involvement. Some sections are non-vocal.

This work is meant to be tremendously uplifting: a conductor must attack it with faith in the positive outcomes of both the music and the theology behind it. Claudio Abbado, in his full-price 1988 live version for DGG (part of a complete cycle), packs a mighty punch, the Berlin Philharmonic performing impeccably. If you're looking for an entry-point recording of the work, then the 1981 version for Sony by Michael Gielen can hardly be bettered. It is budget-price and performed with a complete understanding of Mahler's special musical identity.

● If you like this, try Bruckner's Symphony No. 8 (284)

Deutsche Grammophon DG 445 843-2 **Cheryl Studer (soprano)/ Syvlia McNair (soprano)/ Andrea Rost (soprano)/ Anne Sofie von Otter (mezzo-soprano)/ Rosemarie Lang (mezzo-soprano)/ Peter Seiffert (tenor)/ Bryn Terfel (bass-baritone)/ Jan-Hendrik Rootering (bass)/**	**Tölz Boys' Choir/ Berlin Radio Chorus/ Prague Philharmonic Chorus/ Berlin Philharmonic Orchestra/ Claudio Abbado** Sony SBK 48281 **Faye Robinson (soprano)/ Margaret Marshall (soprano)/ Hildegard Heichele (soprano)/**	**Ortrun Wenkel (contralto)/ Hildegard Laurich (contralto)/ Mallory Walker (tenor)/ Richard Stilwell (baritone)/ Simon Estes (bass-baritone)/ Hesse Radio Choir/ Frankfurt Kantorei/ Frankfurt Singakademie/ Limberg Cathedral Children's Choir/Frankfurt Opera Orchestra/Michael Gielen**

Bruch

241) KOL NIDREI

Kol Nidrei is a meditation based on a collection of Hebrew themes, an exploration of folk music which shows a deep communion with and understanding of the impulses behind such musical expression. In its ten or so minutes it moves through a number of themes but shifts its mood little from the lament with which it opens. The cumulative effect is of a vocal lament with empathetic accompaniment.

Ofra Harnoy gives a heartfelt reading of the work in collusion with Sir Charles Mackerras and the London Philharmonic. Her big, full tone and naturally romantic, plastic phrasing suit the music perfectly, allowing it time and space to develop but avoiding bathos. The recorded sound is full and well balanced. There is less orchestral presence in the sound on the Naxos recital by Maria Kliegel and conductor Gerhard Markson with the Irish National Symphony. Kliegel's sound is also not well captured. For the full effect, then, eschew the budget price for once and go with Harnoy and Mackerras.

> ★
> RCA RD 60757
> **Ofra Harnoy (cello)/**
> **London Philharmonic**
> **Orchestra/**
> **Sir Charles Mackerras**
>
> ✔
> Naxos 8.550519
> **Maria Kliegel (cello)/**
> **Ireland National**
> **Symphony Orchestra/**
> **Gerhard Markson**

● If you like this, try Brahms's Violin and Cello Concerto in A minor (314)

Mozart

242) MASS IN C MINOR K427 (GREAT)

Mozart was not the most pious of men, and his church music was usually written to fulfil a commission. The Mass in C minor was an exception, written by the composer as a gesture of reconciliation between himself and his father after he had married against Leopold's express wishes. It has come down to posterity as a fragment: the evidence points to Mozart using material from pre-existing Masses to complete the missing sections for its only performance in his lifetime. It is huge in scope and employs forces unusually large for the time, including no less than four soloists.

Both Claudio Abbado and Nikolaus Harnoncourt have approached this great work with a clear eye: they have not attempted to guess when it comes to reconstructing the unknown missing parts, having recorded only those parts which Mozart wrote or authorised. The Harnoncourt version has tremendous power and dignity, but the Abbado has a rewarding warmth of expression which makes it a worthy first choice.

> ★
> Sony SK 46671
> **Barbara Bonney (soprano)/**
> **Arleen Augér (soprano)/**
> **Hans-Peter Blochwitz (tenor)/**
> **Robert Holl (bass)/**
> **Berlin Radio Chorus/Berlin**
> **Philharmonic Orchestra/**
> **Claudio Abbado**
>
> Teldec 4509 95991-2
> **Krisztina Laki (soprano)/**
> **Zsuzsanna Dénes (soprano)/**
> **Kurt Equiluz (tenor)/**
> **Robert Holl (bass)/**
> **Vienna State Opera Chorus/**
> **Vienna Concentus Musicus/**
> **Nikolaus Harnoncourt**

● If you like this, try Rossini's *Stabat Mater* (357)

J. S. Bach

243) CANTATA BWV140 'WACHET AUF'

BACH: CANTATAS
EASTER · OSTERN · PÂQUES
Bleib bei uns BWV 6
Erfreut euch, ihr Herzen BWV 66
JOHN ELIOT GARDINER

The Monteverdi Choir · The English Baroque Soloists

BWV140, composed in 1731, is not one of Bach's longer cantatas: it has seven constituent sections and is written for relatively modest forces, although a small chamber group is included. The text comes from the Bible passages dealing with the wise and foolish virgins. It has a sense of event rare in the overall context of Bach's cantatas, and this stimulated him to some of his greatest music within the genre. Nevertheless, this superb work would probably be an acquired taste for specialists were it not for the particularly happy inspiration of the fourth section, the chorale 'Zion hört die Wachter singen'. This, a solo for tenor voice and accompaniment,

Deutsche Grammophon
Archiv 431 809-2
**Ruth Holton (soprano)/
Michael Chance (alto)/
Anthony Rolfe Johnson
(tenor)/Stephen Varcoe
(baritone)/Monteverdi
Choir/English Baroque
Soloists/John Eliot Gardiner**

Hänssler 98 857
**Arleen Augér (soprano)/
Aldo Baldin (tenor)/Philippe
Huttenlocher (baritone)/
Stuttgart Gächinger
Kantorei/Württemberg
Chamber Orchestra/
Helmuth Rilling**

clearly pleased Bach, who himself made an arrangement of it for organ. The work became even better known through its orchestral transcription by Stokowski. Since then many have beaten a path to the original (and best) incarnation. Of the current recordings, the most emotionally involving and correctly interpreted remain those by John Eliot Gardiner on Deutsche Grammophon Archiv and Helmuth Rilling on Hänssler.

● If you like this, try Monteverdi's *Vespers* (201)

Tchaikovsky

244) EUGENE ONEGIN

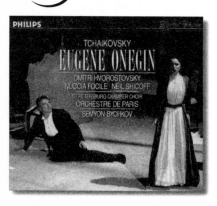

PHILIPS

TCHAIKOVSKY
EUGENE ONEGIN
DMITRI HVOROSTOVSKY
NUCCIA FOCILE · NEIL SHICOFF
ST PETERSBURG CHAMBER CHOIR
ORCHESTRE DE PARIS
SEMYON BYCHKOV

It is sometimes forgotten just how much of a committed opera composer Tchaikovsky was: eight operas were given in his lifetime, of which only *The Queen of Spades* and *Eugene Onegin* have retained their place in the general repertoire, although *Mazeppa* is recorded from time to time. *Eugene Onegin* deals in lyrical terms with a story taken from Pushkin – a melancholy tale of love out of step. The love in question is that of young Tatyana for Eugene Onegin, a feckless, Byronic hero. The pivot of the story is Tatyana and her changing circumstances as she realises her love for Onegin will not finally be returned.

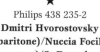

Philips 438 235-2
**Dmitri Hvorostovsky
(baritone)/Nuccia Focile
(soprano)/St Petersburg
Chamber Choir/Paris
Orchestra/Semyon Bychkov**

Sony S2K 45539
**Yuri Mazurok (baritone)/
Anna Tomowa-Sintow
(soprano)/Sofia National
Opera Chorus/Sofia Festival
Orchestra/Emil Tchakarov**

She ends the opera years later a sophisticate in St Petersburg, spurning the disgraced Onegin and remaining loyal to her new husband. Both recordings listed here feature some Russian singers, though the Bychkov has a cast nearer the age and outlook of the characters they portray. This, and their outstanding voices, makes his the recording to look out for.

● If you like this, try R. Strauss's *Der Rosenkavalier* (132)

Schubert

245) STRING QUARTET NO. 14 IN D MINOR
(DEATH AND THE MAIDEN)

Schubert is the great exception to the rule that chamber music is not a medium of popular appeal. His string quartet, which contains a variation on his own song 'Der Tod und das Mädchen' (Death and the Maiden) in the bleak second movement, is the perfect illustration. This is because it is uncompromising music, written with great force of feeling and pushing the known boundaries of string quartet writing to the limit and beyond.

★
Decca 436 843-2
Takács String Quartet

Harmonia Mundi
HMC90 1408/9
Melos Quartett

Both quartets represented here play with tremendous vitality. They show a deep understanding of and sympathy with Schubert. Both are completely recommendable, but if there has to be a choice, the luminous quality of the recording and the incredible internal balance of the Takács Quartet must place them as first choice.

● If you like this, try Tchaikovsky's String Quartet No. 1 (318)

Gounod

246) MORS ET VITA

Gounod's name will forever be associated with *Faust* (251), and rightly so. However, Gounod himself did not see it that way, and from middle age, having experienced a religious reawakening of sorts, he began turning his compositional talents towards oratorios. *Mors et Vita* (Death and Life) was conceived as such. Gounod's essentially lyric style became progressively simpler and more naïve as he grew older, and this, plus the anodyne text, guaranteed

✔
ASV CDDCA 878
**Royal Philharmonic
Orchestra/
Yondani Butt**

★
EMI CDS 754459 2
**Toulouse Capitole
Orchestra/
Michel Plasson**

Mors et Vita a short shelf life: it has languished unheard for many years, apart from a single orchestral passage, 'Judex'. This section has gained an independent following and is occasionally recorded separately. The ASV recording with the RPO and Yondani Butt is one such version. The complete *Mors et Vita* is currently on an EMI import disc featuring Barbara Hendricks and conducted by Michel Plasson. It can be obtained from retailers on special order.

● If you like this, try Gounod's *Faust* (251)

Dvořák

247) SLAVONIC DANCES

The *Slavonic Dances* were a relatively early success for Dvořák, beginning their successful progress around the concert halls of the world in the early 1880s. There is no mystery as to why, for the music has charm in great quantity, and the natural energy of dance music to boot. The general mood of these pieces (there are two series of them, both with eight dances each) is uncomplicated and free-spirited, as if the listener were eavesdropping on a local village festival while the locals were informally celebrating and enjoying themselves. This is a series of expertly conceived musical snapshots which reek of the culture of Bohemia.

> ★
> Supraphon SU-3422-2
> **Czech Philharmonic**
> **Orchestra/**
> **Sir Charles Mackerras**
>
> ✔
> Supraphon 11 1916-2
> **Czech Philharmonic**
> **Orchestra/**
> **Karel Sejna**

It is only right that two recordings from the Czech national label Supraphon represent these works. Of the two, the 1999 CD from Mackerras has the ideal combination of brio and fine, modern recording balance. The excellent mid-price Sejna is from 1959 and in good sound for the time.

● If you like this, try Liszt's *Hungarian Rhapsody* No. 2 (249)

Bernstein

248) CANDIDE OVERTURE

Leonard Bernstein's career as a composer was somewhat chequered, his huge successes, such as *On the Town* and *West Side Story*, interspersed with damp squibs which, although containing outstanding music, often failed to catch the public's attention or praise. *Candide* was such a

> ★ ✔
> Sony SMK 63085
> **New York Philharmonic**
> **Orchestra/**
> **Leonard Bernstein**

theatrical project. Its music has largely been neglected – all but the Overture, of course, which has won a permanent place in the concert hall.

The best man for the job of conducting this joyful, tongue-in-cheek and rumbustious music is Bernstein himself. Although the complete *Candide* (which Bernstein recorded more than once) is not currently available on disc, the Overture comes on a mid-price Sony reissue accompanied by orchestral music from *Fancy Free, West Side Story* and *On the Waterfront*, so this is an unalloyed joy from top to bottom. No need to look farther.

● If you like this, try Copland's *Rodeo* (306)

Liszt

249) HUNGARIAN RHAPSODY NO. 2

Liszt's marvellous gift for arrangement and paraphrase led his *Hungarian Rhapsodies* – both for piano and for orchestra – to become immensely popular during his lifetime. This second Rhapsody, with its changes of pace, its fierce dance rhythms, its famous rallying melodic motifs, is so widely known that even people with no knowledge of Liszt's existence can whistle the chirpy main theme. The 1998 version by Hungarian Iván

★
Philips 456 570-2
**Budapest Festival Orchestra/
Iván Fischer**

✔
Mercury 432 015-2
London Symphony Orchestra/Antal Dorati

Fischer and his Budapest Festival Orchestra is hard to top, its inflections being so apposite, its exhilaration at the music it is performing completely consuming. This is no theme park – this is suddenly the real thing, with the thigh-booted peasants dancing in front of you. Another Hungarian, Antal Dorati, makes a big splash with the London Symphony from 1963 for Mercury, but the much-vaunted sound can no longer hold up so well, and the orchestra's phrasing is not as idiomatic as Fischer's.

● If you like this, try Brahms's Symphony No. 4 (155)

J. S. Bach

250) CANTATA BWV208

This cantata has a text dealing with the joys of the hunt on a glorious day, and a series of arias, recitatives and duets which makes it one of the longer examples of the genre. Most of the music is unremarkable for Bach, but one aria, sung by one of the goddesses on the hunt, has a most exquisite accompaniment from two woodwinds (in the original played by recorders). Set against that common but always exciting walking bass line is a delightful little arabesque, the two mock Pan-pipes

✔
Teldec 4509 97501-2
Arnold Schoenberg Choir/Vienna Concentus Musicus/Nikolaus Harnoncourt

★ ✔
Naxos 8.550643
**Hungarian Radio Chorus/
Failoni Chamber Orchestra/
Mátyás Antál**

in harmony as the singer delivers her praise of the magnificence of nature.

Neither performance here stints on the joy felt by the participants in the hunt, nor does it make the music too extravagant: all is kept in proper check. The Harnoncourt, at mid-price, gives the listeners a full text and authentic instruments; the Antál none and modern instruments. The average listener may just prefer the comfort of the Naxos disc.

● If you like this, try Monteverdi's *Vespers* (201)

Gounod

251) FAUST

Faust could be described as a producer's favourite DIY opera, considering the number of versions of it which have been presented to audiences since its 1859 première. This is due to the fact that Gounod's original version lasted more than four hours and its first producer demanded copious cuts and rearrangements. Thus no definitive performing version exists.

The recommended versions are two of the more scrupulous attempts to arrive at something close to Gounod's original intentions. Rizzi's effort for Teldec is based on the 1972 revised critical edition and restores many of the cuts made in the first handful of productions. A strong cast means the singing is top-notch. The Chandos set conducted by David Parry leaves Faust's drinking song in place rather than shifting it to the appendix, but the English translation works very well and the singers are a strong cast pulling together. For a really French experience stick with Rizzi; for opera without libretto in hand, try Parry.

★
Teldec 4509 90872-2
Jerry Hadley (tenor)/
Cecilia Gasdia (soprano)/
Welsh National Opera
Orchestra & Chorus/
Carlo Rizzi

Chandos CHAN 3014
Paul Charles Clarke (tenor)/
Mary Plazas (soprano)/
Geoffrey Mitchell Choir/
Philharmonia Orchestra/
David Parry

● If you like this, try Gounod's 'Ave Maria' (272)

Vaughan Williams

252) THE WASPS – OVERTURE

Written in 1909 for a new production of *The Wasps* by Aristophanes, this gives a very different picture of the composer than much of his other, more pastoral music. Vaughan Williams creates a wonderful set of musical pictures of the comedy the audience is about to enjoy, and includes at least one very memorable melody, played by the strings high above the brass and woodwinds. This is a small masterpiece of mood-setting and has long been a favourite short piece at concerts and festivals.

★ ✔
Chandos CHAN 8330
London Philharmonic
Orchestra/
Vernon Handley

✔
RCA GD 90501
London Symphony
Orchestra/
André Previn

Both Vernon Handley and André Previn are established experts in the field of Vaughan Williams interpretation. Previn's performance dates from the early 1970s when he was recording a first-rate cycle of the complete Vaughan Williams symphonies for RCA. It is now available at mid-price. Mid-price is also the mark for Vernon Handley's 1984 recital for Chandos. This has a wonderful inner life to it and is brilliantly recorded. It comes with a gripping *Serenade to Music* and four beautiful Delius tone poems.

● If you like this, try Vaughan Williams's Symphony No. 5 (268)

J. S. Bach
253) GOLDBERG VARIATIONS

This famous work for keyboard (there are as many great recordings on harpsichord as there are on piano) has such a strong intellectual basis that a keyboard giant such as Glenn Gould could spend years pondering the musical architecture he felt underpinned it. Thus his famous 1981 recording was a thorough rethink of his youthful ideas on the work. It was also an intellectual and artistic *tour de force* which won Gould just about every award going. It is now available at mid-price and should be a cornerstone of any collection.

Yet the set made for Hyperion by Russian pianist Tatyana Nikolaieva in 1992 carries just as much artistic authority, even though its viewpoint is one of utter poeticism. The music has the grace and poise of Chopin, the melodies the vocal quality of opera. It is a masterly and entrancing set. It, too, won awards galore. But the Gould is the better starting-point, giving the listener a clear idea of the music, and being at mid-price.

Sony SMK 64126
Glenn Gould (piano)

Hyperion CDA 66589/
Tatyana Nikolaieva (piano)

● If you like this, try Bach's Cello Suites (174)

Elgar
254) POMP & CIRCUMSTANCE MARCHES

The five great marches gathered together under this title are widely seen as some of the most 'English' of all English classical music: a few bars of any of the five and any music lover the world over will know where they come from. March No. 1 contains the 'Land of Hope and Glory' refrain in its middle section.

This is music that must be played to the hilt, but the musicianship cannot in any way afford to be slapdash, or the result will sound unintentionally comic. Sir John Barbirolli and the New Philharmonia manage a vivid and exciting account of all five on an all-Elgar EMI disc which also contains *Froissart* and *Cockaigne* and is at mid-price. Andrew Davis, as a means of cooling off after the serious business of producing a fine rendition of Elgar's Symphony No. 1, gives us Marches Nos 1, 3 and 4, all in excellent heart and good 1991 sound.

EMI CDM 566323 2
**New Philharmonia Orchestra/
Sir John Barbirolli**

Teldec 9031 73278-2
**BBC Symphony Orchestra/
Andrew Davis**

● If you like this, try Parry's *Jerusalem* (370)

Mozart
255) PIANO CONCERTO NO. 27 K595

The concerto is a highly personal statement, for Mozart wrote it for his own use. The maturity and serenity it holds are those which come upon a man who is leaving the first flushes of youth behind and reaching out for the balance and good sense which he believes middle age may hold for him. There is a minor stylistic shift within it, for the spotlight is more firmly fixed upon the piano soloist than before, the orchestra asked to accompany more often than directly participate in the elucidation of the themes and musical arguments being enacted and resolved in the three movements.

★
Sony SK 46485
Murray Perahia (piano)/
Chamber Orchestra
of Europe

✔
Deutsche Grammophon
DG 453 079-2
Friedrich Gulda (piano)/
Vienna Philharmonic
Orchestra/
Claudio Abbado

As elsewhere with Mozart, Murray Perahia cannot be faulted for his playing or his directing of the Chamber Orchestra of Europe: this is a thoroughly fulfilling recording and one need not look further at full price. At mid-price there are the 1976 vintage delights of Friedrich Gulda and Claudio Abbado (available only in a two-CD set of Mozart piano concertos).

● If you like this, try Schubert's Piano Trio in B flat (376)

Delius
256) LA CALINDA

This exotic dance, scored in bright, dashing colours and given an unusually sprightly tempo by the composer, is excerpted from a Delius opera, *Koanga*. It was Delius's young helper, Eric Fenby, who arranged it for orchestra as a short concert piece, the form that made it so popular today. The opera still languishes in obscurity.

★ ✔
EMI CMS 565119 2
Robert Tear (tenor)/
Hallé Orchestra/
Sir John Barbirolli

Unicorn UKCD 2073
Royal Philharmonic
Orchestra/
Eric Fenby

Oddly enough, outstanding performances of *La Calinda* are not thick on the ground at present. The recording by Sir John Barbirolli and the Hallé Orchestra dates back to the late 1960s, but it remains a stunning display of vigour, so out of character with Delius's usual lyrical and meditative approach. Another noteworthy recording was made in the early 1980s by Eric Fenby himself for the Unicorn-Kanchana label. Unfortunately, although the performance (and the music on the rest of the disc) is a delight, there is something about the recording that robs it of much of its immediacy. This leaves Barbirolli's interpretation as the best place to go.

● If you like this, try Delius's *On Hearing the First Cuckoo in Spring* (259)

Beethoven

257) FANTASIA FOR PIANO, CHORUS AND ORCHESTRA (CHORAL FANTASIA) OP. 80

Many commentators have pointed out that the *Fantasia* is something of a dress rehearsal for the Ninth Symphony, and there are enough parallels to make this a worthwhile observation. While there is obviously no role for a piano in the symphony, the idea of the *Fantasia*, with its variations based around a common theme, has its echoes in the Ninth. Even more directly, the work's resolution in a choral salute gives a strong suggestion of what was to come for Beethoven.

Both versions listed here are committed, thoughtful performances. Listening to Robert Levin on the fortepiano accompanied by John Eliot Gardiner reminds you that there simply is not a great deal in the earlier version of the piano to recommend it. For all but the committed few, the sound undermines the impact of the artistry. With the Beaux Arts Trio this is not a problem, for they are using conventional instruments. Considering that the level of artistry is comparable, for the average listener the choice is clear.

Archiv 447 771-2
**Robert Levin (piano)/
Monteverdi Choir/
Orchestre Révolutionnaire
et Romantique/
John Eliot Gardiner**

★

Philips 438 005-2
**Menahem Pressler (piano)/
Mid-German Radio Chorus/
Beaux Arts Trio/
Leipzig Gewandhaus
Orchestra/Kurt Masur**

● If you like this, try Beethoven's Triple Concerto (159)

Offenbach

258) ORPHÉE AUX ENFERS

It is easy to forget just how exhilarating this music can be when performed by top-flight singers and musicians, particularly when it is based on the original 1858 Bouffes-Parisiens production rather than the elaborated, sumptuous Théâtre de la Gaieté version of 1874. This latter production softened the satire and took the edge off the cutting observations that made the original such racy fun. Our recommendation, the EMI Marc Minkowski recording released in 1999 and starring Natalie Dessay and Laurent Naouri, bases itself on the lean and mean (and shorter) 1858 version, but beefs it up by including the

EMI CDS 556725 2
**Yann Beuron (tenor)/
Natalie Dessay (soprano)/
Lyon Opéra Orchestra
& Chorus/Grenoble
Chamber Orchestra/
Marc Minkowski**

Sony S2K 66616
**David Fieldsend (tenor)/
Mary Hegarty (soprano)/
D'Oyly Carte Opera
Orchestra & Chorus/
John Owen Edwards**

'unmissable' parts from 1874. It brings a heady whiff of excitement, of licence, back into the old warhorse. The D'Oyly Carte recording, from 1994, also takes the 1858 version as its starting-point, adding in some potent morsels from 1874: the recording is in English, with no libretto, and is recommended for those who simply want to sit back and enjoy the music.

● If you like this, try J. Strauss's *Die Fledermaus* (229)

Delius

259) ON HEARING THE FIRST CUCKOO IN SPRING

This wonderful slow waltz-metre dance of spring is the first of *Two Pieces for Small Orchestra* (the other being 'Summer Night on the River') which summarise Delius's intense responses to the world around him. The images he conjures with his small orchestra include the cuckoo itself (nonchalantly evoked by a single clarinet) and a whole range of effects – the wind through the trees, the rustle of grass, the sounds of other living creatures – all encompassed within this almost elegiac slow dance.

Delius's first great champion was Sir Thomas Beecham, and his recordings remain definitive, even if they are currently deleted. In their stead, then, the recommendation goes to the great latter-day Delius and Vaughan Williams interpreter, Andrew Davis, whose sensitivity to texture and atmosphere, together with his clear view of the music's overall pattern, makes this a well-recorded winner. Barbirolli's is a warm, sensual mid-sixties account.

● If you like this, try Debussy's *La Mer* (266)

> ★
> Teldec 4509 990845-2
> **BBC Symphony Orchestra/**
> **Andrew Davis**
>
> ✔
> EMI CMS 565 119 2
> **Hallé Orchestra/**
> **Sir John Barbirolli**

Schubert

260) AVE MARIA D839

Schubert's famous 'Ave Maria', a simple and passionate plea to the mother of Christ, is actually a setting of lines from Sir Walter Scott's poem 'The Lady of the Lake'. For this plea, Schubert has created a most beautiful piano accompaniment.

The melody is not complex, but it requires singing of strength and delicacy. Its original scoring was for soprano and piano, but it has been arranged for any number of combinations, including whole choirs. The two recommendations here stick to the original setting. Irmgard Seefried is accompanied by the faultless Erik Werba and her voice is pure as a bell. A more modern recording comes from Marjana Lipovšek, with the great Geoffrey Parsons at the piano. Her rich voice also gives this music directness and power. Hers is an all-Schubert programme from 1987, and includes three-language lyrics for all the songs. Both recordings are on Orfeo.

> Orfeo C297921B
> **Irmgard Seefried (soprano)/**
> **Erik Werba (piano)**
>
> ★
> Orfeo C159871A
> **Marjana Lipovšek**
> **(mezzo-soprano)/**
> **Geoffrey Parsons (piano)**

● If you like this, try Caccini's 'Ave Maria' (194)

Franck

261) VIOLIN SONATA

César Franck wrote just one violin sonata, but it has held a position of prominence in classical music since its première in 1886. The reason is not hard to find: it is a work with gentle lyricism at its heart, a characteristic it shares with another famous work by Franck, the *Symphonic Variations* for piano and orchestra.

Midori's version on Sony, recorded in 1997, is a wonderfully controlled interpretation. In keeping a taut rein on many of the idiosyncrasies that can creep into chamber interpretation she produces a model performance. In this she is helped greatly by her pianist, Robert McDonald, and by sensitive Sony engineering. Two good budget-price versions also exist. The 1990 Naxos recital from Takako Nishizaki is technically expert, but runs into some interpretative difficulties, while the Arte Nova recording from 1998, with Mirijam Contzen, finds a middle path between the two. The programme is also good, having the Debussy and the first Saint-Saëns violin sonatas as CD partners.

★

Sony SK 63331
Midori (violin)/
Robert McDonald (piano)

✔

Arte Nova 74321 59233-2
Mirijam Contzen (violin)/
Valéry Rogatchev (piano)

● If you like this, try Beethoven's Violin and Piano Sonata No. 5 (308)

Brahms

262) ACADEMIC FESTIVAL OVERTURE OP. 80

Brahms wrote his overture in 1880 as a gesture of thanks to a university that had awarded him an honorary doctorate. Evidently in good spirits and well disposed towards the University of Breslau and its lucky students, he fashioned the ten-minute piece out of various drinking songs. This had the clearly intended effect of making it a breezy and informal affair, full of little jokes and winking asides. Not content with making his pleasure known through the music alone, he also scored this entertaining trifle for the largest orchestra of his career, making sure that it would be heard at full volume in any setting. At no point do the spirits flag or enjoyment lessen: this is fun from start to finish. Played with great gusto, the version by Daniel Barenboim is an obvious front-runner on CD today. The Supraphon recording by Jiri Belohlávek accompanies the Second Symphony and the very different *Tragic Overture*.

★

Erato 4509 95194-2
Chicago Symphony
Orchestra/
Daniel Barenboim

Supraphon SU1990-2
Czech Philharmonic
Orchestra/
Jiri Belohlávek

● If you like this, try Brahms's *Variations on a theme by Haydn* (353)

MacCunn
263) LAND OF THE MOUNTAIN AND THE FLOOD

For a popular piece of music this work doesn't get recorded that often. Less often still does Scottish composer Hamish MacCunn get a whole CD to himself: in fact, the Hyperion disc recommended here remains the only one solely given over to MacCunn's orchestral music. A shame really, because although *Mountain and the Flood*, a piece written, incredibly enough, when MacCunn was still a teenager, fully deserves its popularity, there is much else besides which deserves a listen.

The composer was not one to simply reach for bombast to get his point over. Luckily for him and us, the BBC Scottish Orchestra's director on this disc, Martyn Brabbins, has chosen to honour this, going instead for sharp contrasts, quick climaxes and ready drama. The music is full enough of incident without the players milking it further. Brabbins has avoided such temptations and has set MacCunn's four compositions on this disc in as sympathetic a light as possible. Celtic romance flourishes splendidly here.

> ★
> Hyperion CDA 66815
> **BBC Scottish Symphony Orchestra/**
> **Martyn Brabbins**

● If you like this, try Warlock's *Capriol* Suite (307)

Chopin
264) ÉTUDE IN E MAJOR OP. 10 NO. 3

It is quite extraordinary how Chopin can take a study in a major key and make it sound profoundly melancholy. Still, that is what he achieves in this, one of his most famous Études. The helter-skelter catalogue of musical events scampers across the landscape in the space of just under four minutes. His Minute Waltz may impress more through its breathtaking artifice, but this work, with its unknowing hints of the inwardness and passion of late Brahms piano music, leaves an indelible stamp on the hearer's mind.

Ashkenazy and Perahia coax a world of imagination and emotional intensity from these four minutes, but Perahia is working with better acoustics and is happy to follow the wayward Chopin just a little further into his interior landscape, thus making the experience all the more memorable. It's a tough choice, and Ashkenazy is at less than full price, but Perahia, in a programme that includes the four *Ballades*, maintains his edge.

> ✔
> Decca 414 127-2
> **Vladimir Ashkenazy (piano)**
>
> ★
> Sony SK 64399
> **Murray Perahia (piano)**

● If you like this, try Liszt's *Liebestraume* No. 3 (273)

Pergolesi
265) STABAT MATER

Pergolesi was dead in his twenty-sixth year and left few examples of his brilliance, but his *Stabat Mater* has been a consistent favourite since its completion in the last year of his life, 1736. The mood is sombre and occasionally despairing as Pergolesi struggles to come to terms with his own hard-pressed mortality. It is an ambitious work, made up of 13 separate settings of texts dealing with Christ's death on the cross.

The Harnoncourt version is scrupulous in its observance of Pergolesi's artistic intentions, his soloists exquisite in their expression. The combination with the Vivaldi *Gloria* is not ideal, but is instructive. Il Seminario Musicale on Virgin Veritas is a 1997 recording of great beauty and tremendous depth of feeling, bringing the full gamut of the work's ambitions to the listener. It is on authentic instruments. Rounding the CD out with the wonderfully inventive *Salve Regina* makes it that special rarity, an all-Pergolesi disc.

> Teldec 9031 76989-2
> **Eva Mei (soprano)/**
> **Marjana Lipovšek**
> **(mezzo-soprano)/Vienna**
> **Concentus Musicus/**
> **Nikolaus Harnoncourt**
>
> ★
>
> Virgin VC 545291 2
> **Véronique Gens (soprano)/**
> **Gérard Lesne (alto)/**
> **Seminario Musicale**

● If you like this, try Rossini's *Stabat Mater* (357)

Debussy
266) LA MER

Debussy's love of nature inspired many of his most famous compositions, but this homage to the elemental majesty of the sea is his most direct portrayal. The first movement is a breathless anticipation and celebration of sunrise over the water. Even more miraculous is the joyful evocation of the sea's changing moods on a bright summer morning which takes up the majority of the second movement, 'Jeux de vagues'. The last movement carries distant echoes of Wagner in its rich drama and colourful orchestration.

> ★
> Deutsche Grammophon
> DG 439 896-2
> **Cleveland Orchestra/**
> **Pierre Boulez**
>
> Sony SK 62599
> **Los Angeles**
> **Philharmonic Orchestra/**
> **Esa-Pekka Salonen**

The conductor and orchestra who manage this complex score achieve a balance between sheer musical dexterity and naturalness of expression. Many duck this challenge and rely on bombast. Both conductors here achieve a wonderful transparency of texture while not neglecting any single aspect of the scoring. Each takes different routes to their end, with Boulez perhaps more clearly revealing the music's inner workings in 'Jeux de vagues', while Salonen's long sunrise is thrilling. Both are worth an unreserved recommendation.

● If you like this, try Britten's *Four Sea Interludes* (288)

Mendelssohn

267) HEAR MY PRAYER

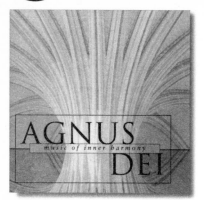

This hymn, based on Psalm 55 and composed in 1844, is famous mostly for the unearthly beauty of the melody that accompanies the last verse, 'O for the wings of a dove', a tune known and loved worldwide by people who have absolutely no idea of its classical source. The work chiefly features the soprano soloist, although the choir helps out in the 'hear my prayer' sections. Most performances are accompanied by organ, adding to the purity of the sound

Hyperion CDA 66359
**Anne Dawson (soprano)/
Corydon Singers/
Matthew Best**

★

Erato 0630 14634-2
**Choir of New
College, Oxford/
Edward Higginbottom**

generated by the young soprano voice – usually a boy soprano from a well-known choir, although there are numerous recordings with outstanding female sopranos. The Hyperion recording under Matthew Best features the Corydon Singers and the outstanding soprano Anne Dawson in an all-Mendelssohn programme. The Erato recording under Edward Higginbottom is a diverse selection from Tavener to Elgar. It features boy soprano Thomas Herford. His vulnerable technique makes the experience perhaps more touching.

● If you like this, try Caccini's 'Ave Maria' (194)

Vaughan Williams

268) SYMPHONY NO. 5

The roots of Vaughan Williams's Fifth Symphony, begun in 1938 and premièred in 1943, lie in the music he wrote for his opera *The Pilgrim's Progress*. Serenity and a sense of divine inspiration are present from the delighted yearning of the initial movement to the *passacaglia* movement which ends it. In between, there are bouts of joy and minutes of the most searing, rhapsodic intensity, as in the Romanza. This is a tightly worked and emotionally fulfilling symphony, very outward-looking, as if bestowing solace,

★
Chandos CHAN 9666
**London Symphony
Orchestra/
Richard Hickox**

✔

RCA GD 90506
**London Symphony
Orchestra/
André Previn**

quite gentle after the fearsome rigours of Vaughan Williams's Fourth.

Richard Hickox gives an intent and closely knit reading of the work on his Chandos disc from 1999, coupling it with religious pieces by Vaughan Williams that have a direct relevance to the symphony. André Previn's 1972 recording for RCA remains an outstanding achievement, and is at mid-price. It is coupled with *Three Portraits from the England of Elizabeth*.

● If you like this, try Vaughan Williams's *English Folk Song Suite* (286)

Hummel
269) TRUMPET CONCERTO IN E

Hummel cast his concerto in E major, a key guaranteed to give the music bright colours owing to the sonority of open strings around the trumpet part. The first movement is quite grand, the second movement, an *andante*, melancholy. However, it is the last movement where Hummel really pulls out the stops for the soloist, giving the trumpet some dashing music to play which recalls the hunt or other aristocratic country pastimes.

The music has to be played in the style of the time and with proper warmth and elegance. John Wallace with the Philharmonia has an incredible bell-like clarity and lightness of tone in his playing, while Wynton Marsalis with the ECO uses a larger tone and is more concerned with the emotions behind the notes than Wallace. Both attack the *allegro molto* of the last movement with relish. Wallace's lightness of tone suits this work more than Marsalis's so, this time, it's Wallace.

★
Nimbus NI 7016
**John Wallace
(trumpet)/Philharmonia
Orchestra/Christopher
Warren-Green**

Sony SK 57497
**Wynton Marsalis (trumpet)/
English Chamber Orchestra/
Raymond Leppard**

● If you like this, try Haydn's Trumpet Concerto in E flat (153)

Sibelius
270) SYMPHONY NO. 1

The great symphonic odyssey by which Sibelius became one of the foremost exponents of the form starts with this work, premièred in the spring of 1899. What is so remarkable is that, even then, his voice as a composer was highly distinctive. In places its subjectivity is quite daring, especially in the way he balances single instruments from sections against each other or against weightier masses of sound. That Sibelius was capable of a lighter touch this early in his long career is shown in the extravagant but unflappable urgency of the *scherzo*.

★
BIS CD 861
**Lahti Symphony Orchestra/
Osmo Vänskä**

Chandos CHAN 6555
**Royal Scottish National
Orchestra/
Sir Alexander Gibson**

This vision, bleak and distinctly Nordic, is brilliantly lit by the Lahti Symphony Orchestra under Osmo Vänskä. They play each part with total conviction and make the whole hang together through this strength of vision. The commitment is equal from the Scottish National with Sir Alexander Gibson, but the angle taken by the recording engineers gives the orchestra a strangely British hue. This leads us to the BIS aggregation's door.

● If you like this, try R. Strauss's *Eine Alpensinfonie* (276)

Puccini

271) LA RONDINE

Strange to think of an opera written by Puccini during his years of fame as a flop, but that's what *La Rondine* has been. The story is a clever rerun of elements from *La Traviata* and *Die Fledermaus*, and though no one dies at the end, the two romantic leads depart with broken hearts to their uncertain futures. Puccini's music is as exquisite as ever, but here he mostly avoids the 'big aria'.

Unsurprisingly, *La Rondine* is not often recorded complete. The two versions on current release are not flawless, but both exhibit considerable spirit. The Domingo/Te Kanawa combination for Maazel's 1983 set for Sony treats it as an opera close to Puccini's *verismo* origins, their emotions large and close to the surface. The 1997 Alagna/Gheorghiu combination for Pappano and EMI reveals a lighter touch and the delicacy which Puccini insisted upon. This may deprive it of some of the drama of the Maazel set, but it reveals the bigger picture the opera is supposed to provide.

★
EMI CDS 556338 2
Angela Gheorghiu (soprano)/Roberto Alagna (tenor)/ London Voices/ London Symphony Orchestra/ Antonio Pappano

Sony M2K 37852
Kiri Te Kanawa (soprano)/ Placido Domingo (tenor)/ Ambrosian Opera Chorus/ London Symphony Orchestra/Lorin Maazel

● If you like this, try Puccini's *Manon Lescaut* (316)

Gounod

272) AVE MARIA

Hundreds of composers and arrangers have been attracted to the beauties of J. S. Bach's music over the centuries. In his 'Ave Maria', Gounod takes the famous opening arpeggios of the first number in Bach's *Well-Tempered Clavier Book 1* as his starting-point and drapes a rather sentimental melody over them. Add the praise to Mother Mary and the transformation into an affecting devotional snippet is complete.

Simplicity and sincerity are essential if such a piece is to be successful. Any hint of showmanship or irony and the whole idea falls flat. The Westminster Cathedral Choir under James O'Donnell manage a Colin Mawby arrangement (tenor, choir and organ) with dignity and devotional decorum on Hyperion's *Panis Angelicus* collection. Jessye Norman also brings dignity and decorum to the music, accompanied by harp only, making it something of a cameo solo piece in this setting (as such it would make the perfect encore to a recital).

★
Hyperion CDA 66669
Westminster Cathedral Choir/ Iain Simcock (organ)/ James O'Donnell

Philips 432 731-2
Jessye Norman (soprano)/ Fabrice Pierre

● If you like this, try Franck's *Panis Angelicus* (175)

Liszt
273) LIEBESTRÄUME NO. 3

Much of Liszt's vast output remains virtually unknown outside a very small circle of musicians and music scholars, but at least the world at large has a generally correct idea that this flamboyant Hungarian genius was one of the supreme piano virtuosos of his (or any other) century. Thus it's no surprise that his most popular piece of music is for solo piano.

★
Hyperion CDA 66593
Leslie Howard (piano)

✔
Naxos 8.553595
Jeno Jandó (piano)

The approach to playing this piece must be rooted in total commitment to the emotional overindulgence being called for. The pianist must sound like someone under the power of love, and happy to be so. Leslie Howard, in his complete survey of Liszt's piano music on Hyperion, manages this to perfection. It must be said, however, that Jeno Jandó, in recital No. 10 of his complete Liszt piano music cycle, is not far behind, although the recorded sound is not quite so sumptuous.

● If you like this, try Chopin's Nocturne in E flat Opus 9 No. 2 (221)

Gershwin
274) PIANO CONCERTO IN F

Some listeners have detected a note of desperation to please in this 1925 concerto, one of Gershwin's most extroverted symphonic works, as if he were straining to meet expectations already heightened by the glorious progress *Rhapsody in Blue* was making in the twelve short months since its première. But this is to be unfair to the relative gains the composer has made. He does not need here to frantically push everything so hard, Broadway style, to make it sound convincing, as the supremely relaxed *adagio* shows. Gershwin has come of age.

★ ✔
Virgin VM 561243 2
**Wayne Marshall
(piano/director)/
Aalborg Symphony
Orchestra**

Erato 0630 19571-2
**Hélène Grimaud (piano)/
Baltimore Symphony
Orchestra/
David Zinman**

Both pianists chosen are young but have themselves come of age as Gershwin interpreters. This is most certainly true of Marshall, who has perhaps the edge in panache over Grimaud, although her fastidious articulating of the music's natural cadences makes her performance work on its own terms. But with Marshall being so well recorded and at mid-price, it seems churlish not to embrace his brash attractions.

● If you like this, try Ravel's Piano Concerto in G (285)

Chopin

275) FANTASIE IMPROMPTU IN C# MINOR OP. 66

This famous piece was not published by Chopin in his lifetime, possibly because he thought it betrayed the influence of other popular composers of the day. Today nobody recalls his rivals and it has become for many a definitive example of Chopin's piano style. Certainly the mercurial changes of mood, direction and tempo, the sudden switch to different melodies signalling these mood swings, the perfect control of the piano's expressive possibilities, are all traits associated with the great Polish composer.

> ✔
> Decca 417 798-2
> **Vladimir Ashkenazy (piano)**
>
> ★
> Sony MK 39708
> **Murray Perahia (piano)**

The two pianists chosen here are both past masters at Chopin. Ashkenazy's sensitive and correct interpretation can be heard on a number of Decca discs at a variety of price points. The one chosen here is a mid-price 'favourites' collection and comes from 1979. Murray Perahia's recording dates from 1985 and contains such melting poetry of touch and phrase as to make it an immediate favourite. This may be a full-price disc still, but it is superb. It contains all four impromptus among its selection.

● If you like this, try Rachmaninov's Prelude in C# minor (386)

Richard Strauss

276) EINE ALPENSINFONIE

This was the last tone poem Strauss wrote. Its individuality is very marked, his trademark harmonic twists and sinuous melodies coming at the listener unabated. In this work, written 'between operas' during the Great War, Strauss takes great delight in giving the listener a detailed musical painting of what it is like to take a stroll through the Austrian Alps. Through its twenty-one sections it is possible to imagine Strauss and his party of fellow-travellers as they move

> ★
> Supraphon 11 0005-2
> **Czech Philharmonic Orchestra/ Zdeněk Košler**
>
> Telarc CD 80211
> **Vienna Philharmonic Orchestra/ André Previn**

through the grassy lower slopes and gradually climb higher. This is not the storm and turmoil of *Ein Heldenleben* or the philosophical angst of *Tod und Verklärung*: this is a whole-hearted reaction to the magnificence of nature. Music of such space and clarity needs a suitably spacious and detailed recording, and it can be readily enough found with the Czech Philharmonic under Zdeněk Košler. Their 1994 version for Supraphon does justice to a meticulous score and a panoramic concept of sound.

● If you like this, try Strauss's *Also Sprach Zarathustra* (315)

Mozart
277) SYMPHONY NO. 39

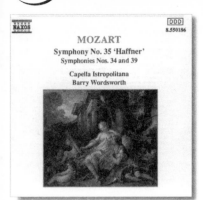

In the summer of 1788 Mozart wrote his last three symphonies, the 39th being the first of the three. It is a work that continues to use the structure and style of the Classical symphony as perfected by Haydn, but it is also a work that, in its ambition, was a pointer to the future. Alas, not to Mozart's own future, for he would be dead in three years' time.

Conductor and orchestra need to relax into this music. Harnoncourt, in his 1984 recording of it for Telarc, seems unable to do so sufficiently, but Trevor Pinnock and the English Concert, while they cannot meet the different demands of the 40th and 41st symphonies in the same set, succeed with No. 39. This is on original instruments, but the sound is not overly harsh. Yet the winner here must be the Capella Istropolitana under Barry Wordsworth, on a Naxos disc that includes Symphonies 34 and 35. This is such a natural and flowing interpretation that, at budget price, it would be foolish to ignore its charms.

Archiv 447043-2
English Concert/
Trevor Pinnock

★ ✔

Naxos 8.550186
Capella Istropolitana/
Barry Wordsworth

● If you like this, try Haydn's Symphony No. 104 (342)

Grieg
278) LYRIC PIECES BOOK 8 OP. 65

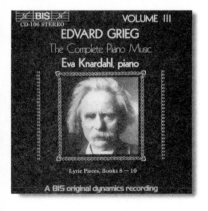

Grieg's popularity as a creator of orchestral favourites obscures the true tenor of his output. Like Debussy, he was a prolific writer of songs and piano music: his *Lyric Pieces* alone cover ten 'books', with each book containing around a half-dozen separate pieces for solo piano covering a grand array of subjects and moods. Considering the natural audience for this type of music, Grieg consciously kept his pieces simple in form and full of greatly enjoyable melody, while the harmonic accompaniment was never off-putting or tangential. One of the most popular, 'Wedding Day at Troldhaugen', comes from Book No. 8 and paints a very gay picture of a celebration.

Both BIS and Naxos have recorded complete cycles of Grieg's piano music. While Naxos's pianist, Einar Steen-Nøkleberg, is the artistic equal of BIS's Eva Knardahl, there is no doubt that the BIS disc triumphs in terms of sound quality.

✔

Naxos 8.553396
Einar Steen-Nøkleberg
(piano)

★

BIS 106
Eva Knardahl (piano)

● If you like this, try Debussy's *Preludes* Book I (352)

Rimsky-Korsakov

279) CAPRICCIO ESPAGNOL OP. 34

ORCHESTRAL SPECTACULAR
España • Boléro • Capriccio Espagnol
Polovtsian Dances • Night on the Bare Mountain

ROYAL PHILHARMONIC ORCHESTRA
Adrian Leaper

1991 Recording Playing Time : 58'13"

The nature of a *capriccio* (or caprice) is that it combines a gamut of themes from source material into a freewheeling fantasia, often displaying virtuoso technique as it does so. On that definition, Rimsky-Korsakov's *Capriccio espagnol* is most definitely correctly titled. It glides in spectacular fashion from one theme to the next, often with brilliant linking passages for solo instrument (violin, woodwind), and its bold orchestration (including mandolins, castanets and other exotic percussion effects) makes a myriad Spanish images flash in front of the listener's eyes.

> ✔
> Decca 443 580-2
> **London Symphony**
> **Orchestra/**
> **Ataulfo Argenta**
>
> ★ ✔
> Naxos 8.550501
> **Royal Philharmonic**
> **Orchestra/**
> **Adrian Leaper**

Considering the composer's emphasis on the spectacular, it is vital for a recording to be in excellent sound and to show off a disciplined and vibrant orchestra. The old Decca showcase album by Ataulfo Argenta holds up capably, considering its vintage (1958), but Adrian Leaper and the RPO on Naxos possess a truly in-depth modern sound on their 1991 collection of big orchestral display numbers, making them a natural first choice.

● If you like this, try Falla's *Nights in the Garden of Spain* (355)

Suppé

280) DICHTER UND BAUER (POET AND PEASANT)

SUPPÉ

Famous Overtures
The Beautiful Galatea • Poet and Peasant
Fatinitza • Jolly Robbers
and others

Slovak State Philharmonic Orchestra (Košice)
Alfred Walter

Boccaccio.

Franz von Suppé has every right to be as closely associated with the heady days of 19th-century Viennese operetta as Johann Strauss. His parade of operetta hits lasted for the best part of three decades and made him internationally famous. In the present day his stage works are rarely heard complete outside of German-speaking countries, but the overtures to many of his most successful works are still popular worldwide. This overture is a case in point.

> ★ ✔
> Naxos 8.553935
> **Slovak State**
> **Philharmonic Orchestra/**
> **Alfred Walter**
>
> EMI CDC7 54056 2
> **Academy of**
> **St Martin-in-the-Fields/**
> **Sir Neville Marriner**

The traditional elements of operetta have to be treated with respect for a great performance of this overture. The orchestra must not indulge in irony or any attempt to undermine the basic naïveté of the genre. These requirements are met by the Slovak State Philharmonic conducted by Alfred Walter for Naxos on an all-Suppé overtures disc with a collection of first-rate performances. Given its success and price level, the full-price Marriner collection on EMI has tough opposition unless you are a Suppé fan looking for strong comparisons.

● If you like this, try J. Strauss's *Tales from the Vienna Woods* (339)

Beethoven
281) MISSA SOLEMNIS

The five sections of this vast and immensely dignified Mass – 'Kyrie', 'Gloria', 'Credo', 'Sanctus' ('Benedictus') and 'Agnus dei' – are all couched in positive terms, even the plea of the Kyrie: 'Lord, have mercy upon us'. The roles of the soprano, alto, tenor and bass soloists are defined by normal liturgical practice, and they are given music that does not try to imitate opera (as opposed to many other composer's efforts). With this intent in mind, a successful performance and recording must find the correct approach for chorus and soloists, avoiding the pitfalls of histrionics and pulling rank. The soloists should 'sit' within the sound spectrum, rather than dominate. The recordings chosen here benefit from this approach, with the extra immediacy of the Harmonia Mundi recording making it a first choice for sound. The Harnoncourt, however, a 'live' recording from 1992, takes some beating at budget price, though it has no texts and spreads onto two CDs.

> Harmonia Mundi HMC90 1557
> **Rosa Mannion (soprano)/**
> **Birgit Remmert (contralto)/**
> **James Taylor (tenor)/**
> **Cornelius Hauptmann (bass)/**
> **Chapelle Royale Choir/**
> **Collegium Vocale/Champs-**
> **Elysées Orchestra/**
> **Philippe Herreweghe**
>
> ★
>
> Teldec 0630 18945-2
> **Eva Mei (soprano)/Marjana**
> **Lipovšek (mezzo-soprano)/**
> **Anthony Rolfe Johnson**
> **(tenor)/Robert Holl (bass)/**
> **Arnold Schoenberg Choir/**
> **Chamber Orchestra**
> **of Europe/**
> **Nikolaus Harnoncourt**

● If you like this, try Berlioz's *Grande messe des morts* (289)

Bruckner
282) SYMPHONY NO. 7

Bruckner occupies a curious position in the development of 19th-century Austrian music. A deeply humble and religious man, a devoted follower of Wagner's blazing progressiveness, he was also on friendly terms with Wagner's arch-rival, the conservative Brahms, who admired his symphonies greatly. Bruckner's Seventh Symphony is elegiac in tone and highly rhapsodic. Compared with his earlier symphonies, this has a peace in its soul which is rarely reached elsewhere. It was completed in the immediate aftermath of Wagner's death, and something of the sorrow that Bruckner felt at this loss can be detected.

> ★
> Deutsche Grammophon
> DG 439 037-2
> **Vienna Philharmonic**
> **Orchestra/**
> **Herbert von Karajan**
>
> RCA 09026 61398-2
> **North German Radio**
> **Symphony Orchestra/**
> **Günter Wand**

Von Karajan always had Bruckner close to his heart: this recording (his last) was made in 1989 and finds him and the orchestra perfectly in step with each other and the music. Günter Wand's more expansive reading of the same work is on a similar plateau, but it is hard to deny Karajan in this mood.

● If you like this, try Mahler's Symphony No. 3 (305)

Rachmaninov

283) PIANO CONCERTO NO. 1 IN F# MINOR OP. 1

Rachmaninov's First Piano Concerto starts with a bang, the pianist imposing himself on both audience and orchestra in the same spectacular display of technique. Two minutes have passed before things calm down and the rhapsodic side of Rachmaninov's creative nature takes a firm grip. Then we know the territory we are in: this is big, soulful concerto country, with a virtuoso young composer eager to impress. By the end of the first movement's *cadenza* he has certainly done that: even Tchaikovsky would have been impressed by the combination of technique and emotionalism.

Decca 425 004-2
**Vladimir Ashkenazy
(piano)/London
Symphony Orchestra/
André Previn**

★

Chandos CHAN 7114 (2)
**Earl Wild (piano)/
Royal Philharmonic
Orchestra/
Jascha Horenstein**

The pianist who successfully scales the technical difficulties of this concerto to inject something special into the music will have unequalled reserves of charisma. Both Ashkenazy and Earl Wild manage this, but the rather forward piano position in the mix hinders rather than helps Ashkenazy's case. Wild's 1965 recording has the right balance, fine sound and brilliant playing. It is also budget-price. Why look farther?

● If you like this, try Tchaikovsky's Piano Concerto No. 2 (331)

Bruckner

284) SYMPHONY NO. 8

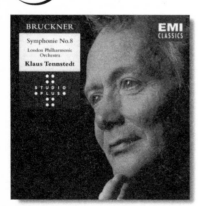

Bruckner's penultimate symphony finds him back in the more tumultuous waters often occupied in his earlier works after the relative equanimity of his Seventh. It is a vast and vastly ambitious symphony, at the time of its writing the longest in the world. This in itself is no recommendation, but Bruckner's individuality, his creativity and his ability to mould huge musical architecture into a living work of art made sure that the music was an artistic triumph.

RCA 09026 68047-2
**NDR Symphony Orchestra/
Günter Wand**

★

EMI CDM 764849 2
**London Philharmonic
Orchestra/
Klaus Tennstedt**

Many conductors attempt this work, but few manage to bring it all together successfully. Günter Wand and Klaus Tennstedt do. Wand's version takes up two CDs, using a new combination of source texts for his 'live' version (the sound suffers a little as a result), while Tennstedt, at mid-price from 1983 and the safety of a studio, sticks to the second official version and brings off a coup.

● If you like this, try Mahler's Symphony No. 6 (372)

Ravel

285) PIANO CONCERTO IN G

It is important to remember that Ravel was a musical fantasist who normally went to great lengths to conceal his emotional world. This he did in a bewildering number of ways. The piano concerto in G is no exception: its first movement is a wonderful example of his ability to wave his creative wand over an orchestra and soloist.

It is no straightforward proposition for pianist and conductor. Nothing must be allowed to droop, most especially the tempo of the second movement. The playing on Hélène Grimaud's CD with the Baltimore Symphony and David Zinman is alert and articulate. It retains flair, a light heart and a steely concentration on the work at hand. An older performance (at budget price) is available on Sony by Philippe Entremont, a superb but today neglected interpreter of Ravel and his French contemporaries.

★
Erato 0630 19571-2
Hélène Grimaud (piano)/
Baltimore Symphony
Orchestra/
David Zinman

✔
Sony SBK 46338
Philippe Entremont (piano)/
Philadelphia Orchestra/
Eugene Ormandy

● If you like this, try Gershwin's Piano Concerto in F (274)

Vaughan Williams

286) ENGLISH FOLK SONG SUITE

Vaughan Williams's love of English folk songs is well known. He openly acknowledged it as a key element in finding his own 'voice' as a composer. Few compositions illustrate this better than this suite of four rollicking versions of old work songs and shanties. The first two are marches which beg to be whistled along with, while the third, a beautiful arrangement of the ballad 'My Bonny Boy', does not so much suggest melancholy as a sweet warmth and love for another human. The fourth and last piece begins as a light-footed march before it opens out into a fully fledged whistle-along once more. The pieces were originally gathered together as a suite for wind orchestra and later rearranged for standard concert orchestra. Both arrangements are given recorded representation here. It is fun to taste the freshness of the original wind arrangements as played by the Royal Northern College of Music Wind Orchestra on Chandos. The 1999 recording is perfection.

★
Chandos CHAN 9697
Royal Northern College
of Music Wind Orchestra/
Tim Reynish

✔
EMI CDM 764022 2
London Symphony
Orchestra/
Sir Adrian Boult

● If you like this, try Vaughan Williams's Symphony No. 2 (364)

Clarke

287) THE PRINCE OF DENMARK'S MARCH
(TRUMPET VOLUNTARY)

Jeremiah Clarke's famous trumpet tune, for a long time mistakenly attributed to Purcell, has been a traditional accompaniment to wedding ceremonies in Britain as long as anyone can remember. The proud melody turns what is unmistakably a march into a graceful procession, deflating any notions of pomp in the ceremony by its elegance.

This short piece has cropped up in many arrangements. The two quoted here stick with tradition, the performance by Stephen Burns on ASV's budget Quicksilva line being correct and very much in the style of the day. It is also one of a handful of performances which puts the March in the context of the rest of Clarke's original Suite, so it represents a bargain. Wynton Marsalis not only manages perfect execution of the piece but brings his fertile imagination to bear on the subject of baroque ornamentation of the melody. This, in a collection dedicated to baroque trumpet music, makes it a disc we'd be foolish to deny ourselves.

✔
ASV CDQS 6081
Stephen Burns (trumpet)/
Ensemble

★
Sony SK 66244
Wynton Marsalis
(trumpet)/English
Chamber Orchestra/
Anthony Newman

● If you like this, try Handel's *Solomon* (56)

Britten

288) FOUR SEA INTERLUDES

These four short orchestral tone poems come from *Peter Grimes* – not Britten's first opera, but his first huge success and first operatic masterpiece. The work is wholly taken up by the sea and the people who make a living from it.

For those who like their Britten without voices, then two modern recordings (both from 1993) give fine interpretations. They both also benefit from brilliant and detailed recorded sound. The Bournemouth Symphony Orchestra and Richard Hickox on Chandos offer great immediacy and beauty in their portraits, and the rest of their programme, including the *Young Person's Guide to the Orchestra*, is attractive. But it is an American who pips Hickox at the post. Leonard Slatkin and the LPO build an atmosphere so strong that it sounds as if the four interludes were excerpted directly from a performance of the complete opera. Slatkin also has the *Young Person's Guide* as well as a dramatic reading of the *Sinfonia da Requiem*.

Chandos CHAN 9221
Bournemouth Symphony
Orchestra/
Richard Hickox

★
RCA 09026 61226-2
London Philharmonic
Orchestra/
Leonard Slatkin

● If you like this, try Elgar's *Sea Pictures* (290)

Berlioz

289) REQUIEM (GRANDE MESSE DES MORTS)

Berlioz was nothing if not fully committed to whatever he was working on at any given time. The *Requiem* requires huge forces for its performance, and while it sets the traditional Latin liturgical text, one continually gets the feeling that a church (or even a cathedral) is not the ideal setting. Perhaps an open-air site would allow it the dimensions it demands. The work is awesome in its scope and drama, its unblinking stare into the terrors of the Last Judgement which Berlioz is sure awaits all mankind. It also has a cataclysmic (and justly famous) moment in the 'Dies irae' when a bank of trumpets anticipate the text and wake the dead. For that alone it is worth the entrance fee. Still outstanding as a recording of this important and difficult work is that by Sir Colin Davis from 1969. His deep empathy for Berlioz and his comprehensive knowledge of the composer's music combine for a classic recording.

★ ✔
Philips 416 283-2
**Ronald Dowd (tenor)/
Wandsworth School Boys'
Choir/London Symphony
Orchestra & Chorus/
Sir Colin Davis**

✔
EMI CZS 569512 2
**Robert Tear (tenor)/
London Philharmonic
Orchestra & Choir/
André Previn**

● If you like this, try Brahms's *Eine deutsches Requiem* (127)

Elgar

290) SEA PICTURES

To call this music ravishing is to underrate it. That it came from the pen of an Englishman only shows what hidden depths this nation has. The poetry Elgar chose to set is hardly the most distinguished of verse, but these pictures of people's physical and emotional relationships with the sea in its various moods obviously suited his larger purpose, regardless of the verse's shortcomings. This is spine-tingling, heart-breakingly beautiful music. Especially when it is sung by Janet Baker with Barbirolli conducting. One of the great benefits of buying the famous du Pré version of Elgar's Cello Concerto is that you get this shattering performance of these five orchestral songs as a bonus. There is another worthy version, affectingly sung by Rosemaria Lang for BIS (and with Wagner's Wesendonck lieder for company), but Baker's 1965 vintage insights remain second to none.

★
EMI CDC 556219-2
**Dame Janet Baker
(mezzo-soprano)/London
Symphony Orchestra/
Sir John Barbirolli**

BIS CD 530
**Rosemaria Lang (soprano)/
Helsingborg Symphony
Orchestra/
Hans-Peter Frank**

● If you like this, try Vaughan Williams's Symphony No. 1 (301)

Nyman
291) THE PIANO

*T*he Piano is a score for the film of the same name, and is calculated to evoke the mystery, sensuality and dreaminess of that movie. Nyman is a thoroughly schooled composer who has written many noted film scores as well as music which his own touring performing group plays in concert throughout the world. This is most definitely film score music – episodic, completely programmatic, and tied to the film from which it came. Nyman must have felt something along these lines himself, or perhaps he needed a version that could be performed live, for he fashioned from the main musical themes here a work he called *The Piano Concerto*. This is cast in more conventionally classical form and is worth investigating in its own right as a different viewpoint on the same thing. Kathryn Stott is the piano soloist on the Argo recording directed by Nyman himself.

● If you like this, try Satie's *Gymnopédies* (131)

Verdi
292) OTELLO

*O*tello was premièred in 1887 and was quickly recognised as a towering operatic achievement. Not only had Verdi made Shakespeare's unfortunate Moor into a convincing creature of Italian opera, he had preserved the tensions and balances between the main protagonists, allowing Iago to be the fulcrum through which all the evil events take place and Desdemona to engage the audience's sympathies even as Otello rages.

It is generally agreed that Placido Domingo has been the great Otello of the past thirty years: he has recorded the role no less than three times. Each version has its own special merits, the latest one on DGG giving the Moor an increased complexity of motivation in his relationship with Iago, but Domingo's first effort, from 1978 and under James Levine's baton, is unbeatable for its singing and vitality. It is also at mid-price with full libretto (and English translation) included.

● If you like this, try Bellini's *Norma* (187)

Bizet

293) L'ARLÉSIENNE SUITE NO. 1

In his short career Bizet wrote fine incidental music for a number of plays, *L'Arlésienne* being by far the most successful. He had drawn together his Suite No. 1 (a second Suite was to follow) from the incidental music within six weeks of the première.

Normally, both *L'Arlésienne* suites appear together on CDs, and our two recommendations are no exception. The ASV Quicksilva compilation conducted by Enrique Bátix combines the *L'Arlésienne* music with a concert suite from Bizet's early opera, *La jolie fille de Perth*, and his charming orchestral suite *Jeux d'enfants*. The performances are effective, the 1994 sound good. A budget price makes this a bargain. It must be said, however, that a few extra pounds are worth finding when it comes to Yan-Pascal Tortelier's version, for the brilliance of the Chandos sound makes this a stand-out. The companion music is the two *Carmen* suites, making a very satisfying programme.

✔
ASV CDQS 6134
Mexico City Philharmonic Orchestra/ Enrique Bátix

★ ✔
Chandos CHAN 7107
Ulster Orchestra/ Yan-Pascal Tortelier

● If you like this, try Mendelssohn's Symphony No. 3 (302)

Boccherini

294) STRING QUINTET OP. 11 NO. 5

Boccherini had an undeniable gift for beautiful melody. His works range from quintets to cello concertos and symphonies, many of which remain unknown to the general public. But the minuets from his quintets became so popular in fashionable society at the end of the 19th century that it amounted to a craze. Remnants of that craze survive in the love of the minuet from this quintet, which is so well known as to be repeatedly mistaken for a striking piece of Mozart chamber music.

★
Deutsche Harmonia Mundi
RD 77159
Smithsonian Chamber Players

✔
Naxos 8.551142
Capella Istropolitana

The two performances chosen here treat the music's charm (and its complexities) with great respect. The Smithsonian Players offer sonorous and refined playing which does not stretch the music out of shape in a bid for effect. Their CD is an all-Boccherini affair. The Capella Istropolitana play a string orchestra arrangement that obeys the minuet tempo but is a little colourless at times. It is Volume 2 of a budget Naxos collection of various 'orchestral classics'.

● If you like this, try Schubert's 'Trout' Quintet (33)

Mahler
295) DAS LIED VON DER ERDE

Mahler's symphonic cycle of songs setting a variety of texts by Chinese poets takes one of his youthful enthusiasms – orchestral lieder – and sets it on its head. As with all late Mahler, the note of reconciliation and acceptance of life is shot through with searing anguish: in fact the first movement, sung by the tenor, is a drunken poet's admission of the ultimate futility of any other action apart from getting drunk. Luckily Mahler lightens up a little with some of the other movements, even managing some good-natured fun along the way.

This is music not to be taken lightly. The famous 1951 Decca version featuring Kathleen Ferrier and Bruno Walter, though suffering from poor sound, is one of the greatest of all classical recordings. The 1960s Klemperer on EMI, though more stoic of mood, is not far behind. For those wanting a modern recording (and one with a baritone instead of a contralto), Sir Simon Rattle's with Peter Sieffert and Thomas Hampson (EMI CDC 556200-2) is as good as any currently available.

> Decca 414 194-2
> **Kathleen Ferrier (contralto)/**
> **Julius Patzak (tenor)/**
> **Vienna Philharmonic**
> **Orchestra/**
> **Bruno Walter**
>
> ★ ✔
>
> EMI CDM 5 66892 2
> **Christa Ludwig**
> **(mezzo-soprano)/**
> **Fritz Wunderlich (tenor)/**
> **New Philharmonia**
> **Orchestra/**
> **Otto Klemperer**

● If you like this, try R. Strauss's *Vier Letzte Lieder* (68)

Sibelius
296) VALSE TRISTE

The *Valse triste* (Sad Waltz) is in fact a dance of death. It was first heard as part of the incidental music for the play *Kuolema* (premièred in 1903). Sibelius later extracted it from the incidental music and fashioned it into a concert morsel. It has been immensely popular ever since, especially in continental Europe. The music begins slowly and wistfully, expounding its melancholy theme before gradually gaining pace and fire.

Sibelius's instruction '*tempo di valse lente*' is closely adhered to by Leif Segerstam and the Danish National Radio Symphony in their 1991 recording for Chandos (now at mid-price). Perhaps too closely, for their rendition takes over six minutes, as against Neeme Järvi's for BIS, which just gets past five minutes. Yet they both work admirably on their own terms. Interestingly, on a separate BIS disc that gives the complete *Kuolema* music, Osmo Vänskä and the Lahti Symphony play the original, shorter version of the *Valse*. Worth looking into.

> ★ ✔
> Chandos CHAN 7075
> **Danish National Radio**
> **Symphony Orchestra/**
> **Leif Segerstam**
>
> BIS CD 610
> **Gothenburg Symphony**
> **Orchestra/**
> **Neeme Järvi**

● If you like this, try Respighi's *Pines of Rome* (330)

Mozart
297) VIOLIN CONCERTO NO. 3 K216

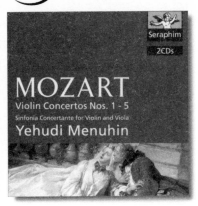

Mozart's five violin concertos have long been favourites among violinists, but they have never been as popular with the general public as his piano concertos. This is perhaps surprising, for there is no lack of melodic invention, even though the works themselves are products of relative youth and so do not possess the remarkable identity of his mature concertos. Yet its combination of naturalness and formal perfection is so typical of his compositional style and so fecklessly charming that this work is hard to resist, even if it does not rank with his greatest.

Deutsche Grammophon
DG 457 746-2
Anne-Sophie Mutter (violin)/
Berlin Philharmonic Orchestra/
Herbert von Karajan

★ ✔
EMI CES 568530 2
Yehudi Menuhin (violin)/
Bath Festival Orchestra

The two recordings recommended here come from proven violin greats; neither is new, but they are at mid-price and offer value for money. Anne-Sophie Mutter's recording comes from early in her career and has the Fifth Concerto as a partner. The Menuhin includes all five concertos and the Sinfonia Concertante K364 on two CDs in good 1960s sound: an excellent way to approach this music.

● If you like this, try Mozart's Violin Concerto No. 4 (390)

Schubert
298) OCTET IN F D803

A product of the intense pain Schubert endured after experiencing the first manifestations of syphilis, the Octet is in the tradition of the serenade, and has an obvious antecedent in Beethoven's Septet Op. 20. The pure Schubertian melody is most often displayed in the *adagio* of the second movement, which has the character of a lullaby sung quietly at the fireside while a storm rages outside.

Decca 448 715-2
Vienna Octet

★
Sony SK 66264
Mozzafiato/
Archibudelli

With music of such a deeply expressive nature, it is a prime requirement to avoid prettification of its complexities. Two current CD versions manage this in quite individual ways. The Vienna Octet on Decca maintain a highly polished surface and smooth sound. They use conventional instruments in a recording dating from 1992. Mozzafiato and Archibudelli use authentic instruments on their Sony recital from 1995, Charles Neidich's clarinet gaining a most attractive timbre as a result. This slight edge gives the Sony performance a wonderful presence, though the Decca version is at considerably less than full price.

● If you like this, try Mendelssohn's Octet (385)

Vivaldi

299) DOUBLE CONCERTO FOR MANDOLINS, STRINGS & CONTINUO RV532

This is another of those chamber concertos by which Vivaldi has established himself far beyond the usual audience for baroque and early music. He knows exactly how to create a large sound from his chamber forces, and also how to create drama from simple ingredients, as the stealthy tread of the second movement, the *andante*, makes clear. Either side of this are two lively *allegros*, the first possessed of a pace which is not far short of a canter, the second a little more stately but no less dramatic in its declamations.

Teldec 4509 91182-2
Il Giardino Armonico Ensemble

★

Hyperion CDA 66160
Paul O'Dette (guitar)/ Robin Jeffrey (guitar)/ Parley of Instruments/ Peter Holman (organ)/ Roy Goodman

Both Il Giardino Armonico and The Parley of Instruments have the measure of this music, stressing its charm and its dramatic qualities but not destroying its miniaturist perfection by swelling the instrumental numbers. Previously we have given the nod to Il Giardino Armonico. This time, to show the closeness of Paul O'Dette's players to the Italians in terms of excellence, the choice falls upon Hyperion's Parley of Instruments.

● If you like this, try Bach's Concerto for Violin No. 2 (356)

Khachaturian

300) MASQUERADE

Khachaturian is mostly known in the West through his ballets *Spartacus, Gayaneh* and *Masquerade*. The score for the latter was written as incidental music for the play by Lermontov. Khachaturian later extracted a concert suite from it, and it is this which has steadily built a following. Khachaturian's music is always very strong on vigorous rhythm and soaring melodies. He often exhibits a folk touch, but his musical language really has its roots in Tchaikovsky's generation of Russian composers.

Naxos 8.554054
St Petersburg State Symphony Orchestra/ André Anichanov

★
Belart 461 007-2
London Symphony Orchestra/ Stanley Black

Recordings of the complete *Masquerade* are rare. Both versions quoted here are of the suite, are at budget price and contain selections from *Gayaneh* and *Spartacus*. The most recent recording is on Naxos and is conducted by André Anichanov. The sound is a trifle cavernous, but the performance is acceptable. The Belart recording goes back to 1978, but Stanley Black whips up tremendous *esprit de corps* from the LSO. This, plus an enticingly immediate recording sound, makes this the preferred choice.

● If you like this, try Smetana's *The Bartered Bride* (381)

BUBBLING UNDER

The Hall of Fame contains 300
pieces of music. Although the next
100 entries do not qualify for the
Hall of Fame Collection, we offer a
recommended recording for each on
the basis that they received plenty of
votes in our annual polls, making
them worthy 'also rans'.

301

Vaughan Williams

SYMPHONY NO. 1
('A SEA SYMPHONY')

Teldec 4509 94550-2
Amanda Roocroft (soprano)/
Thomas Hampson (baritone)/
BBC Symphony Orchestra & Chorus/
Andrew Davis

302

Mendelssohn

SYMPHONY NO. 3
('SCOTTISH')

RCA 74321 20286-2
Leipzig Gewandhaus Orchestra/
Kurt Masur

303

Schubert

DIE FORELLE
(THE TROUT)

Deutsche Grammophon DG 445 294-2
Bryn Terfel (baritone)/
Malcolm Martineau (piano)

304

Weber

CLARINET CONCERTO
NO. 2 IN E FLAT

Teldec 0630 15428-2
Sharon Kam (clarinet)/
Leipzig Gewandhaus Orchestra/
Kurt Masur

305

Mahler

SYMPHONY NO. 3
IN D MINOR

Deutsche Grammophon DG 410 715-2
Jessye Norman (soprano)/
Vienna Boys' Choir/
Vienna State Opera Concert Choir/
Vienna Philharmonic Orchestra/
Claudio Abbado

306

Copland

RODEO

Sony Classical SK46559-2
London Symphony Orchestra/
Aaron Copland

307

Warlock

CAPRIOL SUITE

Chandos CHAN 8808
Ulster Orchestra/
Vernon Handley

308

Beethoven

VIOLIN AND PIANO
SONATA NO. 5 IN F
OP. 24 ('SPRING')

Deutsche Grammophon DG 457 619-2
Anne-Sophie Mutter (violin)/
Lambert Orkis (piano)

309

Beethoven

PIANO SONATA NO. 23 IN F MINOR OP. 57 ('APPASSIONATA')

Deutsche Grammophon DG 447 404-2
Wilhelm Kempff (piano)

310

Glazunov

THE SEASONS

Telarc CD 80347
**Minnesota Orchestra/
Edo de Waart**

311

J. Strauss II

CASANOVA (NUNS' CHORUS)

SilvaScreen SILVAD 3602
**Lesley Garrett (soprano)/
Crouch End Festival Chorus/
RP Concert Orchestra/
James Holmes**

312

Glinka

RUSLAN AND LYUDMILA OVERTURE

BIS CD 570
**Malmö Symphony Orchestra/
James DePriest**

313

Walton

CROWN IMPERIAL

EMI CDM 567222 2
**Royal Liverpool Philharmonic Orchestra/
Sir Charles Groves**

314

Brahms

VIOLIN AND CELLO CONCERTO IN A MINOR OP. 102

Teldec 0630 13137-2
**Gidon Kremer (violin)/
Clemens Hagen (cello)/
Concertgebouw Orchestra, Amsterdam/
Nikolaus Harnoncourt**

315

R. Strauss

ALSO SPRACH ZARATHUSTRA

RCA 09026 68225-2
**Bavarian Radio Symphony Orchestra/
Lorin Maazel**

316

Puccini

MANON LESCAUT

Decca 440 200-2
**Mirella Freni (soprano)/
Luciano Pavarotti (tenor)/
New York Metropolitan Opera
Orchestra & Chorus/
James Levine**

317

Berlioz

HAROLD IN ITALY

Philips 416 431-2
**Nobuko Imai (viola)/
London Symphony Orchestra/
Sir Colin Davis**

318

Tchaikovsky

STRING QUARTET NO. 1

Teldec 4509 90422-2
Borodin Quartet

319

Grieg

PEER GYNT SUITE NO. 2

Decca 425 857-2
**San Francisco Symphony
Orchestra & Chorus/
Herbert Blomstedt**

320

Haydn

CELLO CONCERTO NO. 1 IN C

Deutsche Harmonia Mundi RD 77757-2
**Anner Bylsma (cello)/
Tafelmusik/
Jeanne Lamon**

321

Joplin

PIANO RAGS

Music Masters 67061-2
William Albright (piano)

322

Schubert

IMPROMPTU NO. 3 IN G FLAT

Supraphon 11 0366-2
Ivan Klansky (piano)

323

Beethoven

SYMPHONY NO. 8

Arte Nova 74321 56341-2
**Zurich Tonhalle Orchestra/
David Zinman**

324

Rachmaninov

VESPERS

Hyperion CDA 66460
**Corydon Singers/
Matthew Best**

325

Khachaturian

GAYANEH

Naxos 8.554054
**St Petersburg State
Symphony Orchestra/
André Anichanov**

326

Dukas

THE SORCERER'S APPRENTICE

Chandos CHAN 6503
**Royal Scottish National Orchestra/
Sir Alexander Gibson**

327

Offenbach

GAITÉ PARISIENNE

Telarc CD 80294
**Cincinnati Pops Orchestra/
Erich Kunzel**

328
Janáček
SINFONIETTA
Supraphon 11 1522-2
**Brno State Philharmonic Orchestra/
Frantisek Jilek**

329
Weber
CLARINET CONCERTO
NO. 1 IN F MINOR
Teldec 0630 15428-2
**Sharon Kam (clarinet)/
Leipzig Gewandhaus Orchestra/
Kurt Masur**

330
Respighi
PINES OF ROME
EMI CDC 747316 2
**Philadelphia Orchestra/
Riccardo Muti**

331
Tchaikovsky
PIANO CONCERTO
NO. 2 IN G
EMI CDC 749940 2
**Peter Donohoe (piano)/
Bournemouth Symphony Orchestra/
Rudolf Barshai**

332
Franck
SYMPHONY
IN D MINOR
EMI CDM 566824 2
**New Philharmonia Orchestra/
Otto Klemperer**

333
Rodrigo
FANTASIA PARA
UN GENTILHOMBRE
Sony SK 37848
**John Williams (guitar)/
Philharmonia Orchestra/
Louis Frémaux**

334
Brahms
RHAPSODY OP. 53
Deutsche Grammophon DG 435 791-2
**Marjana Lipovšek (mezzo-soprano)/
Ernst Senff Chorus/
Berlin Philharmonic Orchestra/
Claudio Abbado**

335
Ponchielli
LA GIOCONDA
Decca 414 349-2
**National Philharmonic Orchestra/
Bruno Bartoletti**

336
Elgar
SYMPHONY NO. 2
Teldec 9031 74888-2
**BBC Symphony Orchestra/
Andrew Davis**

337
Barber
VIOLIN CONCERTO
RCA 09026 68283-2
**Kyoko Takezawa (violin)/
St Louis Symphony Orchestra/
Leonard Slatkin**

338

Chopin

POLONAISE IN A FLAT
OP. 53 ('HEROIC')

Deutsche Grammophon DG 457 711-2
Maurizio Pollini (piano)

339

J. Strauss II

TALES FROM THE VIENNA WOODS

Telarc CD 80098
**Cincinnati Pops Orchestra/
Erich Kunzel**

340

Mozart

SERENADE NO. 10 IN B FLAT

Sony SK 58950
**Berlin Philharmonic Orchestra/
Zubin Mehta**

341

Mozart

FLUTE CONCERTO NO. 1 IN G K313

Philips 442 148-2
**Konrad Hünteler (flute)/
Eighteenth Century Orchestra/
Frans Brüggen**

342

Haydn

SYMPHONY NO. 104 IN D ('LONDON')

RCA 09026 62549-2
**Philharmonia Orchestra/
Leonard Slatkin**

343

Schubert

PIANO SONATA NO. 21 IN B FLAT D960

Naxos 8.550475
Jeno Jandó (piano)

344

Chopin

POLONAISE IN A OP. 40 NO. 1 ('MILITARY')

Deutsche Grammophon DG 457 711-2
Maurizio Pollini (piano)

345

Tchaikovsky

MARCHE SLAVE OP. 31

Deutsche Grammophon DG 429 984-2
**Gothenburg Symphony Orchestra/
Neeme Järvi**

346

Clara Schumann

PIANO CONCERTO IN A MINOR OP. 7

Koch Int 371692
**Angela Cheng (piano)/
Women's Philharmonic Orchestra/
JoAnn Falletta**

347

Mahler

SYMPHONY NO. 9 IN D

Sony SM2K 64452-2
**Columbia Symphony Orchestra/
Bruno Walter**

348

Haydn

SYMPHONY NO. 94 IN G ('SURPRISE')

Naxos 8.550114
**Capella Istropolitana/
Barry Wordsworth**

349

Chopin

PRELUDE OP. 28 NO. 15 IN D FLAT ('RAINDROP')

Sony S2K 53468
Vladimir Horowitz

350

Haydn

SYMPHONY NO. 101 IN D ('CLOCK')

Naxos 8.550114
**Capella Istropolitana/
Barry Wordsworth**

351

Rachmaninov

VOCALISE OP. 34 NO. 14

EMI CDM 566 982 2
**London Symphony Orchestra/
André Previn**

352

Debussy

PRELUDES BOOK 1

Decca 452 022-2
Jean-Yves Thibaudet (piano)

353

Brahms

VARIATIONS ON A THEME BY HAYDN

RCA 74321 24206-2
**Staatskapelle Dresden/
Kurt Sanderling**

354

Dvořák

STRING QUARTET IN F ('AMERICAN')

Linn CKD 098
Schidlof Quartet

355

Falla

NIGHTS IN THE GARDEN OF SPAIN

Auvidis Valois V 4724
**Rafael Orozco (piano)/
Spanish National Youth Orchestra/
Edmon Colomer**

356

J. S. Bach

CONCERTO FOR VIOLIN NO. 2 IN E BWV1042

Sony SK 66265
Jeanne Lamon (violin)/Tafelmusik

357

Rossini

STABAT MATER

Philips 426 312-2
**Carol Vaness (soprano)/
Cecilia Bartoli (mezzo-soprano)/
Francisco Araiza (tenor)/
Feruccio Furlanetto (bass)/
Bavarian Radio Chorus & Symphony Orchestra/
Semyon Bychkov**

358

Beethoven
SYMPHONY NO. 4

EMI CDM 566795 2
**Philharmonia Orchestra/
Otto Klemperer**

359

J. S. Bach
CONCERTO FOR VIOLIN NO. 1 IN A MINOR
BWV1041

Sony SK 66265
**Jeanne Lamon (violin)/
Tafelmusik**

360

Ravel
LE TOMBEAU DE COUPERIN

Erato 0630 14331-2
**Lyon Opéra Orchestra/
Kent Nagano**

361

Schubert
WINTERREISE

Deutsche Grammophon DG 447 421-2
**Dietrich Fischer-Diskau (baritone)/
Jorg Demus (piano)**

362

Vaughan Williams
SERENADE TO MUSIC

EMI CDM 764022 2
**Sheila Armstrong (soprano)/
Norma Burrows (soprano)/
Ian Partridge (tenor)/
London Philharmonic Orchestra/
Sir Adrian Boult**

363

Humperdinck
HÄNSEL UND GRETEL

EMI CDS 754022 2
**Anne Sofie von Otter (mezzo-soprano)/
Barbara Bonney (soprano)/
Tölz Boys' Choir/
Bavarian Radio Symphony Orchestra/
Jeffrey Tate**

364

Vaughan Williams
SYMPHONY NO. 2
('A LONDON SYMPHONY')

RCA GD 90501
**London Symphony Orchestra/
André Previn**

365

Debussy
ARABESQUES

Sony SBK 48174
Philippe Entremont (piano)

366

Mozart
OBOE CONCERTO

Classic FM 75605 57001-2
**Nicholas Daniel (oboe)/
Britten Sinfonia/
Nicholas Cleobury**

367

Wagner
DER FLIEGENDER HOLLÄNDER

Philips 442 103-2
**Franz Crass (bass)/
Anja Silja (soprano)/
Bayreuth Festival Orchestra & Chorus/
Wolfgang Sawallisch**

368

Satie

GNOSSIENNE NO. 1

BIS CD 317
Roland Pontinen (piano)

369

Mozart

PIANO CONCERTO NO. 24 IN C MINOR
K491

Decca 452 888-2
**Clifford Curzon (piano)/
London Symphony Orchestra/
Istvan Kertesz**

370

Parry

JERUSALEM

Hyperion CDA 66273
**St George's Chapel Choir/
Roger Judd (organ)/
Christopher Robinson**

371

Marcello

OBOE CONCERTO IN D MINOR

Supraphon 11 1290-2
**Gabriela Krcova (oboe)/
Musica Bohemica/
Jaroslav Krcek**

372

Mahler

SYMPHONY NO. 6 IN A MINOR

Sony SMK 60208
**New York Philharmonic Orchestra/
Leonard Bernstein**

373

Bruckner

SYMPHONY NO. 4

RCA 09026 68047-2
**NDR Symphony Orchestra/
Günter Wand**

374

Mozart

SONATA FOR KEYBOARD NO. 11 IN A K331

Deutsche Grammophon DG 429 739-2
Maria-Joao Pires (piano)

375

Dvořák

SYMPHONY NO. 7 IN D MINOR

Chandos CHAN 9391
**Czech Philharmonic Orchestra/
Jiri Bélohlávek**

376

Schubert

PIANO TRIO IN B FLAT

Harmonia Mundi HMU90 7094
**Stanley Ritchie (violin)/
Myron Lutzke (cello)/
Steven Lubin (piano)**

377

Stainer

THE CRUCIFIXION

Chandos CHAN 9551
**Martyn Hill (tenor)/
Michael George (bass)/
BBC Singers/Leith Hill Festival Singers/
Margaret Philips (organ)/
Brian Kay**

378

Rachmaninov

SYMPHONIC DANCES

Melodiya 74321 32046-2
**Moscow Philharmonic Orchestra/
Kyrill Kondrashin**

379

Falla

THE THREE-CORNERED HAT

Auvidis Valois V 4642
**Maria Lluisa Muntada (soprano)/
Spanish National Youth Orchestra/
Edmon Colomer**

380

Glière

HARP CONCERTO OP. 74

Chandos CHAN 9094
**Rachel Masters (harp)/
City of London Sinfonia/
Richard Hickox**

381

Smetana

THE BARTERED BRIDE

Supraphon 11 0040-2
**Drahomíra Tikalová (soprano)/
Ivo Zídek (tenor)/
Eduard Haken (baritone)/
Prague National Theatre Chorus & Orchestra/
Zdeněk Chalabala**

382

Chopin

BALLADE NO. 1 IN G MINOR

Sony SK 64399
Murray Perahia (piano)

383

Lalo

SYMPHONIE ESPAGNOLE OP. 21

Decca 460 007-2
**Kyung-Wha Chung (violin)/
Montreal Symphony Orchestra/
Charles Dutoit**

384

Kodály

HÁRY JÁNOS

Decca 443 006-2
**Philharmonia Hungarica/
Antal Dorati**

385

Mendelssohn

OCTET

Sony SK48307
**Archibudelli/
Smithsonian Chamber Players**

386

Rachmaninov

PRELUDE OP. 3 NO. 2 IN C# MINOR

Decca 443 841-2
Vladimir Ashkenazy (piano)

387

Donizetti

L'ELISIR D'AMORE

Naxos 8.660045-6
**Alessandra Ruffini (soprano)/
Vincenzo La Scola (tenor)/
Hungarian State Opera Orchestra & Chorus/
Pier Giorgio Morandi**

388

Walton

BELSHAZZAR'S FEAST

Chandos CHAN 8760
**Gwynne Howell (bass)/
Bach Choir/Philharmonia Orchestra/
Sir David Willcocks**

389

Schubert

DER HIRT AUF DEM FELSEN

Deutsche Grammophon DG 453 082-2
**Gundula Janowitz (soprano)/
Irwin Gage (piano)**

390

Mozart

VIOLIN CONCERTO NO. 4 IN D K218

EMI CES 568530 2
**Yehudi Menuhin (violin)/
Bath Festival Orchestra**

391

Hérold

LA FILLE MAL GARDÉE

Decca 430 196-2
**Royal Opera House Orchestra/
John Lanchberry**

392

Mozart

HORN CONCERTO NO. 2 IN E FLAT K417

Sony SK 53369
**Ab Koster (horn)/
Tafelmusik/Bruno Weil**

393

Villa-Lobos

BACHIANAS BRASILEIRAS NO. 5

EMI CDC 747433 2
**Barbara Hendricks (soprano)/
Eldon Fox (cello)/
Royal Philharmonic Orchestra Cellos/
Enrique Batiz**

394

Franck

SYMPHONIC VARIATIONS FOR PIANO AND ORCHESTRA

Auvidis Valois V 4764
**Danielle Laval (piano)/
Bordeaux-Aquitaine
National Orchestra/
Alain Lombard**

395

Chabrier

ESPAÑA

EMI CDC 749652 2
**Toulouse Capitole Orchestra/
Michel Plasson**

396

J. Strauss II

EMPEROR WALTZ

RCA 09026 68160-2
**Chicago Symphony Orchestra/
Fritz Reiner**

397

Wagner

RIENZI

Orfeo C34695D
René Kollo (tenor)/
Cheryl Studer (soprano)/
Bavarian State Opera
Orchestra & Chorus/
Wolfgang Sawallisch

398

J. Williams

SCHINDLER'S LIST

Sony S2K 51333 (Greatest Hits 1969–1999)
London Symphony Orchestra/
John Williams

399

Britten

THE YOUNG PERSON'S GUIDE TO THE ORCHESTRA

RCA 09026 61226-2
London Philharmonic Orchestra/
Leonard Slatkin

400

Suppé

LIGHT CAVALRY

Naxos 8.553935
Slovak State Philharmonic Orchestra/
Alfred Walter

STATISTICS

In this section, you'll find a final
100 popular pieces, plus the Top
50s and new entries for each
year's Hall of Fame.

The Hall of Fame Collection
Bottom 100

401
Rimsky-Korsakov: *The Legend of Tsar Saltan*

402
Schumann: *Träumerei*

403
Corelli: *Concerto Grosso* Op. 6 No. 8

404
Mozart: Symphony No. 29 in A

405
J. S. Bach: *St John Passion*

406
Beethoven: Piano Sonata No. 21 in C
Op. 53

407
Weber: *Invitation to the Dance*

408
Ravel: String Quartet

409
Chopin: Étude Op. 10 No. 12 in C minor

410
Shostakovich: Symphony No. 7 in C
('Leningrad')

411
Sullivan: *The Yeomen of the Guard*

412
Schubert: 'Ständchen'

413
Bruckner: Symphony No. 9

414
Ravel: *Introduction and Allegro*

415
Lloyd Webber: *Requiem*

416
Handel: *Judas Maccabaeus*

417
Leoncavallo: *I Pagliacci*

418
Wolf-Ferrari: *Jewels of the Madonna*

419
Wagner: *Parsifal*

420
J. S. Bach: *Christmas Oratorio*

421
Finzi: Clarinet Concerto in C minor
Op. 31

422
Grofé: *Grand Canyon Suite*

423
Mozart: Horn Concerto No. 3 in E flat,
K447

424
Charpentier: Prelude to a Te Deum in D

425
Mozart: *Toy Symphony*

426
Bartók: *Concerto for Orchestra*

427

Chopin: Nocturne Op. 27 No. 2 in D flat

428

Boyce: Symphony No. 4 in F major

429

Duruflé: *Requiem*

430

Addinsell: *The Warsaw Concerto*

431

Mozart: Horn Concerto No. 1 in D, K412

432

Delibes: *Sylvia*

433

Schubert: Symphony No. 3 in D

434

Verdi: *Don Carlos*

435

Tchaikovsky: *Variations on a Rococo Theme*
Op. 33

436

Haydn: Mass No. 11 in D minor

437

Delius: *Florida Suite*

438

Rossini: *The Silken Ladder*

439

Sarasate: *Zigeunerweisen*

440

Weber: *Oberon* Overture

441

Saint-Saëns: Violin Concerto No. 3
in B minor Op. 61

442

Shostakovich: Piano Concerto No. 1
in C minor

443

Vaughan Williams: Symphony No. 3
('Pastoral')

444

Massenet: *El Cid*

445

Gershwin: *Porgy and Bess*

446

Prokofiev: *Peter and the Wolf*

447

Shostakovich: Symphony No. 10 in E minor

448

Handel: *Samson*

449

Vivaldi: *Concerto for Two Trumpets*

450

Bruch: Violin Concerto No. 3 in D

451

Sullivan: *The Mikado*

452

Handel: *Rinaldo*

453

Stanley: Trumpet Voluntary Op. 5 No. 5

454

Sinding: *Rustle of Spring*

455

Liszt: Piano Concerto No. 1 in E flat

456

Mozart: *Coronation Mass*

457
Jenkins: *Palladio*

458
Nielsen: *Aladdin*

459
Britten: *War Requiem*

460
Purcell: 'Come ye sons of art'

461
Brahms: Clarinet Quintet in B minor
Op. 115

462
Lehár: *Gold and Silver Waltz* Op. 79

463
Prokofiev: Symphony No. 5 in B flat

464
J. S. Bach: *Magnificat* in D, BWV243

465
Catalani: *La Wally*

466
Beethoven: Piano Concerto No. 2
in B flat

467
Rossini: *Italian Girl in Algiers*

468
Sibelius: Symphony No. 7 in C

469
Berlioz: *Damnation of Faust*

470
Sullivan: *Pineapple Poll*

471
Anon: 'Greensleeves'

472
Handel: *Semele*

473
Chopin: Waltz Op. 64 No. 1 in D flat
('Minute')

474
Litolff: *Concerto Symphonique* No. 3 in E flat
Op. 45

475
J. S. Bach: *Partita* No. 2 in D minor

476
Sullivan: *The Pirates of Penzance*

477
R. Strauss: *Ein Heldenleben* Op. 40

478
Balfe: *The Bohemian Girl*

479
Donizetti: *Don Pasquale*

480
Tchaikovsky: *Manfred Symphony* Op. 58

481
Handel: Harp Concerto Op. 4 No. 6

482
Jenkins: *Adiemus 2 – Cantata Mundi*

483
Purcell: *Funeral music for Queen Mary*

484
Rachmaninov: Symphony No. 1

485
Parry: *I Was Glad*

486
Brahms: Sextet No. 1 in B flat Op. 18

487
Schubert: *An die Musik*

488
Albinoni: Oboe Concerto in B flat major
Op. 7 No. 3

489
J. S. Bach: Orchestral Suite No. 2 in B minor,
BWV1067

490
Brahms: *Hungarian Dance* No. 7

491
Waldteufel: *Les Patineurs*

492
Handel: Organ Concerto No. 13 in F

493
Williams: *Star Wars*

494
Haydn: Cello Concerto No. 2 in D

495
Rachmaninov: Symphony No. 3 in
A minor

496
Schubert: Fantasy for Piano in C major,
D760

497
Respighi: *Ancient Airs and Dances*

498
Schubert: *Deutsche Messe*

499
Horner: *Braveheart*

500
Albeniz: *Suite española* No. 1

Top 50
1999

1 **Bruch**: Violin Concerto No. 1
2 **Rachmaninov**: Piano Concerto No. 2
3 **Mozart**: Clarinet Concerto
4 **Elgar**: Cello Concerto in E minor
5 **Vaughan Williams**: *The Lark Ascending*
6 **Beethoven**: Symphony No. 6 (Pastoral)
7 **Beethoven**: Piano Concerto No. 5
8 **Beethoven**: Symphony No. 9 (Choral)
9 **Saint-Saëns**: Symphony No. 3 (Organ)
10 **Elgar**: *Enigma Variations*
11 **Mahler**: Symphony No. 5
12 **Pachelbel**: Canon in D
13 **Barber**: *Adagio for Strings*
14 **Grieg**: Piano Concerto in A minor
15 **Mozart**: Piano Concerto No. 21 (*Elvira Madigan*)
16 **Mendelssohn**: Violin Concerto in E minor
17 **Bizet**: *Les Pêcheurs de Perles*
18 **Fauré**: *Requiem*
19 **Mascagni**: *Cavalleria Rusticana*
20 **Holst**: *The Planets Suite*
21 **J. S. Bach**: Concerto for Two Violins
22 **Vivaldi**: *Le Quattro Stagione*
23 **Rodrigo**: *Concierto de Aranjuez*
24 **Albinoni**: *Adagio*

25 **Handel**: *Messiah*
26 **Dvořák**: Symphony No. 9
27 **Beethoven**: Violin Concerto
28 **Shostakovich**: *The Gadfly*
29 **Rachmaninov**: Rhapsody on a theme of Paganini
30 **Allegri**: *Miserere*
31 **Rachmaninov**: Piano Concerto No. 3
32 **Mozart**: *Requiem*
33 **Sibelius**: *Finlandia*
34 **Vaughan Williams**: *Fantasia on a theme of Thomas Tallis*
35 **Beethoven**: Symphony No. 7
36 **Rachmaninov**: Symphony No. 2
37 **Chopin**: Piano Concerto No. 2
38 **Shostakovich**: Piano Concerto No. 2
39 **Schubert**: 'Trout' Quintet
40 **Prokofiev**: *Romeo and Juliet*
41 **Beethoven**: Symphony No. 5
42 **Massenet**: 'Meditation' from *Thaïs*
43 **Chopin**: Piano Concerto No. 1
44 **Fauré**: *Cantique de Jean Racine*
45 **Verdi**: *Nabucco*
46 **Beethoven**: Sonata No.14 Op. 27 No. 2 ('Moonlight')
47 **J. S. Bach**: *Brandenburg Concertos*
48 **Tchaikovsky**: Piano Concerto No. 1
49 **Rimsky-Korsakov**: *Scheherezade*
50 **Mozart**: Flute and Harp Concerto

New Entries
1999

80 **Rutter**: *Requiem*

169 **Ravel**: Concerto for Piano
and Orchestra in G

212 **Satie**: *Gnossienne No. 1*

236 **Preisner**: *Requiem for my Friend*

267 **Vivaldi**: *Gloria*

268 **Lloyd Webber**: *Requiem*

283 **Haydn**: Symphony No. 101 in D

296 **Tchaikovsky**: String Quartet No. 1

297 **Debussy**: *Arabesques*

298 **Williams**: *Star Wars*

299 **Khachaturian**: *Gayaneh*

Top 50
1998

1 **Bruch**: Violin Concerto No. 1
2 **Rachmaninov**: Piano Concerto No. 2
3 **Mozart**: Clarinet Concerto
4 **Beethoven**: Symphony No. 6 (Pastoral)
5 **Vaughan Williams**: *The Lark Ascending*
6 **Mahler**: Symphony No. 5
7 **Saint-Saëns**: Symphony No. 3 (Organ)
8 **Elgar**: *Enigma Variations*
9 **Elgar**: Cello Concerto in E minor
10 **Beethoven**: Piano Concerto No. 5
11 **Pachelbel**: Canon in D
12 **Barber**: *Adagio for Strings*
13 **Bizet**: *Les Pêcheurs de Perles*
14 **Allegri**: *Miserere*
15 **Fauré**: *Requiem*
16 **Mozart**: Piano Concerto No. 21 (*Elvira Madigan*)
17 **Beethoven**: Symphony No. 9 (Choral)
18 **Vivaldi**: *Le Quattro Stagione*
19 **Grieg**: Piano Concerto in A minor
20 **Mascagni**: *Cavalleria Rusticana*
21 **Mendelssohn**: Violin Concerto in E minor
22 **Holst**: *The Planets Suite*
23 **Rodrigo**: *Concierto de Aranjuez*
24 **Albinoni**: *Adagio*

25 **Mozart**: *Requiem*
26 **Rimsky-Korsakov**: *Scheherezade*
27 **Dvořák**: Symphony No. 9
28 **J. S. Bach**: Concerto for Two Violins
29 **Handel**: *Messiah*
30 **Sibelius**: *Finlandia*
31 **Vaughan Williams**: *Fantasia on a Theme of Thomas Tallis*
32 **Verdi**: *Nabucco*
33 **Fauré**: *Cantique de Jean Racine*
34 **Beethoven**: Symphony No. 5
35 **Prokofiev**: *Romeo and Juliet*
36 **Puccini**: *Madama Butterfly*
37 **Massenet**: *'Meditation' from Thaïs*
38 **Beethoven**: Symphony No. 7
39 **Beethoven**: Violin Concerto
40 **Orff**: *Carmina Burana*
41 **Beethoven**: Sonata No.14 Op. 27 No. 2 ('Moonlight')
42 **Tchaikovsky**: Symphony No. 6 'Pathétique'
43 **Puccini**: *La Bohème*
44 **Rachmaninov**: Symphony No. 2
45 **Shostakovich**: *The Gadfly*
46 **Smetana**: *Má Vlast*
47 **Grieg**: *Peer Gynt Suite No. 1*
48 **Delibes**: *Lakmé*
49 **J. S. Bach**: *Brandenburg Concertos*
50 **Verdi**: *Requiem*

New Entries
1998

53 **Tavener**: *Song for Athene*

75 **Horner**: *Titanic*

76 **McCartney**: *Standing Stone*

120 **Bruch**: Violin Concerto No. 2

182 **Vivaldi**: Double Concerto for Two Mandolins

193 **Vivaldi**: *Nulla in mundo pax sincera*

197 **Mozart**: Violin Concerto No. 4

206 **Bruch**: Violin Concerto No. 3

209 **Schubert**: Impromptu No. 3 in G flat

213 **Jenkins**: *Adiemus II: Cantata Mundi*

225 **Khachaturian**: *Masquerade*

255 **Mozart**: Sonata for Keyboard No. 11 (*Rondo alla turca*)

258 **Chen Kang** and **Ho Zhan Hao**: *Butterfly Lover's Violin Concerto*

259 **R. Strauss**: 'Also sprach Zarathustra'

263 **Rodrigo**: *Fantasia para un gentilhombre*

264 **Mozart**: Serenade No. 10 in B flat for 13 wind instruments

266 **Clara Schumann**: Piano Concerto

274 **Weber**: Clarinet Concerto No. 2

275 **Walton**: *Crown Imperial*

276 **Copland**: *Rodeo*

277 **Tchaikovsky**: *Marche slave*

278 **J. Clarke**: *Prince of Denmark's March (Trumpet Voluntary)*

285 **Barber**: Violin Concerto

286 **Shostakovich**: Symphony No. 7

288 **Parry**: *Jerusalem*

292 **Mozart**: Violin Concerto No. 3

295 **Saraste**: *Zigeunerweisen*

296 **Jenkins**: *Palladio*

300 **Glazunov**: *The Seasons*

Top 50
1997

1. **Bruch**: Violin Concerto No. 1
2. **Rachmaninov**: Piano Concerto No. 2
3. **Beethoven**: Symphony No. 6 (Pastoral)
4. **Elgar**: Cello Concerto in E minor
5. **Mozart**: Clarinet Concerto
6. **Elgar**: *Enigma Variations*
7. **Beethoven**: Piano Concerto No. 5
8. **Mozart**: Piano Concerto No. 21 (*Elvira Madigan*)
9. **Bizet**: *Les Pêcheurs de Perles*
10. **Barber**: *Adagio for Strings*
11. **Mahler**: Symphony No. 5
12. **Beethoven**: Symphony No. 9 (Choral)
13. **Vivaldi**: *Four Seasons*
14. **Pachelbel**: Canon in D
15. **Mascagni**: *Cavalleria Rusticana*
16. **Saint-Saëns**: Symphony No. 3 (Organ)
17. **Vaughan Williams**: *The Lark Ascending*
18. **Dvořák**: Symphony No. 9 ('From the New World')
19. **Fauré**: *Requiem*
20. **Handel**: *Messiah*
21. **Mendelssohn**: Violin Concerto in E minor
22. **Holst**: *The Planets Suite*
23. **Verdi**: *Nabucco*
24. **Rachmaninov**: Piano Concerto No. 3
25. **Albinoni**: *Adagio*
26. **Grieg**: Piano Concerto in A minor
27. **Rimsky-Korsakov**: *Scheherezade*
28. **J. S. Bach**: Concerto for Two Violins
29. **Beethoven**: Violin Concerto
30. **Schubert**: *'Trout' Quintet*
31. **Sibelius**: *Finlandia*
32. **Orff**: *Carmina Burana*
33. **Allegri**: *Miserere*
34. **Rodrigo**: *Concierto de Aranjuez*
35. **Puccini**: *La Bohème*
36. **Mozart**: *Requiem*
37. **Beethoven**: Symphony No. 5
38. **Tchaikovsky**: Piano Concerto No. 1
39. **Smetana**: *Má Vlast*
40. **Rachmaninov**: Symphony No. 2
41. **Prokofiev**: *Romeo and Juliet*
42. **Beethoven**: Sonata No.14 Op. 27 No. 2 ('Moonlight')
43. **Beethoven**: Symphony No. 7
44. **Puccini**: *Madama Butterfly*
45. **Grieg**: Peer Gynt Suite No. 1
46. **Tchaikovsky**: Symphony No. 6 'Pathétique'
47. **Verdi**: *Aida*
48. **Fauré**: *Cantique de Jean Racine*
49. **J. S. Bach**: *Brandenburg Concertos*
50. **Handel**: *Solomon*

New Entries
1997

127 **Vivaldi**: Mandolin Concerto, RV425

134 **Jenkins**: *Adiemus: Songs of Sanctuary*

179 **Caccini**: 'Ave Maria'

187 **Verdi**: *La Forza del Destino*

189 **Barber**: *Agnus Dei*

195 **Shostakovich**: Jazz Suite No. 2

203 **Verdi**: *Il Trovatore*

204 **Zipoli**: *Elevazione*

207 **Lehár**: The Merry Widow

210 **Litolff**: Concerto Symphonique No. 4

220 **J. S. Bach**: Cello Suites

226 **Shostakovich**: Jazz Suite No. 1

229 **Franck**: Sonata for Violin and Piano in A

231 **Rameau**: *Les Indes Galantes*

235 **Tchaikovsky**: *Eugene Onegin*

239 **Suppé**: *Poet and Peasant Overture*

242 **Gounod**: *Faust*

243 **Offenbach**: *Orpheus and the Underworld*

246 **Bruckner**: Symphony No. 7

247 **Elgar**: Pomp and Circumstance March No. 4

254 **J. Strauss II**: *'Nuns' Chorus' from Casanova*

255 **Bruckner**: Symphony No. 8

259 **Puccini**: *La Rondine*

260 **Joplin**: *Piano Rags*

261 **Bernstein**: *Candide Overture*

262 **Rachmaninov**: Piano Concerto No.1

263 **Wagner**: *Götterdämmerung*

264 **Delius**: *On Hearing the First Cuckoo in Spring*

267 **Grieg**: Lyric Pieces No. 8

268 **MacCunn**: *Land of the Mountain and the Flood*

272 **Liszt**: *Liebestraume* No. 3

273 **Weber**: Clarinet Concerto No. 1

279 **Grieg**: Peer Gynt Suite No.2

281 **Elgar**: *Sea Pictures*

282 **Nyman**: *The Piano*

286 **Gershwin**: Piano Concerto in F

287 **Vaughan Williams**: English Folk Song Suite

288 **Ravel**: Piano Concerto in G

289 **J. S. Bach**: Concerto for Violin No. 1

290 **Beethoven**: Piano Sonata No. 23 ('Appassionata')

291 **Smetana**: *The Bartered Bride*

297 **Sibelius**: *Valse Triste*

299 **Glinka**: *Russlan and Ludmila Overture*

Top 50
1996

1 **Bruch**: Violin Concerto No. 1
2 **Rachmaninov**: Piano Concerto No. 2
3 **Beethoven**: Symphony No. 6 (Pastoral)
4 **Mozart**: Clarinet Concerto
5 **Beethoven**: Symphony No. 9 (Choral)
6 **Elgar**: Cello Concerto in E minor
7 **Elgar**: *Enigma Variations*
8 **Beethoven**: Piano Concerto No. 5
9 **Mozart**: Piano Concerto No. 21 (Elvira Madigan)
10 **Handel**: *Messiah*
11 **Vivaldi**: *Four Seasons*
12 **Mahler**: Symphony No. 5
13 **Pachelbel**: Canon in D
14 **Bizet**: *Les Pêcheurs de Perles*
15 **Dvořák**: Symphony No. 9 ('From the New World')
16 **Barber**: *Adagio for Strings*
17 **Albinoni**: *Adagio*
18 **Vaughan Williams**: *The Lark Ascending*
19 **Beethoven**: Symphony No. 5
20 **Mendelssohn**: Violin Concerto in E minor
21 **Rimsky-Korsakov**: *Scheherezade*
22 **Fauré**: *Requiem*
23 **Saint-Saëns**: Symphony No. 3 (Organ)

24 **Mozart**: *Requiem*
25 **Beethoven**: Symphony No. 7
26 **J. S. Bach**: Concerto for Two Violins
27 **Schubert**: *'Trout' Quintet*
28 **Mascagni**: *Cavalleria Rusticana*
29 **Grieg**: Piano Concerto in A minor
30 **Delibes**: *Sylvia*
31 **Rodrigo**: *Concierto de Aranjuez*
32 **Beethoven**: Violin Concerto
33 **Allegri**: *Miserere*
34 **Verdi**: *Aida*
35 **Orff**: *Carmina Burana*
36 **Tchaikovsky**: Symphony No. 6 'Pathétique'
37 **Tchaikovsky**: Piano Concerto No. 1
38 **Tchaikovsky**: *1812 Overture*
39 **Beethoven**: Sonata No.14 Op. 27 No. 2 ('Moonlight')
40 **Vaughan Williams**: *Fantasia on a Theme of Thomas Tallis*
41 **Sibelius**: *Finlandia*
42 **Mozart**: *Eine Kleine Nachtmusik*
43 **Puccini**: *La Bohème*
44 **Prokofiev**: *Romeo and Juliet*
45 **Rachmaninov**: Symphony No. 2
46 **Tchaikovsky**: *Romeo and Juliet*
47 **Sibelius**: Symphony No. 2
48 **Ravel**: *Bolero*
49 **Grieg**: *Peer Gynt* Suite No. 1
50 **Puccini**: *Madama Butterfly*

SELECTED CHARTS

Top Composers

Based on number of entries in the Hall of Fame Collection

1	Mozart	23
2	Beethoven	20
3	Tchaikovsky	13
4	Elgar	12
5	J. S. Bach	11
6	Schubert	10
7	Brahms	9
=8	Sibelius	8
=8	Verdi	8
=10	Vivaldi	7
=10	Wagner	7
=12	Dvořák	6
=12	Handel	6
=12	Mahler	6
=12	Mendelssohn	6
=12	Puccini	6
=12	Saint-Saëns	6
=12	Vaughan Williams	6
=19	Rachmaninov	5
=19	Shostakovich	5
=21	Bruch	4
=21	Bizet	4
=21	Chopin	4
=21	Grieg	4
=21	Gounod	4
=21	Ravel	4

Top Orchestras

Based on number of recommended recordings

1 **London Symphony Orchestra** (1, 2, 5, 6, 11, 14, 19, 21, 36, 49, 70, 72, 78, 79, 86, 91, 94, 95, 106, 116 (twice), 125 (twice), 126, 139, 165, 167, 179, 198, 211, 217, 222, 236, 249, 252, 268 (twice), 271 (twice), 279, 283, 286, 289, 290, 300)

2 **Berlin Philharmonic** (2, 7, 8, 21, 23, 36, 40, 41, 68, 77, 82, 94, 103, 111, 119, 150, 152, 171, 182, 206, 212, 223, 226, 237, 240, 242, 297)

3 **Vienna Philharmonic** (4, 7, 9, 10, 32, 35, 39, 45, 52, 54, 55, 74, 90, 92, 117, 118, 132, 134, 136, 200, 215, 229, 255, 276, 282, 285)

4 **Philharmonia** (8, 29, 32, 35, 43, 60, 63, 64, 70, 79, 81, 93, 96 (twice), 120, 127, 132, 138, 153, 231, 251, 269)

5 **London Philharmonic** (1, 17, 28, 37, 42, 68, 76, 97, 125, 170, 178, 186, 206, 225, 241, 252, 284, 288, 289)

6 **Royal Concertgebouw** (31, 54, 57, 85 (twice), 90, 100, 107, 119, 136, 171, 196, 203, 204, 213, 229, 233)

7 **Royal Philharmonic** (2, 5, 69, 72, 84, 95, 123, 141, 143, 193, 222, 231, 246, 256, 279, 283)

8 **English Chamber** (3, 10, 16, 30, 128 (twice), 163 (twice), 207, 232, 269, 287)

=9 **Chicago Symphony** (28 (twice), 57 (twice), 72, 98, 155, 161, 237, 262)

=9 **Czech Philharmonic** (20, 21, 47, 110 (twice), 164, 247 (twice), 262, 276)

=9 **Royal Scottish National** (5, 23, 40, 104, 121, 122, 177, 213, 227, 270)

=12 **Chamber Orchestra of Europe** (4, 10, 29, 135, 138, 205, 224, 255, 281)

=12 **Gothenburg Symphony** (34, 48, 51, 63, 65, 145, 181, 202, 296)

=14 **La Scala** (37, 55, 96, 115, 130, 147, 156, 187)

=14 **Leipzig Gewandhaus** (1, 20, 92, 109, 111, 159, 205, 257)

=14 **Tafelmusik** (7, 26, 59, 83, 87, 114, 166, 197)

=17 **National Philharmonic** (17, 115, 147, 153, 187, 200, 292)

=17 **New York Philharmonic** (74, 94, 100, 107, 126, 192, 248)

=17 **Philadelphia** (15, 43, 53, 78, 159, 177, 285)

=17 **Staatskapelle Dresden** (3, 82, 99, 146, 149, 155, 164)

Top Conductors

Based on number of recommended recordings

= 1 **Claudio Abbado** (2, 7, 10, 36, 41, 55, 74, 103, 138, 150, 171, 182, 206, 237, 240, 242, 255)

= 1 **Nikolaus Harnoncourt** (4, 54, 57, 90, 100, 107, 135, 136, 140, 197, 205, 207, 229, 242, 250, 265, 281)

3 **Neeme Järvi** (34, 40, 47, 48, 51, 63, 65, 121, 122, 145, 181, 202, 213, 227, 296)

4 **Herbert von Karajan** (23, 39, 41, 45, 55, 68, 92, 94, 132, 152, 229, 282, 297)

5 **Daniel Barenboim** (28, 57, 72, 82, 117, 118, 155, 161, 189, 215, 238, 262)

6 **Sir John Barbirolli** (5, 6, 9, 42, 154, 158, 222, 254, 256, 259, 290)

= 7 **Sir Adrian Boult** (1, 6, 11, 23, 95, 148, 170, 178, 186, 286)

= 7 **André Previn** (2, 36, 49, 70, 91, 252, 268, 276, 283, 289)

= 9 **Riccardo Chailly** (37, 53, 129, 130, 147 (twice), 156, 196, 204)

= 9 **Sir Colin Davis** (19, 63, 65, 85, 86, 139, 224, 225, 289)

= 9 **Antal Dorati** (51, 79, 106, 125, 160, 161, 214, 239, 249)

= 9 **Sir Charles Mackerras** (73, 78, 84, 94, 110, 120, 141, 241, 247)

= 9 **Kurt Masur** (1, 20, 92, 94, 109, 111, 159, 205, 257)

= 9 **David Zinman** (4, 8, 32, 35, 81, 113, 162, 274, 285)

= 15 **Philippe Herreweghe** (18, 30, 71, 80, 127, 135, 217, 281)

= 15 **Sir Simon Rattle** (6, 7, 11, 74, 148, 150, 176, 206)

= 17 **Richard Hickox** (104, 116, 162, 217, 236, 268, 288)

= 17 **Mariss Jansons** (15, 28, 43, 45, 85, 92, 152)

= 17 **Adrian Leaper** (69, 72, 85, 123, 154, 228, 279)

= 20 **Karl Böhm** (4, 77, 90, 120, 134, 136)

= 20 **Carlo Maria Giulini** (60, 64, 79, 96, 138, 220)

= 20 **Eugene Ormandy** (15, 43, 78, 159, 177, 285)

Top Pianists

Based on number of recommended recordings

1 **Murray Perahia** (10, 64, 79, 128, 163, 182, 255, 264, 275)
2 **Vladimir Ashkenazy** (2, 36, 49, 221, 264, 275, 283)
3 **Mitsuko Uchida** (10, 119, 128, 163, 171)
= 4 **Alfred Brendel** (7, 33, 44, 206)
= 4 **Emil Gilels** (44, 111, 169, 223)
= 4 **Jeno Jandó** (22, 33, 182, 273)
= 4 **Wilhelm Kempff** (44, 119, 169, 172)

Top Violinists

Based on number of recommended recordings

= 1 **Kyung-Wha Chung** (1, 31, 70, 91, 95, 96)
= 1 **Kennedy** (11, 16, 31, 148, 186, 228)
= 3 **Yehudi Menuhin** (26, 96, 148, 209, 297)
= 3 **Maxim Vengerov** (1, 20, 57, 137, 234)
= 5 **Jascha Heifetz** (31, 57)
= 5 **Midori** (95, 261)
= 5 **Isaac Stern** (159, 230)
= 5 **Joseph Suk** (20, 52)

The Essential 20

These pieces should be at the heart of any
classical collection, but they would also make a
nice compact classical library on their own

1   **Vivaldi**: *Four Seasons* (16)
2   **Elgar**: Cello Concerto (5)
3   **Pachelbel**: Canon in D (13 – the I Musici recording also has
    Albinoni's *Adagio* and Mozart's *Eine Kleine Nachtmusik*, also
    essential in any record collection)
4   **Mendelssohn**: Violin Concerto (20 – coupled with the Hall of Fame
    No.1, Bruch's Violin Concerto, on Maxim Vengerov's recording)
5   **Tchaikovsky**: Piano Concerto No. 1 (41 – the BIS recording also has
    the Grieg Piano Concerto)
6   **Holst**: *The Planets Suite* (23)
7   **Allegri**: *Miserere* (25 – the Choir of New College also performs other
    essential choral work on their recording)
8   **Rodrigo**: *Concierto de Aranjuez* (29)
9   **Rachmaninov**: Piano Concerto No. 3 (36 – the Decca recording has all
    four Rachmaninov piano concertos with Ashkenazy performing)
10 **Vaughan Williams**: *Fantasia on a Theme of Thomas Tallis* (42)
11 All the **Beethoven** symphonies (4, 8, 32, 35, 81, 323, 358)
12 **Bach**: *Brandenburg Concertos* (46)
13 **Bach**: Cello Suites (174)
14 **Mozart**: *Requiem* (30)
15 **Elgar**: *Enigma Variations* (6)
16 **Mozart**: Clarinet Concerto (3)
17 **Handel**: *Water Music* (83)
18 **Beethoven**: Piano Sonata No.14 ('Moonlight') (44 – select a recording
    that also features Sonatas Nos 8, 21 and 23)
19 **Bizet**: *Carmen* (76)
20 **Puccini**: *La Bohème* (37)

20 Must-have Recordings

Keith Shadwick's choice of superlative CDs

3   **Mozart**: Clarinet Concerto (EMI/Meyer)

4   **Beethoven**: Symphony No. 6 (Deutsche Grammophon/Böhm)

9   **Mahler**: Symphony No. 5 (EMI/Barbirolli)

10   **Mozart**: Piano Concerto No. 21 (Sony/Perahia)

12   **Bizet**: *Les Pêcheurs de Perles* (RCA/Cellini)

16   **Vivaldi**: *The Four Seasons* (Teldec/Antonini)

31   **Beethoven**: Violin Concerto (RCA/Heifetz – also features Brahms's Violin Concerto)

68   **R. Strauss**: *Vier Letzte Lieder* (Deutsche Grammophon/Karajan)

76   **Bizet**: *Carmen* (EMI/Beecham)

98   **J. Strauss II**: *The Blue Danube* (RCA/Reiner)

111   **Brahms**: Piano Concerto No. 2 (Deutsche Grammophon/Gilels)

113   **Górecki**: Symphony No. 3 (Nonesuch/Zinman)

120   **Mozart**: *Così fan tutte* (EMI/Böhm)

138   **Mozart**: *Don Giovanni* (EMI/Giulini)

179   **Debussy**: *Prélude à l'Après-midi d'un Faune* (Sony/Salonen)

222   **Delius**: *The Walk to the Paradise Garden* (EMI/Barbirolli)

229   **J. Strauss II**: *Die Fledermaus* (Decca/Karajan)

288   **Britten**: *Four Sea Interludes* (RCA/Slatkin)

295   **Mahler**: *Das Lied von der Erde* (EMI/Klemperer)

352   **Debussy**: *Preludes Book 1* (Decca/Thibaudet)

Top 20 Relaxing Classics

These tracks are all included on
the Classic FM CD *Relax* (CFMCD30)

1   **Bruch**: Violin Concerto No.1 in G minor
    (2nd Movement – *adagio*)(1)
2   **Rachmaninov**: Piano Concerto No. 2 in C minor
    (2nd Movement – a*dagio sostenuto*) (2)
3   **Mahler**: Symphony No. 5 in C sharp minor
    (4th Movement – *adagietto*) (9)
4   **Vaughan Williams**: *The Lark Ascending* (11)
5   **Pachelbel**: Canon in D (13)
6   **Barber**: *Adagio for Strings* (14)
7   **Mascagni**: *Intermezzo* from *Cavalleria Rusticana* (17)
8   **Grieg**: Piano Concerto in A minor (2nd Movement – *adagio*) (22)
9   **Albinoni**: Adagio in G minor (24)
10 **Allegri**: *Miserere* (25)
11 **Rodrigo**: *Concierto de Aranjuez* (2nd Movement – *adagio*) (29)
12 **Vaughan Williams**: *Fantasia on a Theme of Thomas Tallis* (42)
13 **Tchaikovsky**: Symphony No. 6 in B minor
    (2nd Movement – *allegro con grazio*) (45)
14 **Rachmaninov**: Rhapsody on a Theme of Paganini – Variation 18 (49)
15 **Massenet**: *Thaïs – Meditation* (52)
16 **Shostakovich**: *The Gadfly* (53)
17 **J. S. Bach**: Air 'on the G String' (105)
18 **Khachaturian**: *Spartacus – adagio* (122)
19 **Satie**: *Gymnopédie No.1* (131)
20 **Fauré**: *Pavane* (142)

Top 20 Stirring Classics

1   **Elgar**: Cello Concerto in E minor (5)
2   **Elgar**: *Enigma Variations* (6)
3   **Beethoven**: Piano Concerto No. 5 in E flat (7)
4   **Beethoven**: Symphony No. 9 'Choral' (8)
5   **Saint-Saëns**: Symphony No. 3 'Organ' (15)
6   **Vivaldi**: *Le Quattro Stagione* (16)
7   **Handel**: *Messiah* (19)
8   **Dvořák**: Symphony No. 9 in E minor 'New World' (21)
9   **Holst**: *The Planets Suite* (23)
10   **Beethoven**: Symphony No. 5 (32)
11   **Sibelius**: *Finlandia* (34)
12   **Orff**: *Carmina Burana* (38)
13   **Prokofiev**: *Romeo and Juliet* ('Dance of the Knights') (40)
14   **Tchaikovsky**: Piano Concerto No.1 in B flat minor (41)
15   **J. S. Bach**: *Brandenburg Concertos* (46)
16   **Smetana**: 'Vltava' from *Má Vlast* (47)
17   **Tchaikovsky**: 1812 Overture (51)
18   **Handel**: *Solomon* ('Arrival of the Queen of Sheba') (56)
19   **Handel**: *Zadok the Priest* (58)
20   **J. S. Bach**: Toccata and Fugue in D minor (61)

Top 20 Operas

1   **Bizet**: *Les Pêcheurs de Perles* (12)
2   **Mascagni**: *Cavalleria Rusticana* (17)
3   **Verdi**: *Nabucco* (27)
4   **Puccini**: *La Bohème* (37)
5   **Puccini**: *Madama Butterfly* (39)
6   **Massenet**: *Thaïs* (52)
7   **Mozart**: *The Marriage of Figaro* (54)
8   **Verdi**: *Aida* (55)
9   **Delibes**: *Lakmé* (62)
10 **Verdi**: *La Traviata* (73)
11 **Bizet**: *Carmen* (76)
12 **Mozart**: *The Magic Flute* (77)
13 **Wagner**: *Tristan and Isolde* (82)
14 **Gluck**: *Orpheus and Eurydice* (87)
15 **Puccini**: *Turandot* (97)
16 **Wagner**: *Tannhäuser* (106)
17 **Dvořák**: *Rusalka* (110)
18 **Puccini**: *Tosca* (115)
19 **Wagner**: *Die Walküre* (117)
20 **Wagner**: *Götterdämmerung* (118)

Top 20 Romantic Classics

1   **Bruch**: Violin Concerto No. 1 in G minor (1)
2   **Rachmaninov**: Piano Concerto No. 2 in C minor (2)
3   **Mozart**: Clarinet Concerto in A (3)
4   **Mozart**: Piano Concerto No. 21 in C (10)
5   **Vaughan Williams**: *The Lark Ascending* (11)
6   **Saint-Saëns**: Symphony No. 3 'Organ' (15)
7   **Grieg**: Piano Concerto in A minor (22)
8   **J. S. Bach**: Double Violin Concerto in D minor (26)
9   **Rimsky-Korsakov**: *Scheherezade* (28)
10 **Beethoven**: Violin Concerto in D major (31)
11 **Puccini**: *Madama Butterfly* (39)
12 **Rachmaninov**: Symphony No. 2 in E minor (43)
13 **Smetana**: 'Vltava' from *Má Vlast* (47)
14 **Rachmaninov**: Rhapsody on a Theme by Paganini (49)
15 **Shostakovich**: 'Romance' from *The Gadfly* (53)
16 **Brahms**: Violin Concerto in D major (57)
17 **Mozart**: Flute and Harp Concerto (66)
18 **Schubert**: String Quintet in C (67)
19 **Tchaikovsky**: *Romeo and Juliet* (72)
20 **Debussy**: *Clair de Lune* (89)

Top 20 20th-Century Classics

1   **Rachmaninov**: Piano Concerto No.2 in C minor (2)

2   **Elgar**: Cello Concerto in E minor (5)

3   **Mahler**: Symphony No. 5 in C# minor (9)

4   **Vaughan Williams**: *The Lark Ascending* (11)

5   **Barber**: *Adagio for Strings* (14)

6   **Holst**: *The Planets Suite* (23)

7   **Rodrigo**: *Concierto de Aranjuez* (29)

8   **Rachmaninov**: Piano Concerto No. 3 in D minor (36)

9   **Orff**: *Carmina Burana* (38)

10   **Puccini**: *Madama Butterfly* (39)

11   **Prokofiev**: *Romeo and Juliet* (40)

12   **Vaughan Williams**: *Fantasia on a Theme by Thomas Tallis* (42)

13   **Rachmaninov**: Symphony No. 2 in E minor (43)

14   **Rachmaninov**: *Rhapsody on a Theme by Paganini* (49)

15   **Shostakovich**: 'Romance' from *The Gadfly* (53)

16   **Sibelius**: Symphony No. 2 in D minor (63)

17   **Sibelius**: Symphony No. 5 in E flat (65)

18   **R. Strauss**: *Vier Letzte Lieder* (68)

19   **Ravel**: *Bolero* (69)

20   **Shostakovich**: Piano Concerto No. 2 (88)

20 Movie Classics

The popularity of these pieces was greatly boosted after they appeared in some very successful movies.

1　**Rachmaninov**: Piano Concerto No. 2 in C minor (2)
 　　[*Brief Encounter/The Seven Year Itch*]
2　**Mozart**: Clarinet Concerto in A major (3) [*Out of Africa*]
3　**Beethoven**: Symphony No. 6 'Pastoral' (4) [*Fantasia*]
4　**Elgar**: Cello Concerto in E minor (5) [*Hilary and Jackie*]
5　**Elgar**: *Enigma Variations* – 'Nimrod' (6) [*Elizabeth*]
6　**Beethoven**: Symphony No. 9 'Choral' (8)
 　　[*Dead Poets' Society/A Clockwork Orange*]
7　**Mahler**: Symphony No. 5 in C# minor (9) [*Death in Venice*]
8　**Mozart**: Piano Concerto No. 21 in C (10) [*Elvira Madigan*]
9　**Bizet**: Duet from *Les Pêcheurs de Perles* (12) [*Gallipoli*]
10　**Pachelbel**: Canon in D (13) [*Ordinary People*]
11　**Barber**: Adagio for Strings (14) [*Platoon/The Elephant Man*]
12　**Saint-Saëns**: Symphony No. 3 'Organ' (15) [*Babe*]
13　**Mascagni**: *Intermezzo* from *Cavalleria Rusticana* (17)
 　　[*Raging Bull/Godfather III*]
14　**Fauré**: *Requiem* (18) [*The Thin Red Line*]
15　**Dvořák**: Symphony No. 9 in E minor 'New World' (21) [*Paradise Road*]
16　**Albinoni**: *Adagio* in G minor (24) [*Gallipoli*]
17　**J. S. Bach**: Double Violin Concerto in D minor (26)
 　　[*Children of a Lesser God*]
18　**Mozart**: *Requiem* (30) [*Amadeus*]
19　**Sibelius**: *Finlandia* (34) [*Die Hard 2*]
20　**Rachmaninov**: Piano Concerto No. 3 in D minor (36) [*Shine*]

Top 20 UK
TV Commercial Themes

These tracks, made memorable in many successful TV
advertisements, are all included on the Classic FM CD
Adverts Hall of Fame (CFMCD26)

1   **Beethoven**: Symphony No. 6 in F 'Pastoral' (5th Movement –
    allegretto) (4)
2   **Elgar**: Cello Concerto in E minor (1st Movement – adagio moderato)
    (5)
3   **Mahler**: Symphony No. 5 in C# minor (4th Movement – adagietto) (9)
4   **Pachelbel**: Canon in D (13)
5   **Barber**: *Adagio for Strings* (14)
6   **Mascagni**: *Intermezzo* from *Cavalleria Rusticana* (17)
7   **Dvořák**: Symphony No. 9 in E minor 'From the New World' (2nd
    Movement – largo) (21)
8   **Holst**: 'Jupiter, the Bringer of Jollity' from *The Planets* (23)
9   **Orff**: 'O Fortuna' from *Carmina Burana* (38)
10 **Smetana**: 'Vltava' from *Má Vlast* (47)
11 **Tchaikovsky**: *1812 Overture* (51)
12 **Handel**: 'Arrival of the Queen of Sheba' from *Solomon* (56)
13 **Mozart**: *Eine Kleine Nachtmusik* (4th Movement – allegro) (59)
14 **Verdi**: 'Dies Irae' from *Requiem Mass* (60)
15 **J. S. Bach**: Toccata & Fugue in D minor (61)
16 **Delibes**: 'Flower Duet' from *Lakmé* (62)
17 **Bizet**: 'Toreador's Song' from *Carmen* (76)
18 **Tchaikovsky**: 'Dance of the Reed-Flutes' from *The Nutcracker* (78)
19 **Gershwin**: *Rhapsody in Blue* (93)
20 **Puccini**: 'Nessun Dorma' from *Turandot* (97)

Top 20 Record Labels

Based on the number of recommendations each record label receives in this book, these are the most successful Hall of Fame recording companies.

	Label	Number of recordings
1	**EMI**	88
2	**Sony**	87
3	**Deutsche Grammophon**	85
4	**Decca**	66
5	**Chandos**	56
= 6	**Teldec**	48
= 6	**Naxos**	48
= 8	**Philips**	44
= 8	**RCA**	44
10	**Hyperion**	26
11	**Erato**	25
= 12	**Harmonia Mundi**	17
= 12	**BIS**	17
= 12	**Telarc**	17
15	**Supraphon**	15
= 16	**Arte Nova**	9
= 16	**Virgin**	9
= 18	**Mercury**	7
= 18	**Belart**	7
= 20	**ASV**	6
= 20	**Hanssler**	6

One-Hit Wonders

Composers who have just one entry
in the Hall of Fame Collection

Allegri	Gorecki	MacCunn	Smetana
Bellini	Holst	Nyman	Schumann
Bernstein	Horner	Orff	Suppé
Boccherini	Hummel	Pachelbel	Tallis
Britten	Jenkins	Paganini	Tárrega
Butterworth	Lehár	Pergolesi	Tavener
Caccini	Litolff	Purcell	Widor
Canteloube	Mascagni	Rodrigo	Zipoli
Clarke	Massenet	Rameau	
Donizetti	Monteverdi	Rutter	
Gluck	McCartney	Satie	

In which century were the pieces in the
Hall of Fame Collection composed? (per cent)

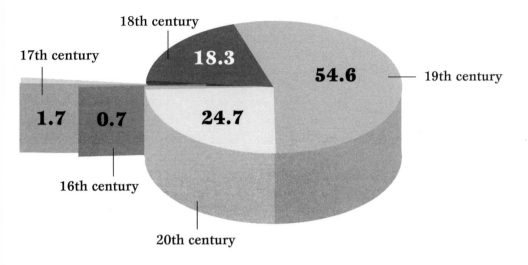

17th century

18th century

1.7   0.7   24.7   18.3   54.6   19th century

16th century

20th century

Index

A

Aalborg Symphony Orchestra 111, 205

Abbado, Claudio 20, 25, 28, 54, 59, 73, 92, 120, 143, 154, 159, 171, 187, 188, 189, 196

Abbondanza, Roberto 169

Academic Festival Overture (Brahms) 199

Academy of Ancient Music 37, 44, 124, 138, 162

Academy of St Martin-in-the-Fields 21, 38, 74, 118, 125, 208

Accardo, Salvatore 88, 114

Adagio (Albinoni) 42

Adagio for Strings (Barber) 32

Addinsell, Richard
  The Warsaw Concerto 233

Adiemus (Jenkins) 131

Agnew, Paul 124

Agnus Dei (Barber) 173

Aida (Verdi) 73

Ainsley, John Mark 124, 177

Akademie Für Alte Musik, Berlin 64, 121

Alagna, Roberto 55, 141, 204

Albéniz, Isaac
  Suite española No. 1 235

Albinoni, Tomasso
  Adagio 42
  Oboe Concerto in B Flat Major 234
  Oboe Concerto in D Minor 186

Aler, John 30, 56, 184

Alessandrini, Rinaldo 169

Allegri, Gregorio
  Miserere 13, 14, 43

Allegri String Quartet 60, 130, 145

Allen, Nancy 84

Almeida, Antonio de 140

Ameling, Elly 172

Amps, Kym 37

Amsterdam Baroque Orchestra 101, 104, 124

Ancerl, Karel 38, 39

Anderson, June 133

Anderson, Mark 180

Andsnes, Leif Ove 40

Anichanov, André 129, 218

Antál, Mátyás 122, 193

Antonini, Giovanni 34

Appalachian Spring (Copland) 131

Araiza, Francisco 141

Archibudelli L' 130, 217

Argenta, Ataulfo 208

Argenta, Nancy 105

Argerich, Martha 59

Arlésienne, L', Suite No. 1 (Bizet) 215

Arroyo, Martina 165

Asch, David van 37

Ashkenazy, Vladimir 20, 54, 67, 81, 179, 200, 206, 210

Ashton, Caroline 36

Atlanta Symphony Orchestra 56, 78

Augér, Arleen 92, 117, 122, 189, 190

Ave Maria (Caccini) 13, 165

Ave Maria (Gounod) 204

Ave Maria (Schubert) 198

Ave Verum Corpus (Mozart) 104

B

Bach, Johann Sebastian
  Brandenburg Concertos 64
  Cantata BWV 140 190
  Cantata BWV 147 122
  Cantata BWV 208 193
  Cello Suites 155
  Christmas Oratorio 232
  Concerto for Two Violins 44
  Concerto for Violin No. 1 in A Minor 226
  Concerto for Violin No. 2 in E 225
  Goldberg Variations 195
  Magnificat 234
  Mass in B Minor 117
  Orchestral Suite No. 2 235
  Orchestral Suites 121
  Partita No. 2 234
  St John Passion 232
  St Matthew Passion 98
  Toccata and Fugue in D Minor 79

Bacquier, Gabriel 80

Baker, Dame Janet 92, 213

Baldin, Aldo 190

Balfe, Michael
  The Bohemian Girl 234

Baltimore Symphony Orchestra 149, 205, 211

Bamberg Symphony Orchestra 40

Banks of Green Willow, The (Butterworth) 178

Barber, Samuel
  Adagio for Strings 32
  Agnus Dei 173
  Violin Concerto 223

Barbieri, Fedora 73

Barbieri di Siviglia, Il (Rossini) 146

Barbirolli, Sir John 14, 23, 24, 27, 60, 145, 147, 179, 195, 196, 198, 213

Barenboim, Daniel 46, 75, 90, 100, 127, 146, 149, 163, 176, 187, 199

Barrell, David 56

Barshai, Rudolf 173

Bartók, Béla
  Concerto for Orchestra 232

Bartoletti, Bruno 163

Bath Festival Orchestra 44, 64, 173, 217

Batiz, Enrique 47, 215

Bavarian Radio Symphony Orchestra 117, 121, 164, 180, 181

Bavarian State Opera Orchestra 91, 94, 187

Bayreuth Festival Orchestra 127, 163, 176

BBC Philharmonic Orchestra 70

BBC Scottish Symphony Orchestra 200

BBC Symphony Orchestra 59, 60, 147, 153, 195, 198

Bean, Hugh 29

Beaux Arts Trio 148

Beckley, Lisa 36

Beecham, Sir Thomas 55, 94

Beethoven, Ludwig van
  Bagatelle in A Minor 160
  Egmont Overture 171
  Fantasia for Piano, Chorus and Orchestra 197
  Fidelio 187
  Missa Solemnis 209
  Piano Concerto No. 1 171
  Piano Concerto No. 2 234
  Piano Concerto No. 3 154
  Piano Concerto No. 4 128
  Piano Concerto No. 5 25
  Piano Sonata No. 8 153
  Piano Sonata No. 14 62
  Piano Sonata No. 21 232
  Piano Sonata No. 23 221
  Piano Trio Op. 97
  Romance for Violin and Orchestra 114
  Symphony No. 3 99
  Symphony No. 4 226
  Symphony No. 5 50
  Symphony No. 6 22
  Symphony No. 7 53
  Symphony No. 8 222
  Symphony No. 9 26
  Triple Concerto 148

Violin and Piano Sonata No. 5
in F 220
Violin Concerto 49
Bell, Joshua 38
Bellini, Vincenzo
Norma 162
Bélohlávek, Jiri 150, 199
Benacková, Gabriela 123
Berbie, Jane 80
Berg, Nathan 48, 158
Bergen Philharmonic Orchestra 40
Bergzoni, Carlo 73, 91, 165
Berlin Philharmonic Orchestra 20,
25, 26, 39, 41, 54, 58, 59, 86, 95,
100, 112, 120, 124, 128, 143, 144,
154, 159, 171, 174, 180, 181, 187,
188, 189, 217
Berlin Radio Symphony Orchestra
72, 86
Berlin Staatskapelle 163
Berlioz, Hector
Damnation of Faust 234
L'Enfance du Christ 184
Harold in Italy 221
Requiem 213
Symphonie Fantastique 103
Bernius, Frieder 105
Bernstein, Leonard 118, 122, 131
Candide Overture 192
Best, Matthew 173, 184, 202
Beuron, Yann 197
Binaudi, Ludovico
Le Onde 13
Biret, Idil 184
Bizet, Georges
Carmen 94
L'Arlésienne Suite No. 1 215
Les Pêcheurs de Perles 12, 30
Symphony in C 166
Bjoerling, Jussi 30, 35, 55, 57, 73,
115
Black, Stanley 218
Blegen, Judith 56
Blochwitz, Hans-Peter 95, 189
Blomstedt, Herbert 66
Blue Danube, The (Strauss) 116
Boccherini, Luigi
String Quintet 215
Boettcher, Wolfgang 85
Bogacz, Pavel 42
Böhm, Karl 22, 95, 108, 128, 135,
136
Boléro (Ravel) 87
Bologna Teatro Comunale Orchestra
133
Bolshoi Theatre Orchestra 61
Bonney, Barbara 72, 95, 172, 189
Bonynge, Richard 80, 167, 168
Borkh, Inge 115
Borodin, Alexander
In the Steppes of Central Asia

159
Prince Igor 130
String Quartet No. 2 7, 155
Borodina, Olga 138
Boskovsky, Willi 77
Boston Symphony Orchestra 27, 49,
54, 81, 83, 181
Bostridge, Ian 48, 98
Boughton, William 152, 178
Boulez, Pierre 27, 164, 181, 201
Boult, Sir Adrian 19, 24, 29, 41, 113,
142, 153, 157, 161, 211
Bournemouth Sinfonietta 176, 178
Bournemouth Symphony Orchestra
157, 212
Bowen, John 37
Bowman, James 105
Boyce, William
Symphony No. 4 233
Brabbins, Martyn 200
Brahms, Johannes
Academic Festival Overture 199
Clarinet Quintet 234
Ein Deutsches Requiem 132
Hungarian Dance No. 7 235
Piano Concerto No. 1 180
Piano Concerto No. 2 124
Rhapsody Op. 53 223
Sextet No. 1 Op. 18 234
Symphony No. 1 150
Symphony No. 2 170
Symphony No. 3 143
Symphony No. 4 146
Variations on a Theme of Haydn
225
Violin and Cello Concerto 221
Violin Concerto 75
Brandenburg Consort 76, 121
Brandis Quintet 85
Bratislava Radio Symphony
Orchestra 133, 161, 182
Bream, Julian 47, 164
Brecknock, John 91
Brendel, Alfred 25, 51, 62, 171
Britten, Benjamin 126
Four Sea Interludes 212
War Requiem 234
Young Person's Guide to the
Orchestra 230
Brown, Iona 74
Brown, William 56
Bruch, Max 11
Kol Nidrei 189
Scottish Fantasy 113
Violin Concerto No. 1 19
Violin Concerto No. 2 186
Violin Concerto No. 3 233
Bruckner, Anton
Symphony No. 4 227
Symphony No. 7 209
Symphony No. 8 210

Symphony No. 9 232
Brüggen, Frans 84, 117, 168
Brymer, Jack 21, 130
Budapest Camerata 156
Budapest Festival Orchestra 193
Budapest Symphony Orchestra 40,
159
Budd, Jeremy 177
Burles, Charles 80
Burns, Stephen 212
Butt, Yondani 191
Butterworth, George
The Banks of Green Willow 178
Bychov, Semyon 190
Byram-Wigfield, Timothy 147

C

Caballé, Monserrat 55, 91, 115
Caccini, Giulio
Ave Maria 13, 165
Cachermaille, Gilles 95
Calinda, La (Delius) 196
Callas, Maria 126, 162
Cambreling, Sylvain 138
Cambridge Singers 68, 176
Candide Overture (Bernstein) 192
Canon in D (Pachelbel) 31
Canteloube, Joseph
Songs of the Auvergne 140
Cantilena 74
Cantique de Jean Racine (Fauré) 68
Capecchi, Renato 72
Capella Istropolitana 31, 42, 135,
145, 207, 215
Capella Reial Instrumental Ensemble
64
Capriccio Italien (Tchaikovsky) 149
Capricorn 42
Carewe, Mary 131
Carey, Colm 68
Carmen (Bizet) 94
Carmina Burana (Orff) 56
Carnival of the Animals (Saint-
Saëns) 119
Carnovich, Daniele 169
Casadesus, Gaby 119
Catalani, Alfredo
La Wally 234
Cavalleria Rusticana (Mascagni) 35
Cellini, Renato 30, 35
Chabrier, Emmanuel
España 229
Chailly, Riccardo 55, 71, 133, 142,
146, 166, 170
Chamber Orchestra of Europe 22, 28,
47, 136, 171, 180, 196, 209
Chance, Michael 105, 117, 190
Chanson de Matin (Elgar) 161
Charpentier, Marc-Antoine
Prelude to a Te Deum 232

Chicago Symphony Orchestra *46, 75, 90, 116, 146, 149, 187, 199*
Chilingirian Quartet *155*
Choir of King's College, Cambridge *43, 151*
Choir of New College, Oxford *43, 76, 173, 202*
Chopin, Frédéric
  Ballade No. 1 in G Minor *228*
  Etude in E Major *200*
  Etude Op. 10 No. 12 *232*
  Fantaisie Impromptu in C# Minor *206*
  Nocturne Op. 9 No. 2 *179*
  Nocturne Op. 27 No. 2 *233*
  Piano Concerto No. 1 *82*
  Piano Concerto No. 2 *97*
  Polonaise in A *224*
  Polonaise in A Flat *224*
  Prelude Op. 28, No. 15 *225*
  Waltz Op. 64 No. 1 *234*
Christie, William *48, 95, 158, 168*
Chung, Kyung-Wha *19, 49, 88, 109, 113, 114*
Chung, Myung-Whun *114, 214*
Church, Charlotte *13*
Cincinnati Pops Orchestra *116, 161*
Cincinnati Symphony Orchestra *69, 87, 166*
City of Birmingham Symphony Orchestra *24, 29, 92, 142, 143, 156*
City of London Sinfonia *35, 68, 149, 176*
Clark, Robert Haydon *172*
Clarke, Jeremiah
  The Prince of Denmark's March *212*
Clarke, Paul Charles *194*
Cleobury, Stephen *43*
Cleveland Orchestra *67, 156, 182, 201*
Cluytens, André *106*
Coburn, Pamela *136*
Collegium Aureum *101, 151*
Collegium Musicum *90 186*
Collegium Vocale Gent Orchestra *98*
Collot, Delphine *136*
Colombara, Carlo *78*
Columbia Jazz Band *111*
Columbia Symphony Orchestra *148, 188*
Concert des Nations *64, 99*
Concertgebouw Orchestra, Amsterdam *49, 103, 108, 118, 122, 128, 136, 154, 166, 170, 175, 185*
Concerto Italiano *169*
Concierto de Aranjuez (Rodrigo) *47*
Conlon, James *57*
Consort of London *172*
Contes d'Hoffman, Les (Hoffmann)

141
Contzen, Miriam *199*
Copland, Aaron
  Appalachian Spring *131*
  Fanfare for the Common Man *152*
  Rodeo *220*
Coppélia (Delibes) *175*
Corelli, Arcangelo
  Concerto Grosso Op. 6 No. 8 *232*
Coronation Ode (Elgar) *120*
Corydon Orchestra *184*
Corydon Singers *173, 202*
Così Fan Tutte (Mozart) *128*
Cossutta, Carlo *138*
Costa, Paolo *169*
Cotrubas, Ileana *91*
Crespin, Régine *134*
Csenki, Agnes *98*
Cser, Péter *98*
Cundari, Emilia *92*
Cura, José *138*
Curry, Diane *78*
Curzon, Clifford *51, 157*
Czech Philharmonic Orchestra *38, 39, 65, 123, 150, 192, 199, 206*

D

Dale, Laurence *177*
Danish National Radio Symphony Orchestra *52, 216*
Danse Macabre (Saint-Saëns) *157*
Danz, Ingeborg *98*
Davidson, Angus *37*
Davies, Arthur *126, 177*
Davis, Andrew *60, 147, 153, 195, 198*
Davis, Sir Colin *37, 81, 83, 103, 104, 138, 180, 181, 213*
Davis, Michael *29*
Dawson, Anne *202*
Dawson, Lynn *105*
De Los Angeles, Victoria *55, 57, 94, 163*
Debussy, Claude
  Arabesques *226*
  La Mer *201*
  Prélude à l'Après-Midi d'un Faune *158*
  Preludes Book 1 *225*
  Suite Bergamasque *107*
Del Mar, Norman *178, 179*
Del Monaco, Mario *115*
Delibes, Léo
  Coppélia *175*
  Lakmé *80*
  Sylvia *233*
Delius, Frederick
  Florida Suite *233*
  La Calinda *196*
  On Hearing the First Cuckoo in

  Spring *198*
  The Walk to the Paradise Garden *179*
Della Casa, Lisa *72*
Demidenko, Nikolai *59, 82, 97*
Dénes, Zsuzsanna *189*
Depriest, James *134*
Dessay, Natalie *80, 95, 141, 197*
Detroit Symphony Orchestra *65, 148, 188*
Dichter und Bauer (Suppé) *208*
Dido and Aeneas (Purcell) *158*
Dohnányi, Oliver *89*
Domingo, Placido *35, 55, 73, 91, 94, 178, 187, 204, 214*
Donath, Helen *117*
Donizetti, Gaetano
  Don Pasquale *234*
  L'Elisir d'Amore *228*
  Lucia di Lammermoor *167*
Donohue, Peter *157*
Dorati, Antal *69, 97, 121, 148, 149, 175, 188, 193*
Doveton, Robin *37*
Dowd, Robert *213*
D'Oyly Carte Opera Orchestra *197*
Dream of Gerontius (Elgar) *126*
Drottningholm Baroque Ensemble *77*
Drottningholm Court Theatre Orchestra *95*
Du Plessis, Christian *91*
Du Pré, Jacqueline *12, 14, 23*
Dukas, Paul
  The Sorcerer's Apprentice *222*
Dunn, Susan *78*
Duruflé, Maurice
  Requiem *233*
Dutoit, Charles *87, 102, 184*
Dvořák, Antonin
  Cello Concerto *112*
  Rusalka *123*
  Serenade for Strings *181*
  Slavonic Dances *192*
  String Quartet in F *225*
  Symphony No. 7 *227*
  Symphony No. 8 *174*
  Symphony No. 9 *39*

E

Edlinger, Richard *31, 42*
Edwards, John Owen *197*
Egmont Overture (Beethoven) *171*
Eighteenth Century Orchestra *84, 117, 168*
Elevazione (Zipoli) *172*
Elgar, Edward
  Cello Concerto *12, 14, 23*
  Chanson de Matin *161*
  Coronation Ode *120*
  Dream of Gerontius *126*

Enigma Variations *24*
Introduction and Allegro for
  Strings *145*
Pomp and Circumstance Marches
  195
Salut d'Amour *182*
Sea Pictures *213*
Serenade for Strings *149*
Symphony No. 1 *153*
Symphony No. 2 *223*
Violin Concerto *142*
Elijah (Mendelssohn) *177*
Elliott, Paul *37*
Emerson Quartet *85*
Enfance du Christ , L' (Berlioz) *184*
English Baroque Soloists *105, 190*
English Chamber Orchestra *21, 28,*
  34, 48, 132, 150, 172, 184, 203,
  212
English Concert *108, 207*
English Consort *76*
English Folk Song Suite (Vaughan
  Williams) *211*
English String Orchestra *178*
English Symphony Orchestra *152*
Enigma Variations (Elgar) *24*
Ensemble Musique Oblique *36*
Entremont, Philippe *107, 119, 211*
Equiluz, Kurt *122, 189*
Erede, Alberto *115*
Estes, Simon *188*
Eugene Onegin (Tchaikovsky) *190*
Exultate, Jubilate (Mozart) *172*

F

Fagotto, Gianpaolo *169*
Failoni Chamber Orchestra *122, 193*
Falla, Manuel de
  Nights in the Garden of Spain *225*
  The Three-Cornered Hat *228*
Fanfare for the Common Man
  (Copland) *152*
Fantasia for Piano, Chorus and
  Orchestra (Beethoven) *197*
Fantasia on a Theme of Thomas
  Tallis (Vaughan Williams) *60*
Farr, Stephen *152*
Fassbinder, Brigitte *117*
Fauré, Gabriel
  Cantique de Jean Racine *68*
  Pavane *139*
  Requiem *36*
Faust (Gounod) *194*
Fenby, Eric *196*
Ferrarini, Alida *133*
Ferras, Christian *44*
Ferrier, Kathleen *216*
Fidelio (Beethoven) *187*
Fieldsend, David *197*
Figueras, Monserrat *169*

Filipova, Elena *78*
Finlandia (Sibelius) *52*
Finley, Gerard *132*
Finnie, Linda *177*
Finzi, Gerald
  Clarinet Concerto *232*
Fiorentino Orchestra *163*
Firebird, The (Stravinsky) *188*
Fischer, Adám *180*
Fischer, Iván *193*
Fischer-Dieskau, Dietrich *72, 132*
Fledermaus, Die (Strauss) *183*
Fleming, Renée *123*
Focile, Nuccia *190*
Forrester, Maureen *92*
Forza del Destino, La (Verdi) *165*
Foster, Lawrence *174, 177*
Four Sea Interludes (Britten) *212*
Franck, César
  Panis Angelicus *156*
  Symphonic Variations for Piano
    and Orchestra *229*
  Symphony in D Minor *223*
  Violin Sonata *199*
Frank, Hans-Peter *213*
Frankfurt Opera Orchestra *188*
Frankfurt Radio Symphony
  Orchestra *166, 170*
Freiburg Baroque Orchestra *34*
Frémaux, Louis *47*
French Radio National Orchestra *94,*
  106, 177
Freni, Mirella *57, 126, 142, 163*
Frey, Paul *163*
Fricsay, Ferenc *26, 72, 187*
  From Holberg's Time (Grieg) *141*

G

Gabrieli Players *74*
Gadfly, The (Shostakovich) *71*
Galante, Inessa *13, 165*
Gallagher, Maureen *173*
Gardelli, Lamberto *45, 165*
Gardiner, John Eliot *47, 105, 168,*
  190, 197
Garrett, Lesley *12–13*
Gasdia, Cecilia *194*
Gáti, Istvan *98, 122*
Gavanelli, Paolo *45*
Gazza Ladra, La (Rossini) *133*
Gedda, Nicolai *78, 94*
Gedge, Nicholas *36*
Gelmetti, Gianluigi *133, 146*
Gens, Véronique *158, 201*
George, Michael *124*
Gergiev, Valery *58, 130, 139, 165*
Gershwin, George
  Piano Concerto in F *205*
  Porgy and Bess *233*
  Rhapsody in Blue *111*

Gheorghiu, Angela *55, 204*
Ghiaurov, Nicolai *78*
Gianni Schicchi (Puccini) *163*
Giardino Armonico *34, 135, 144, 218*
Gibson, Sir Alexander *23, 41, 120,*
  157, 203
Gielen, Michael *188*
Gilels, Emil *62, 124, 153, 180*
Giulini, Carlo Maria *78, 82, 97, 114,*
  178
Glazunov, Alexander
  The Seasons *221*
Glemser, Bernd *67*
Glière, Reinhold
  Harp Concerto *228*
Glinka, Mikhail
  Ruslan and Lyudmila Overture
    221
Gluck, Christoph Wilibald
  Orfeo ed Euridice *105*
Gobbi, Tito *45, 163*
Goldberg Variations (Bach) *195*
Goltz, Gottfried von der *34*
Goodman, Roy *121, 144, 218*
Gorchakova, Galina *165*
Górecki, Henryk
  Symphony No. 3 *8–9, 125*
Görne, Matthias *98*
Gothenburg Symphony Orchestra *52,*
  66, 69, 81, 83, 141, 159, 169, 216
Götterdämmerung (Wagner) *127*
Gould, Glenn *195*
Gounod, Charles
  Ave Maria *204*
  Faust *194*
  Mors et Vita *191*
  St Cecilia Mass *177*
Gran Canaria Philharmonic
  Orchestra *103*
Grande Ecurie *105, 140*
'Greensleeves' (Anon) *234*
Greensleeves Fantasia (Vaughan
  Williams) *147*
Gregorian, Gegam *165*
Grieg, Edvard
  From Holberg's Time *141*
  Lyric Pieces Book 8 *207*
  Peer Gynt Suite No. 1 *66*
  Peer Gynt Suite No. 2 *222*
  Piano Concerto in A Minor *40*
Grimaud, Hélène *205, 211*
Grofé, Ferde
  Grand Canyon Suite *232*
Groop, Monica *177*
Gruberová, Edita *167, 183*
Guadagno, Anton *45*
Gueden, Hilde *72, 134, 183*
Guest, George *48*
Guglielmo Tell (Rossini) *142*
Gulda, Friedrich *28, 196*
Gymnopédies (Satie) *134*

H

Hadley, Jerry 78, 194
Haefliger, Ernst 187
Hagegård, Haken 56
Haidan, Delphine 80
Haitink, Bernard 121, 170, 175, 185
Hála, Josef 70
Halasz, Michael 23
Hallé Orchestra 24, 196, 198
Hampson, Thomas 72
Handel, George Friederic
    Harp Concerto Op. 4 No. 6 234
    Judas Maccabeus 232
    Messiah 37
    Music for the Royal Fireworks
        151
    Organ Concerto No. 13 235
    Rinaldo 233
    Samson 233
    Semele 234
    Serse 140
    Solomon 74
    Water Music Suite 1 101
    Zadok the Priest 76
Handley, Vernon 174, 194
Hanover Band 140
Harnoncourt, Nikolaus 22, 72, 75,
    108, 118, 122, 136, 138, 167, 171,
    172, 183, 189, 193, 201, 209
Harnoy, Ofra 189
Harper, Heather 37
Hauptmann, Cornelius 209
Haydn, Franz Josef
    Cello Concerto No. 1 in C 222
    Cello Concerto No. 2 235
    Die Schöpfung 167
    Mass in D Minor 233
    Symphony No. 94 225
    Symphony No. 101 225
    Symphony No. 104 224
    Trumpet Concerto 145
Hear My Prayer (Mendelssohn) 202
Hebrides Overture (Mendelssohn) 89
Hegarty, Mary 197
Heichele, Hildegard 188
Heifetz, Jascha 49, 75
Helsingborg Symphony Orchestra
    213
Helsinki Philharmonic Orchestra 52,
    119
Hendricks, Barbara 30, 177
Hering, Jörg 167
Hermann, Roland 117
Hernandez, Cesar 78
Hérold, Ferdinand
    La Fille Mal Gardée 229
Herreweghe, Philippe 36, 48, 89, 98,
    132, 136, 177, 209
Heynis, Aafje 185
Hickox, Richard 120, 126, 149, 177,
    186, 202, 212
Higginbottom, Edward 42, 43, 173,
    202
Hill, David 76, 93, 147, 152
Hill, Martyn 56
Hogwood, Christopher 37, 124, 162,
    181
Holl, Robert 167, 189, 209
Hollweg, Werner 183
Holman, Peter 144, 218
Holocek, Heinz 134
Holst, Gustav
    The Planets 14, 41
Holton, Ruth 190
Horenstein, Jascha 20, 210
Horner, James
    Braveheart 235
    Titanic 12, 151
Howard, Leslie 205
Howell, Gwyn 126
Hummel, Johann Nepomuk
    Trumpet Concerto 203
Humperdinck, Engelbert
    Hänsel und Gretel 226
Hungarian Rhapsody No. 2 (Liszt)
    193
Hungarian State Opera Orchestra 78
Hungarian State Philharmonic
    Orchestra 98
Hungarian State Symphony
    Orchestra 180
Hünteler, Konrad 84
Huttenlocher, Philippe 190
Hvorostovsky, Dmitri 190
Hysanek, Leonie 187

I

I Musici 31, 42
I Musici de Montréal 119, 155
I Solisti Veneti 135, 186
Ifokoski, Soile 177
Immerseel, Jos van 25
In the Steppes of Central Asia
    (Borodin) 159
Indes Galantes, Les (Rameau) 168
Indianapolis Symphony Orchestra 32
Introduction and Rondo (Saint-
    Saëns) 185
Irish National Symphony Orchestra
    189
Israel Philharmonic Orchestra 82,
    113, 185
Istomin, Eugene 148, 183

J

Janácek, Leos
    Sinfonietta 223
Jandó, Jeno 40, 51, 159, 205
Janowitz, Gundula 86
Jansons, Mariss 33, 46, 61, 63, 103,
    110, 144
Järvi, Neeme 52, 58, 65, 66, 69, 81,
    83, 129, 141, 159, 169, 175, 182,
    216
Jean, Kenneth 88
Jeffrey, Robin 218
Jellard, Frances 37
Jenkins, Karl 12
    Adiemus 131
    Adiemus 2 – Cantata Mundi 234
    Palladio 233
Jerusalem, Siegfried 100, 176
Jochum, Eugen 117, 124, 180
Johnson, Anthony Rolfe 184, 190,
    209
Johnson, Emma 21
Joplin, Scott
    Piano Rags 222

K

Kampoli, Alfredo 113
Kamu, Okko 52, 119
Kang, Dong-Suk 185
Karajan, Herbert von 41, 57, 59, 63,
    73, 86, 110, 112, 134, 144, 183,
    209, 217
Karelia Suite (Sibelius) 119
Katowice Radio Symphony Orchestra
    185
Kavacos, Leonidas 109
Kempe, Rudolf 113
Kempff, Wilhelm 62, 128, 153, 154
Kendall, William 48
Kennedy, (Nigel) 29, 34, 49, 142,
    161, 182
Kenny, Yvonne 48
Kertesi, Ingrid 122
Kertesz, Istvan 39
Khachaturian, Aram
    Gayaneh 222
    Masquerade 218
    Spartacus 129
Kiehr, Maria Cristina 169
Kilanowicz, Zofia 125
King, Robert 76, 162
King's Consort 76, 162
Kirkby, Emma 13, 37, 124, 138, 158,
    162
Kirov Opera Orchestra 58, 130, 139,
    165
Kirshbaum, Ralph 23
Kiss, Rózsa 98
Kissin, Evgeni 54
Kitaenko, Dmitri 40, 129, 166, 170
Klansky, Ivan 154
Kleiber, Carlos 50, 53, 91, 100
Kleiber, Erich 72
Klemperer, Otto 26, 53, 99, 132, 216
Kliegel, Maria 23, 189

Kmentt, Waldemar *183*
Knardahl, Eva *207*
Kocsis, Zoltán *107*
Kodály, Zoltán
    Háry János *228*
Kodaly Quartet *51*
Kol Nidrei (Bruch) *189*
Kollo, René *100*
Kónya, Sándor *164*
Koopman, Ton *79, 101, 103, 124*
Kooy, Peter *36*
Korpás, Ferenc *98*
Korsten, Gerard *180*
Kosler, Zdenek *206*
Koster, Ab *125*
Köth, Erika *183*
Kovács, Lászlo *156*
Köves, Péter *98*
Kremer, Gidon *75*
Kubelik, Rafael *39, 65, 164, 174*
Kuchar, Theodore *71*
Kunde, Gregory *80*
Kunzel, Erich *69, 116, 161*
Kyrkjebø, Sissel *151*

L

La Bohème (Puccini) *55*
Lafont, Jean-Philippe *177*
Lahti Symphony Orchestra *83, 109, 119, 203*
Laki, Krisztina *189*
Lakmé (Delibes) *80*
Lalo, Edouard
    Symphonie Espagnole *228*
Lamon, Jeanne *44, 101, 151*
Land of the Mountain and the Flood (MacCunn) *200*
Lang, Rosemarie *188, 213*
Lark Ascending, The (Vaughan Williams) *29*
Larmore, Jennifer *94*
Lasarev, Alexander *59*
Latvian National Symphony Orchestra *165*
Laurich, Hildegard *188*
Layton, Stephen *176*
Leaper, Adrian *87, 90, 103, 130, 145, 182, 208*
Lear, Evelyn *95*
Ledger, Philip *184*
Legrand, Michel *134*
Lehár, Franz
    Die Lustige Witwe *168*
    Gold and Silver Waltz *234*
Leinsdorf, Erich *27, 115*
Leipzig Gewandhaus Orchestra *19, 38, 110, 123, 124, 148, 171, 197*
Leipzig Radio Orchestra *141*
Leitner, Ferdinand *128*
Lenárd, Ondrej *161*

Leoncavallo, Ruggero
    I Pagliacci *232*
Leonskaya, Elisabeth *124*
Leppard, Raymond *21, 32, 145, 172, 203*
Les Arts Florissants Orchestra *48, 95, 158, 168*
Lesne, Gérard *201*
Levin, Robert *197*
Levine, James *35, 70, 162, 178, 214*
Liebeck, Anne *56*
Lied von der Erde, Das (Mahler) *216*
Lieutenant Kijé Suite (Prokofiev) *182*
Ligeti, Andras *40, 159*
Lind, Eva *141*
Lindley, Simon *93*
Lipovšek, Marjana *117, 138, 183, 198, 201, 209*
Liszt, Franz
    Hungarian Rhapsody No. 2 *193*
    Liebesträume No. 3 *205*
    Piano Concerto No. 1 *233*
Litolff, Henry
    Concerto Symphonique No. 3 *234*
    Piano Concerto No. 4 *157*
Litton, Andrew *157*
Lloyd Webber, Andrew
    Requiem *13, 232*
Lohengrin (Wagner) *163*
Lombard, Alain *80*
London Baroque *31*
London Festival Orchestra *56*
London Philharmonic Orchestra *19, 35, 46, 55, 60, 86, 94, 115, 131, 153, 157, 161, 171, 181, 189, 194, 210, 212, 213*
London Sinfonietta *125*
London Symphony Orchestra *19, 20, 23, 24, 29, 32, 37, 39, 54, 67, 88, 90, 96, 97, 104, 109, 112, 113, 121, 126, 131, 138, 151, 152, 158, 167, 174, 177, 179, 186, 193, 194, 202, 204, 208, 210, 211, 213, 218*
López-Cobos, Jesús *87, 166*
Los Angeles Philharmonic Orchestra *82, 97, 158, 169, 201*
Lott, Felicity *128*
Loughran, James *184*
Lucia di Lammermoor (Donizetti) *167*
Ludwig, Christa *78, 128, 134, 216*
Lustige Witwe, Die (Lehár) *168*
Lyon Opéra Orchestra *140, 141, 160, 175, 177, 197*

M

Má Vlast (Smetana) *65*
Ma, Yo-Yo *112, 119, 155*
Maazel, Lorin *109, 204*
MacCunn, Hamish

Land of the Mountain and the Flood *200*
Mackerras, Sir Charles *91, 96, 102, 112, 123, 128, 139, 189, 192*
Madama Butterfly (Puccini) *57*
Magee, Emily *163*
Magnus, Elisabeth von *124, 136, 138*
Mahler, Gustav
    Das Lied von der Erde *216*
    Symphony No. 1 *143*
    Symphony No. 2 *92*
    Symphony No. 3 *220*
    Symphony No. 4 *156*
    Symphony No. 5 *8, 13, 27*
    Symphony No. 6 *227*
    Symphony No. 8 *188*
    Symphony No. 9 *224*
Malgoire, Jean-Claude *105, 140*
Malmö Symphony Orchestra *134*
Mannion, Rosa *95, 209*
Manze, Andrew *44*
Marcello, Alessandro
    Oboe Concerto in D Minor *227*
Margiono, Charlotte *72*
Markert, Annette *48*
Markson, Gerhard *189*
Marriner, Sir Neville *21, 38, 118, 125, 208*
Marsalis, Wynton *145, 203, 212*
Marshall, Margaret *188*
Marshall, Wayne *33, 111, 205*
Mascagni, Pietro
    Cavalleria Rusticana *14, 35*
Masquerade (Khachaturian) *218*
Massenet, Jules
    El Cid *233*
    Meditation from 'Thaïs' *13, 70*
Masterson, Valerie *91*
Masur, Kurt *19, 38, 110, 112, 123, 124, 148, 171, 197*
Mazurov, Yuri *190*
McCartney, Paul
    Standing Stone *14, 174*
McCreesh, Paul *74*
McDonald, Robert *199*
McLaughlin, Marie *128*
McGegan, Nicholas *140*
McNair, Sylvia *56, 105, 138, 188*
Meditation from 'Thaïs' (Massenet) *70*
Medlam, Charles *31*
Mehta, Zubin *82, 113, 115, 185*
Mei, Eva *201, 209*
Meier, Waltraud *92, 100, 187*
Meistersinger von Nürnberg, Die (Wagner) *164*
Mellon, Agnes *36*
Melos Quartett *85, 191*
Melstead, Linda *44*
Mendelssohn, Felix
    A Midsummer Night's Dream *136*

Elijah *177*
Hear My Prayer *202*
Hebrides Overture *89*
Octet *228*
Symphony No. 3 *220*
Symphony No. 4 *123*
Violin Concerto in E minor *38*
Menuhin, Sir Yehudi *44, 64, 114,
142, 173, 217*
Mer, La (Debussy) *201*
Merrill, Robert *30*
Mesdag, Matthijs *124*
Mesple, Mady *80*
Messiah (Handel) *37*
Mexico City Philharmonic Orchestra
215
Mexico State Symphony Orchestra *47*
Mey, Guy de *169*
Meyer, Sabine *21*
Midori *113, 199*
Midsummer Night's Dream
(Mendelssohn) *136*
Milanov, Zinka *73*
Millet, Danielle *80*
Millo, Aprile *178*
Milnes, Sherrill *142*
Minkowski, Marc *197*
Minneapolis Symphony Orchestra
69, 149, 175
Minton, Yvonne *126*
Miricioiu, Nelly *35*
Miserere (Allegri) *43*
Missa Solemnis (Beethoven) *209*
Monoyios, Ann *167*
Monte Carlo Opera Orchestra *80*
Monteverdi, Claudio
Vespers *1610 169*
Montreal Symphony Orchestra *87,
102, 106*
Morandi, Pier Giogio *78*
Mordkovitch, Lydia *186*
Moreno, Alfonso *47*
Mors et Vita (Gounod) *191*
Moscow Philharmonic Orchestra *129*
Moser, Thomas *94*
Mozart, Wolfgang Amadeus
Ave Verum Corpus *104*
Clarinet Concerto *21*
Clarinet Quintet *130*
Coronation Mass *233*
Così Fan Tutte *128*
Die Zauberflöte *95*
Exultate, Jubilate *172*
Flute and Harp Concerto *84*
Flute Concerto No. 1 *224*
Horn Concerto No. 1 *233*
Horn Concerto No. 2 *229*
Horn Concerto No. 3 *232*
Horn Concerto No. 4 *125*
Le Nozze di Figaro *72*
Mass in C Minor *189*

Oboe Concerto *226*
Piano Concerto No. 20 *150*
Piano Concerto No. 21 *28*
Piano Concerto No. 23 *132*
Piano Concerto No. 24 *227*
Piano Concerto No. 27 *196*
Requiem *48*
Serenade 'Eine Kleine
Nachtmusik' *77*
Serenade No. 10 *224*
Sinfonia Concertante *173*
Sonata for Keyboard No. 11 in A
227
Symphony No. 29 *232*
Symphony No. 39 *207*
Symphony No. 40 *108*
Symphony No. 41 *135*
Toy Symphony *232*
Vesperae Solonnes de Confessore
124
Violin Concerto No. 3 *217*
Violin Concerto No. 4 *229*
Mozart-Ensemble *84*
Mozzafiato *217*
Mukk, Jósef *98, 122, 156*
Muller-Brachmann, Hanno *48*
Mullova, Viktoria *183*
Munch, Charles *49, 181*
Munich Philharmonic Orchestra *214*
Murray, Ann *117*
Music for the Royal Fireworks
(Handel) *151*
Mussorgsky, Modest
Night on the Bare Mountain *187*
Pictures at an Exhibition *120*
Mutter, Anne-Sophie *70, 217*

N

Nabucco (Verdi) *45*
Nagano, Kent *140, 141, 160, 175*
National Philharmonic Orchestra *35,
126, 142, 145, 162, 168, 214*
Nazareth, Daniel *159*
NDR Symphony Orchestra *143, 170,
210*
Neary, Martin *152*
Neidlich, Charles *130*
Nelson, Judith *37, 138*
Németh, Judit *98, 122*
Neumann, Václav *123*
New Philharmonia Orchestra *27, 29,
41, 142, 195, 216*
New York Metropolitan Opera
Orchestra *178*
New York Philharmonic Orchestra
92, 112, 118, 122, 131, 164, 192
Newman, Anthony *212*
Nielsen, Carl
Aladdin *234*
Night on the Bare Mountain

(Mussorgsky) *187*
Nikolaieva, Tatyana *195*
Nilsson, Birgit *115*
Nishizaki, Takako *88*
Norma (Bellini) *162*
Norman, Jessye *141, 177, 204*
Norrington, Roger *140*
Norris, David Owen *119*
North German Radio Symphony
Orchestra *49, 209*
Northern Sinfonia *120*
Norwegian Chamber Orchestra *141*
Nozze di Figaro, Le (Mozart) *72*
Nucci, Leo *133, 163*
Nulla in Mundo Pax Sincera
(Vivaldi) *13, 162*
Nutcracker Suite, The (Tchaikovsky)
96
Nyman, Michael
The Piano *214*

O

Oberfrank, Géza *98*
Obraztsova, Elena *73*
O'Dette, Paul *144, 218*
O'Donnell, James *43, 68, 104, 156,
204*
Oelze, Christiane *98, 132*
Offenbach, Jacques
Gaité Parisienne *222*
Les Contes d'Hoffman *141*
Orphée aux Enfers *197*
On Hearing the First Cuckoo in
Spring (Delius) *198*
O'Neill, Dennis *35*
Onofri, Enrico *34*
Orchestra of La Scala, Milan *55, 73,
126, 133, 142, 146, 162*
Orchestra of the Age of
Enlightenment *140*
Orchestra of the English National
Opera *91*
Orchestra of the German State
Opera, Berlin *187*
Orchestre de Champs Elysées *48, 89,
132, 136, 177, 209*
Orchestre Révolutionnaire et
Romantique *197*
Orfeo ed Euridice (Gluck) *105*
Orff, Carl
Carmina Burana *56*
Orlandi, Ugo *135*
Ormandy, Eugene *33, 61, 96, 148,
157, 211*
Orphée aux Enfers (Offenbach) *197*
Orpheus Chamber Orchestra *84, 173*
Oslo Philharmonic Orchestra *33, 63,
110, 144*
Ostman, Arnold *95*
Otello (Verdi) *214*

Otto, Lisa 95
Oxford Camerata 36
Oxford Schola Cantorum 68
Ozawa, Seiji 54

P

Pachelbel, Johann
    Canon in D 14, 31
Palma, Susan 84
Palmer, Felicity 126
Panis Angelicus (Franck) 156
Panzarella, Anna Maria 48
Pappano, Antonio 204
Paris Opéra-Bastille Orchestra 214
Paris Opéra-Comique Orchestra 80
Paris Orchestra 57, 190
Parker, Helen 37
Parley of Instruments 144, 218
Parrott, Andrew 158
Parry, David 35, 194
Parry, Hubert
    I Was Glad 234
    Jerusalem 227
Parsons, Geoffrey 198
Pärt, Arvo
    Spiegl im Spiegl 13
Patzak, Julius 216
Pavane (Fauré) 139
Pavane pour une Infante Défunte
    (Ravel) 160
Pavarotti, Luciano 57, 115, 126, 133, 142
Peacock, Adrian 37
Pears, Sir Peter 126
Pêcheurs de Perles, Les (Bizet) 30
Peer Gynt Suite No. 1 (Grieg) 66
Perahia, Murray 28, 82, 97, 132, 150,
    159, 196, 200, 206
Pergolesi, Giovanni
    Stabat Mater 201
Perlea, Jonel 73
Perlot, Pierre 186
Peters, Roberta 95
Pettinger, Peter 161, 182
Philadelphia Orchestra 33, 61, 71, 96,
    148, 157, 211
Philharmonia Orchestra 26, 47, 50, 53,
    61, 78, 81, 82, 88, 97, 99, 111, 114,
    128, 132, 134, 145, 184, 194, 203
Philharmonic Orchestra of La Scala,
    Milan 114
Philips, Todd 173
Phillips, Peter 147
Piano, The (Nyman) 214
Piau, Sandrine 136
Pick-Hieronimi, Monica 45
Pictures at an Exhibition
    (Mussorgsky) 120
Pierre, Fabrice 204
Pinnock, Trevor 108, 207
Pittsburgh Symphony Orchestra 109

Planets, The (Holst) 41
Plasson, Michel 30, 80, 139, 191
Plazas, Mary 194
Pletnev, Mikhail 63
Plishka, Paul 78
Plowright, Rosalind 177, 178
Podger, Rachel 44
Poell, Alfred 72
Polish National Radio Symphony
    Orchestra 65, 67, 125
Pollini, Maurizio 25, 154, 171
Polyphony 176
Pomp and Circumstance Marches
    (Elgar) 195
Ponchielli, Amilcare
    La Gioconda 223
Pöntinen, Roland 40
Pople, Ross 56
Popp, Lucia 86
Power-Biggs, Edward 33
Prégardien, Christoph 48
Preisner, Zbigniew
    Requiem for My Friend 13
Prélude à l'Après-Midi d'un Faune
    (Debussy) 158
Pressler, Menahem 197
Preston, Simon 76, 79, 138
Prêtre, Georges 91, 177
Previn, André 20, 54, 67, 88, 109,
    183, 194, 202, 206, 210, 213
Price, Dame Margaret 100
Prince Igor (Borodin) 130
Prince of Denmark's March (Clarke)
    212
Pritchard, Sir John 114
Prokofiev, Sergei
    Lieutenant Kijé Suite 182
    Peter and the Wolf 233
    Romeo and Juliet 58
    Symphony No. 1 129
    Symphony No. 5 234
Protschka, Josef 167, 183
Puccini, Giacomo
    Gianni Schicchi 163
    La Bohème 55
    La Rondine 204
    Madama Butterfly 57
    Manon Lescaut 221
    Tosca 126
    Turandot 8, 115
Purcell, Henry
    'Come, Ye Sons of Art' 234
    Dido and Aeneas 158
    Funeral Music for Queen Mary 234
Pyatt, David 125

Q

Quasthoff, Thomas 98
Quattro Stagione, Le (Vivaldi) 34
Quilico, Gino 30

R

Rachlin, Julian 109
Rachmaninov, Sergey
    Piano Concerto No. 1 12, 210
    Piano Concerto No. 2 8, 11, 20
    Piano Concerto No. 3 8, 12, 54
    Prelude Op. 3 No. 2 228
    Rhapsody on a theme of Paganini
        67
    Symphonic Dances 228
    Symphony No. 1 234
    Symphony No. 2 61
    Symphony No. 3 235
    Vespers 222
    Vocalise 225
Radetzky March (Strauss) 161
Ragin, Derek Lee 105
Rahbari, Alexander 133
Rameau, Jean-Philippe
    Les Indes Galantes 168
Raskin, Judith 156
Rattle, Sir Simon 24, 25, 29, 92, 142,
    143, 156, 171
Ravel, Maurice
    Boléro 87
    Daphnis et Chloé 181
    Introduction and Allegro 232
    Le Tombeau de Couperin 226
    Pavane pour une Infante Défunte
        160
    Piano Concerto in G 211
    String Quartet 232
RCA Italiana Opera Orchestra 91
RCA Victor Symphony Orchestra 30,
    35, 55
Recuerdos de la Alhambra (Tárrega)
    164
Reiner, Fritz 46, 75, 116, 187
Remmert, Birgit 209
Resigno, Nicola 126
Respighi, Ottorino
    Ancient Airs and Dances 235
    Pines of Rome 223
Rév, Livia 179
Reynish, Tim 211
Rhapsody in Blue (Gershwin) 111
Rhapsody on a theme of Paganini
    (Rachmaninov) 67
Ricci, Ruggiero 19
Ricciarelli, Katia 73
Richter, Sviatoslav 59
Rigby, Jean 184
Rigoletto (Verdi) 133
Rilling, Helmuth 98, 122, 190
Rimsky-Korsakov, Nikolai
    Capriccio Espagnol 208
    Scheherazade 46
    The Legend of Tsar Saltan 232
Rite of Spring, The (Stravinsky) 148
Rizzi, Carlo 194

Robbin, Catherine 124
Robinson, Faye 188
Robson, Anthony 186
Rodrigo, Joaquín
  Concierto de Aranjuez 47
  Fantasia para un Gentilhombre
  223
Rogatchev, Valéry 199
Rogé, Pascal 107, 160, 184
Romance for Violin and Orchestra
  (Beethoven) 114
Rome Opera Orchestra 57, 73, 115,
  163
Romeo and Juliet Overture
  (Tchaikovsky) 90
Rondine, La (Puccini) 204
Roocroft, Amanda 156
Rootering, Jan-Hendrik 188
Rosamunde (Schubert) 185
Rose, Leonard 148, 183
Rosenkavalier, Der (Strauss) 134
Rossini, Gioacchino
  Guglielmo Tell 142
  Il Barbieri di Siviglia 146
  La Gazza Ladra 8, 133
  La Scala di Seta 233
  L'Italiana in Algieri 234
  Stabat Mater 225
Rost, Andrea 188
Rostropovich, Mstislav 85, 112
Royal Concertgebouw Orchestra 72,
  75, 183
Royal Liverpool Philharmonic
  Orchestra 214
Royal Northern College of Music
  Wind Orchestra 211
Royal Opera House Orchestra 167
Royal Philharmonic Orchestra 20, 23,
  87, 90, 102, 113, 130, 139, 140,
  165, 179, 184, 191, 196, 208, 210
Royal Scottish National Orchestra 23,
  41, 58, 120, 129, 157, 175, 182,
  203
Rubens, Sibylla 48, 98
Rubsam, Wolfgang 79
Rusalka (Dvořák) 123
Russian National Orchestra 63
Rutter, John 36, 68
  Requiem 13, 176

S

Sabata, Victor de 126
Saint-Saëns, Camille
  Carnival of the Animals 119
  Danse Macabre 157
  Introduction and Rondo 185
  Piano Concerto No. 2 184
  Samson et Dalila 138
  Symphony No. 3 33
  Violin Concerto No. 3 233

Salomaa, Petteri 177
Salonen, Esa-Pekka 58, 158, 169, 201
Salut d'Amour (Elgar) 182
Samson et Dalila (Saint-Saëns) 138
San Francisco Symphony Orchestra
  66
Sanderling, Kurt 128, 143, 146, 150,
  154
Santa Cecilia Academy Orchestra,
  Rome 115, 178
Santini, Gabriele 57, 163
Sarasate, Pablo
  Zigeunerweisen 233
Saraste, Jukka-Pekka 166
Satie, Erik
  Gnossienne No. 1 227
  Gymnopédies 134
Savall, Jordi 64, 99, 169
Scalchi, Gloria 78
Schade, Michael 98
Scharinger, Anton 72, 117
Scheherazade (Rimsky-Korsakov) 46
Schiff, Heinrich 82, 97, 183
Schlick, Barbara 124
Schneider, Peter 163
Scholars Baroque Ensemble 37
Scholl, Andreas 98, 140
Schöne, Wolfgang 122
Schöpfung, Die (Haydn) 167
Schreier, Peter 117
Schubert, Franz
  An die Musik 234
  Ave Maria 198
  Der Hirt auf dem Felsen 229
  Deutsche Messe 235
  Die Forelle 220
  Fantasy for Piano 235
  Impromptu No. 3 in G Flat 222
  Impromptus 154
  Octet in F 217
  Piano Sonata No. 21 224
  Piano Trio in B Flat 227
  Rosamunde 185
  Ständchen 232
  String Quartet No. 14 in D Minor
  191
  String Quintet in C 85
  Symphony No. 3 233
  Symphony No. 5 136
  Symphony No. 8 122
  Symphony No. 9 in C 118
  'Trout' Quintet 51
  Winterreise 226
Schumann, Clara
  Piano Concerto in A Minor 224
Schumann, Robert
  Piano Concerto in A Minor 159
  Träumerei 232
Schwarzkopf, Elisabeth 78, 86, 128,
  132, 134
Scimone, Claudio 135, 186

Scottish Chamber Orchestra 128, 166
Scottish Fantasy (Bruch) 113
Scotto, Renata 35, 162, 214
Sea Pictures (Elgar) 213
Seefried, Irmgard 72, 198
Segerstam, Leif 40, 52, 216
Seiffert, Peter 163, 188
Sejna, Karel 192
Selig, Franz-Josef 98
Seminario Musicale 201
Serafin, H. 162
Serenade 'Eine Kleine Nachtmusik'
  (Mozart) 77
Serenade for Strings (Dvořák) 181
Serenade for Strings (Elgar) 149
Serenade for Strings (Tchaikovsky)
  180
Serse (Handel) 140
Shaw, Robert 56, 78
Shelley, Howard 111
Shepherd, Adrian 74
Shirley-Quirk, John 37, 126
Shostakovich, Dmitri
  Jazz Suite No. 1 166
  Jazz Suite No. 2 170
  Piano Concerto No. 1 233
  Piano Concerto No. 2 106
  Symphony No. 5 175
  Symphony No. 7 232
  Symphony No. 10 233
  The Gadfly 8, 71
Shostakovich, Dmitri (Jr) 106
Shostakovich, Maxim 106
Sibelius, Jean
  Finlandia 52
  Karelia Suite 119
  Symphony No. 1 203
  Symphony No. 2 81
  Symphony No. 5 83
  Symphony No. 7 234
  The Swan of Tuonela 169
  Valse Triste 216
  Violin Concerto 109
Siegfried (Wagner) 176
Siepi, Cesare 72
Simcock, Iain 68, 104, 156, 204
Simionato, Guilietta 73
Simon, Geoffrey 90
Sinding, Christian
  Rustle of Spring 233
Sinfonia of London 60, 145, 147
Sinopoli, Giuseppe 94
Sitkovetsky, Dmitri 89, 123
Slatkin, Leonard 32, 56, 66, 212
Sleeping Beauty, The (Tchaikovsky)
  139
Slovak Philharmonic Orchestra 88,
  89, 116, 159, 208
Smetana, Bedrich
  Má Vlast 65
  The Bartered Bride 228

Smith, Jennifer *117*
Smithsonian Chamber Players *215*
Söderström, Elisabeth *134*
Sofia Festival Orchestra *190*
Solomon (Handel) *74*
Solti, Sir Georg *55, 94, 127, 176*
Song for Athene (Tavener) *152*
Songs of the Auvergne (Canteloube)
    140
Soyer, Roger *80*
Spagnoli, Pietro *169*
Spartacus (Khachaturian) *129*
Spem in Alium (Tallis) *147*
St Cecilia Mass (Gounod) *177*
St Hedwig's Cathedral Choir, Berlin
    26
St Louis Symphony Orchestra *32, 56,
    66*
St Matthew Passion (Bach) *98*
St Petersburg State Symphony
    Orchestra *129, 218*
Staatskapelle Dresden *21, 100, 117,
    141, 143, 146, 150*
Stabat Mater (Pergolesi) *201*
Stade, Frederica von *140*
Stader, Maria *72*
Stainer, Sir John
    The Crucifixion *227*
Standage, Simon *186*
Standing Stone (McCartney) *174*
Stanley, John
    Trumpet Voluntary *453*
Stasio, Anna di *178*
State Symphony Orchestra *96*
Steen-Nøkleberg, Einar *207*
Steffano, Guiseppe di *126*
Stern, Isaac *148, 183*
Stewart, Thomas *164*
Stich-Randall, Teresa *134*
Stilwell, Richard *188*
Stockley, Miriam *12, 131*
Storck, Helga *84*
Stott, Kathryn *214*
Strauss, Johann I
    Radetzky March *161*
Strauss, Johann II
    Casanova *13, 221*
    Die Fledermaus *183*
    Emperor Waltz *229*
    Tales from the Vienna Woods *224*
    The Blue Danube *116*
Strauss, Richard
    Also Sprach Zarathustra *221*
    Der Rosenkavalier *134*
    Ein Heldenleben *234*
    Eine Alpensinfonie *206*
    Vier Letzte Lieder *86*
Stravinsky, Igor
    The Firebird *188*
    The Rite of Spring *148*
Streit, Kurt *95*

Studer, Cheryl *92, 141, 163, 168,
    188, 214*
Stuttgart Bach Collegium *98, 122*
Stutzmann, Nathalie *48*
Suite Bergamasque (Debussy) *107*
Suk, Josef *38, 70*
Suliotis, Elena *45*
Sullivan, Sir Arthur
    Pineapple Poll *234*
    The Mikado *233*
    The Pirates of Penzance *234*
    The Yeomen of the Guard *232*
Sumi Jo *95, 141*
Summerly, Jeremy *36, 68*
Suppé, Franz von
    Dichter und Bauer *208*
    Light Cavalry *230*
Sutherland, Dame Joan *80, 115, 167,
    168*
Svetlanov, Evgeni *61, 96*
Swan Lake (Tchaikovsky) *102*
Swan of Tuonela, The (Sibelius) *169*
Symphonie Fantastique (Berlioz)
    103
Szell, George *86, 156, 182*
Szokolay, Balázs *160*

T

Tafelmusik *25, 44, 77, 101, 105, 125,
    151, 167*
Takács String Quartet *191*
Tallis, Thomas
    Spem in Alium *147*
Tallis Scholars *147*
Tannhäuser (Wagner) *121*
Tárrega, Francisco
    Recuerdos de la Alhambra *13,
    164*
Tate, Jeffrey *28, 132, 141, 150*
Tavener, John
    Song for Athene *9, 13, 152*
Taverner Players *158*
Taylor, James *209*
Tchaikovsky, Piotr Ilyich
    1812 Overture *69*
    Capriccio Italien *149*
    Eugene Onegin *190*
    Manfred Symphony *234*
    Marche Slave *224*
    Piano Concerto No. 1 *59*
    Piano Concerto No. 2 *223*
    Romeo and Juliet Overture *90*
    Serenade for Strings *180*
    String Quartet No. 1 *222*
    Swan Lake *102*
    Symphony No. 4 *144*
    Symphony No. 5 *110*
    Symphony No. 6 *63*
    The Nutcracker Suite *96*
    The Sleeping Beauty *139*

    Variations on a Rococo Theme
    233
    Violin Concerto *88*
Tchakarov, Emil *190*
Te Kanawa, Kiri *204*
Tear, Robert *196, 213*
Tebaldi, Renata *73, 115*
Tennstedt, Klaus *19, 49, 86, 210*
Terfel, Bryn *188*
Thibaudet, Jean-Yves *67*
Thielemann, Christian *50*
Thomas, David *37, 158*
Thomson, Bryden *29, 60*
Tilson Thomas, Michael *32, 111, 158*
Titanic (Horner) *151*
Toccata and Fugue in D Minor
    (Bach) *79*
Tomlinson, John *176*
Tomowa-Sintow, Anna *190*
Tønnesen, Terje *141*
Torchinsky, Yuri *70*
Tortelier, Yan-Pascal *33, 70, 111, 139,
    215*
Tosca (Puccini) *126*
Toulouse Capitole Orchestra *30, 80,
    139, 191*
Tracey, Ian *93*
Traviata, La (Verdi) *91*
Tristan und Isolde (Wagner) *100*
'Trout' Quintet (Schubert) *51*
Trovatore, Il (Verdi) *178*
Troxell, Richard *57*
Troyanos, Tatiana *94*
Tumagian, Eduard *133*
Turandot (Puccini) *115*
Turin Radio Symphony Orchestra
    133
Türk, Gerd *169*
Turovsky, Yuli *119, 155*
Tuscan Orchestra *146*

U

Uchida, Mitsuko *28, 128, 132, 150,
    154*
Ugorski, Antal *160*
Ukraine National Symphony
    Orchestra *71*
Ulster Orchestra *33, 89, 123, 139,
    174, 215*
Upshaw, Dawn *125, 140*

V

Vaduva, Leontina *141*
Valse Triste (Sibelius) *216*
Van Allan, Richard *184*
Van Dam, José *80*
Van Der Kamp, Harry *117, 167*
Van Der Meel, Nico *117*
Vänskä, Osmo *83, 109, 119, 203*

Vanzo, Alain 80
Varcoe, Stephen 36, 190
Varviso, Silvio 134
Vaughan Williams, Ralph
  English Folk Song Suite 211
  Fantasia on a theme of Thomas
    Tallis 60
  Greensleeves Fantasia 147
  Serenade to Music 226
  Symphony No. 1 220
  Symphony No. 2 226
  Symphony No. 3 233
  Symphony No. 5 202
  The Lark Ascending 13, 29
  The Wasps Overture 194
Vengerov, Maxim 19, 38, 75, 185
Verdi, Giuseppe
  Aida 73
  Don Carlos 233
  Il Trovatore 178
  La Forza del Destino 165
  La Traviata 91
  Nabucco 45
  Otello 214
  Requiem 78
  Rigoletto 133
Verebits, Ibolya 98
Verona Arena Orchestra 45
Vesperae Solonnes de Confessore
  (Mozart) 124
Vester, Frans 84
Vienna Concentus Musicus 138, 172,
  189, 193, 201
Vienna Mozart Ensemble 77
Vienna Octet 51, 217
Vienna Philharmonic Orchestra 22,
  25, 27, 28, 50, 53, 57, 63, 70, 72,
  73, 92, 108, 110, 127, 134, 135,
  136, 168, 176, 183, 196, 206, 209,
  216
Vienna State Opera Orchestra 45
Vienna Symphony Orchestra 59, 138,
  167
Vier Letzte Lieder (Strauss) 86
Villa-Lobos, Heitor
  Bachianas Brasileiras No. 5 229
Vilumanis, Alexander 165
Vivaldi, Antonio
  Chamber Concerto 144
  Concerto for Two Trumpets 233
  Double Concerto for Mandolins,
    Strings and Continuo 218
  Gloria in D 138
  Le Quattro Stagione 34
  Mandolin Concerto 135
  Nulla in Mundo Pax Sincera 13,
    162
Von Otter, Anne Sofie 188
Vonk, Hans 21

W

Wächter, Eberhard 134
Wagner, Richard
  Der Fliegende Holländer 226
  Die Meistersinger von Nürnberg
    164
  Die Walküre 127
  Götterdämmerung 127
  Lohengrin 163
  Parsifal 232
  Rienzi 230
  Siegfried 176
  Tannhäuser 121
  Tristan und Isolde 100
Wakefield, John 37
Waldteufel, Emile
  Les Patineurs 235
Walk to the Paradise Garden, The
  (Delius) 179
Walker, Mallory 188
Walker, Sarah 48
Walküre, Die (Wagner) 127
Wallace, John 145, 203
Wallfisch, Raphael 112
Walter, Alfred 208
Walter, Bruno 92, 216
Walton, William
  Belshazzar's Feast 229
  Crown Imperial 221
Wand, Günter 143, 170, 209, 210
Warlock, Peter
  Capriol Suite 220
Warren-Green, Christopher 145, 203
Wasps Overture, The (Vaughan
  Williams) 194
Water Music Suite 1 (Handel) 101
Watkinson, Carolyn 37, 138
Watts, Helen 37, 122
Weber, Carl Maria
  Clarinet Concerto No. 1 223
  Clarinet Concerto No. 2 220
  Invitation to the Dance 232
  Oberon Overture 233
Weil, Bruno 25, 77, 125, 167
Weir, Gillian 33

Welsh National Opera Orchestra 194
Wenkel, Ortrun 188
Wen-Sinn 85
Werba, Erik 198
Westminster Abbey Choir 152
Westminster Cathedral Choir 43, 68,
  76, 104, 156, 204
White, Willard 177
Widor, Charles Marie
  Symphony No. 5
Wild, Earl 20, 210
Wildner, Johannes 116
Williams, John (guitarist) 47
Williams, John
  Schindler's List 230
  Star Wars 235
Wilson-Johnson, David 48
Winchester Cathedral Choir 76, 147,
  152
Wispelway, Pieter 155
Wit, Antoni 65, 67, 125, 185
Witsenburg, Edward 84
Wolf-Ferrari, Ermanno
  Jewels of the Madonna 232
Wordsworth, Barry 135, 207
Wunderlich, Fritz 95, 216
Württemberg Chamber Orchestra 190

X

Xue Wei 88

Y

Yepes, Narcisco 164
Ying Huang 57
York, Deborah 162

Z

Zadok the Priest (Handel) 76
Zampieri, Giuseppe 183
Zauberflöte, Die (Mozart) 95
Zehetmair Quartet 51
Zilberstein, Lilya 20, 54, 120
Zimerman, Krystian 82, 97
Zinman, David 22, 26, 50, 53, 99,
  125, 149, 205, 211
Zipoli, Domenico
  Elevazione 13, 172
Zurich Tonhalle Orchestra 22, 26,
  50, 53, 99